D1015019

Biodiesel America

How to Achieve Energy Security,
Free America From Middle-East Oil Dependence,
and Make Money Growing Fuel

Josh Tickell

Edited by:

Meghan Murphy & Claudia Graziano

the Biodiesel America Organization
and the National Biodiesel Board

www.BiodieselAmerica.org • www.Biodiesel.org

Cover design by George Foster. Book layout and design by Richard Blackledge. Transcription by Charlene Taylor and Bonnie Picone.

Published by Yorkshire Press

1st Edition

Printed in the United States of America

ISBN: 978-0-9707227-4-4

Library of Congress Control Number: 2005905020

Discounts on bulk purchases are available to distributors, wholesalers, retailers and on-line stores. Please call 877-834-4826.

Individual copies can be purchased on-line at:
www.BiodieselAmerica.org or by contacting

Bookmasters
P.O. Box 388
Ashland, OH 44805
800-266-5564
or
419-281-1802

ACKNOWLEDGEMENTS

This book was made possible through the generous contribution of time, expertise, and work by the following individuals: Joe Jobe, Jenna Higgins, Scott Hughes, Amber Pearson, Bev Thessen, Desiree Hale, Donnell Rehagen, Lola Helming, Scott Tremain, Tammy Sachse, and Tom Verry of the National Biodiesel Board; Steve Howell, Alan Weber, and Leland Tong of Marc IV Consulting; Darryl Brinkmann, Bob Metz, and Mark Palmer of the American Soybean Association; Robert McCormick of The National Renewable Energy Laboratory, United States Department of Energy; Shelley Launey of Clean Cities, United States Department of Energy; Linda Bluestein and Shabnam Fardanesh of the Office of Energy Efficiency and Renewable Energy, United States Department of Energy; Janet Kopenhaver of Eye on Washington; Karen Edwards of the KCE Group; Monte Shaw of the Renewable Fuels Association; Greg Anderson of the United Soybean Board; Jeff Irvin of the Petroleum Marketers Association of America; Paul Nazzaro of Advanced Fuel Solutions; Jennifer Weaver and Brendan Prebo of the Renaissance Creative Group; Jeff Nelson of Stepan Company; Bob Clark of Imperial Western Products; Nile Ramsbottom and Gary Haer of West Central Soy; Fred Wellons of Baker Commodities; Rudi Wiedemann of Biodiesel Solutions; Bob and Kelly King of Pacific Biodiesel; Russ Teall of Biodiesel Industries; Hart Moore of Griffin Industries; Gene Gebolys of World Energy; Steven Hobbs of BE Bio-Energy; Matthew Simmons of Simmons and Company; Julian Darley of The Post Carbon Institute; Dr. Morton Grosser, author of *Diesel, The Man and His Engine*; David Blume, author of *Alcohol Can Be A Gas!*; Mo Mellady of PlanetCheck; Mark Wienand of Liquid Solar; Peter Nester of Cornell University; Dr. Arthur Weaver and Robb Jetty of Renovus Energy; the Cornell University Librarians; Greg Reitman of Blue Water Entertainment; Chip Rosenbloom of Utopia Pictures; Carol Gaskin of Editorial Alchemy; Trudie Martineau; and Richard Blackledge of the Biodiesel America Organization.

I wish to express special gratitude toward Mary Devereux and Brooks Trotter, Brian Tickell and Jo Milikan, Gene and Deborah Dupre Wheeler, and Grant and Judy Dupre.

This book is dedicated to the farmers.

As the caretakers of the Earth they hold the key to our future.

TABLE OF CONTENTS

1   Foreword • Fuel For Thought

9   Introduction • The Road to Freedom

15   Chapter 1 • America's Crude History

37   Chapter 2 • The End of Cheap Oil

57   Chapter 3 • Diesel: The Man and His Vision

83   Chapter 4 • Alternative Fuels 101

117   Chapter 5 • Farming Fuel

155   Chapter 6 • Got Biodiesel?

183   Chapter 7 • Biodiesel Goes to Washington

203   Chapter 8 • Biodiesel's Speedy Growth

221   Chapter 9 • Turning Biodiesel Into Bucks

241   Chapter 10 • The Road Ahead

259   What You Can Do Now

265   Bibliography

283   Glossary

299   Endnotes

327   Index

Fuel for Thought

By *Joe Jobe*
Chief Executive Officer
National Biodiesel Board

"The Middle East had long been the crossroads where Asia, Africa, and Europe met. Now its oil is the lifeblood of modern industry, the Persian Gulf region is the heart that pumps it, and the sea routes around the Gulf are the jugular through which that lifeblood passes."

President Richard M. Nixon

When I was in grade school in the 1970s, I was taught that we would run out of oil within twenty years. I remember a specific discussion with my mother on a trip home from my grandparents' farm in southern Missouri. The conversation we had during that car ride would affect my perspective on oil for the rest of my life. I asked my mom where oil came from, why we were running out, and why it seemed to matter so much. My mother was a schoolteacher and was particularly good at making complex things understandable to young ones.

A favorite family activity at my grandparents' farm was to hunt for arrowheads left behind by the Osage Indians. Oil, she explained, is a little like our treasured Indian arrowheads. Because the Osage Indians are long gone, there are only a certain number of Indian arrowheads left on the farm to find. Once we find the last of them, the arrowhead hunting will be over. Likewise, she said, there is only so much oil in the ground. Once we find the last of the oil, there won't be any more to use in our cars and trucks and tractors.

This concerned me a great deal. I questioned her about what was going to happen when the oil disappeared – will I not be able to drive a car when I get older? At that moment she reverted from teacher to mother, realizing that a seven-year-old ought not be so troubled by such weighty matters. "Honey," she said, "don't you worry. They will figure something out; they always do."

I didn't know who "they" were, but I sure hoped "they" would be able to figure something out soon. As it turned out, the Embargo-era predictions that our world oil supplies would be depleted in twenty years were wrong. Our fears about the end of oil have been blunted by years of false alarms. Decades of U.S. policy aimed at keeping energy prices artificially low have contributed to our economic prosperity, but have also created an indignant sense of entitlement to cheap gasoline. The term "energy crisis" is hardly used anymore. Living with the threat of an energy crisis for so long seems to have lulled us into thinking that it is no longer a threat.

The Oil Jugular

Fuel is virtually the only consumer staple for which prices are posted daily on billboards outside the stores in which it is sold. When prices rise, drivers complain as though their sacred rights have been violated. Complaints turn quickly to theories of conspiracy. "They" must be at it again to gouge us for more money. These same people are unwilling to recognize the role they play as consumers of a limited energy supply.

Almost no one disputes that oil is a finite resource that is being depleted all the time. What are matters of dispute are how much oil is recoverable and how much consumption will grow over the next decades as the world continues to industrialize. Even more important, and more controversial, is the question of when global production of oil will peak due to depleted supplies. Serious estimates range anywhere from less than five to more than forty years. Peak oil production, it is believed, is likely to trigger significant decreases in petroleum supply and increases in petroleum prices. But even before oil production peaks, oil prices should continue to rise over time due to the increasing costs of exploration and extraction. (The arrowheads will become harder to find, and it will be increasingly more difficult to recover the ones that are left.)

The evidence indicates that major shifts of oil supply and price are likely to occur within the next few decades if not sooner. That means that these energy shifts should be expected by the time my children are around my age now. How we as a society can address this coming challenge is the focus of this book.

Oil is like no other commodity. It impacts all salable products and services, from their production to their distribution and consumption. It is inextricably linked to the health of our economy and of the environment, even to our very existence. With such a strong reliance on a single source of energy, replacing that energy source requires an enormous amount of time and effort. Not only must we research and develop energy alternatives, but we must also create consumer acceptance and grow an industry to manufacture and market them.

The Road to Energy Independence

The first step on the road to energy independence is conservation. America makes up approximately 5% of the world population, but we consume approximately 25% of the world's oil. Americans now consume more energy per capita than any other people on Earth.

Americans have a long history of instilling in their children that wasting food is immoral. The fact that there are people starving in the world means that to waste food is shameful. As a result, America donates more food aid to poor countries than any other nation. On the other hand, Americans seem to have the opposite attitude toward energy. One's ability to flagrantly use larger amounts of energy is a desirable symbol of status and prestige. Overuse of energy is not currently a source of shame, and certainly not connected to a moral obligation. It will take a committed effort to change this attitude toward energy to one of conservation.

The second step toward energy independence is to embrace a coordinated strategy of energy options. As people think about answers to our energy problems, there is a natural tendency to search for that single source of energy that will replace oil in our transportation sector. I call this the "silver bullet" approach. The public discourse about hydrogen fuel cells, for example, has led many Americans to believe that the "silver bullet" has already been found. A commonly held belief is that this alternative is just being fine-tuned, and will certainly be implemented before the price of oil gets too high. While hydrogen may one day contribute to our energy supply, its contributions are many years away. The search for a silver bullet solution leads many to discount strategies that cannot single-handedly displace all of our petroleum needs.

The truth is that there is no silver bullet solution to our energy problem. Limiting ourselves to a single source of transportation energy is the reason we have a problem now. What is needed is a diversified portfolio of energy options–an array of energy sources, policies, and strategies that will improve our overall energy picture. This is what I call the "silver buckshot solution." I'm not sure who first coined this phrase, but it is the approach that simply makes the most sense.

As this book points out, biodiesel is positioned to play a prominent role in our new energy economy. Grown on American soil, biodiesel has an energy balance four times greater than petroleum diesel. Thus, every gallon of biodiesel that we produce and consume extends our petroleum supply by four gallons. Biodiesel also has a closed carbon cycle, dramatically reducing CO_2. More than any other renewable fuel, biodiesel fits seamlessly into our existing transportation infrastructure. Growing crops for biodiesel production does not displace the production of food crops. Instead, these biodiesel crops actually increase America's ability to grow food by putting more protein meal onto the food market. In addition, the use of biodiesel generates domestic jobs in the manufacturing sector and displaces imported petroleum, which makes up one third of our national trade deficit.

Growing Awareness

I first met Josh Tickell in 1999, not long after being appointed the Executive Director of the National Biodiesel Board. I was working to restructure an organization and to refocus efforts to help launch an industry that at that time had almost no sales. Josh was working on publishing, speaking, graduate film studies, and talking to anyone who would listen about biodiesel. Over the years I've watched Josh's writing, speaking, publishing, and filmmaking skills evolve. But I believe his most important talent is one that he possessed when I first met him. He is a natural educator. He believes in the value of talking to people, of communicating with them on a personal level, of patiently answering all of their questions. His talent and sincerity come through in all that he does. I believe that this book, *Biodiesel America*, is an important piece of work that will have a positive impact on our country.

Because my career is in the energy sector, I spend a lot of time thinking about energy. I also spend a lot of time talking to others who think a lot about energy. During my work, I am often reminded of my mother's answer to her young son's concerns: "They will figure something out; they always do." I now believe my mother was correct. But I have also come to realize that there is no "they." The only "they" is us. There are no men in black suits and sunglasses sitting on cold fusion, waiting for the right time to introduce it. It is up to us as individuals to implement the solutions that will carry us forward into a brighter future.

A Call to Action

President Nixon referred to the Straits of Hormuz in the Persian Gulf as the "strategic choke point on the West's oil jugular." This analogy was starkly illustrated in October 2000 when terrorists blew a sizable hole in the side of the *USS Cole* in the Straits of Hormuz. Had the Cole sunk, the artery through which roughly a third of the world's oil courses every day would have become perilously clogged, leading to sudden and significant global economic damage.

President Jimmy Carter closed out the 1970s by speaking directly about the Straits of Hormuz. President Carter had made great progress in energy conservation, reducing overall petroleum consumption by 8% in the previous year. At the time of his speech, war was raging in Afghanistan, fifty Americans were being held hostage in Iran, and Soviet military forces were within three hundred miles of the Straits. He stated, "Our excessive dependence on foreign oil is a clear and present danger to our Nation's security. . . . The need has never been more urgent. At long last, we must have a clear, comprehensive energy policy for the United States."

Twenty-five years later the situation has dramatically worsened. At the time of the 1973 Arab Oil Embargo, America imported approximately 30% of its oil. Today, imports make up about 60% of our oil supply and account for approximately one third of our national trade deficit. The top-ten list of countries supplying our oil reads more and more like a Who's Who of terrorist nations. Our dependence on these nations has made us vulnerable.

It is time we heeded President Carter's passionate call to action. Neither the government nor private industry will solve our energy problems. It is not the government's job to dictate how we should behave. It is our job as citizens to dictate how our government should behave. Our personal impact on the world–our allocation of resources, our footprint on the environment, our development and use of energy and new technologies, and our level of awareness–is something we can all affect and have a moral obligation to affect. We cannot wait for "them" to come and save us. The task is ours.

Introduction

by Josh Tickell

The Road to Freedom

The year was 1996. I was a college student on a semester abroad in Europe. The focus of my studies was agriculture and energy—the two cornerstones of our society. While working on a small organic farm in former East Germany, I saw something that changed my life. We were harvesting fields of yellow flowering plants and crushing their seeds to extract vegetable oil. The oil was taken to a large stainless steel machine owned cooperatively by the local farmers. Inside that machine, something incredible happened: the vegetable oil that we had pressed from the yellow *rapeseed* was transformed into a fuel that could run in any diesel engine. The farmers called this fuel *biodiesel*. To the farmers, the process was a routine operation. To me, it represented a complete revolution in thinking. If we could simply "grow" our own fuel, then why was America so fixated on petroleum?

I returned to college, where I studied chemistry and engineering. I learned to make biodiesel in the lab and, with the help of a few sympathetic engineers, designed a portable machine to make biodiesel from used cooking oil that I collected for free from fast food restaurants. I towed this "Green Grease Machine," as it was affectionately called, behind a ten-year-old diesel-powered Winnebago, which my college friends and I had covered in brightly painted sunflowers. We dubbed the little motor home "The Veggie Van." My month long post college tour in the van turned into a two-year cross-country journey. During what became known as the *Veggie Van Voyage,* I was interviewed on *The Today Show*, *CNN*, *Dateline,* and in over one hundred newspapers and magazines. I used the voyage as a means to meet with farmers, scientists, politicians, celebrities, and engineers in order to assess the potential for a viable national biodiesel industry.

Because the Veggie Van was visually enticing, people from just about every walk of life-from young men in fast red cars at stoplights to children on field trips to elderly Bible study groups on their way to lunch—would stop and ask me questions. "How does it run?" "Where do you get your fuel?" and of course, "How fast does it go?" From New York City to Los Angeles and from the Great Lakes to the Texas badlands, Americans embraced the Veggie Van. The experience interacting with people across the country instilled in me a tremendous reverence for America, as well as the many people who live in this great nation.

My adventure and research also prompted me to write my first book, *From the Fryer to the Fuel Tank – The Complete Guide to Using Vegetable Oil as an Alternative Fuel.* By then I had testified as a biodiesel expert in front of the Arizona Senate Committee on the Environment and I was speaking regularly at college campuses across the nation. I would soon be offered a position as a contractor for The National Biodiesel Board, working to promote biodiesel. I gained a deep respect for this organization and their director, Joe Jobe, whom I have now watched work diligently for the better part of a decade to create consensus among people on all sides of the biodiesel issue.

When I first learned about biodiesel in 1996, there were only three fleets in the U.S. using the fuel in trials. By 1997, we had received over one million actual visitors to the Veggie Van web site at www.VeggieVan.org. By 1999, the height of the Internet boom, enthusiasm had exploded for this "new" fuel. Chat groups, blogs, web sites, how-to sites, biodiesel products, conferences, and courses began springing up online. By 2005, there were more than 300 fleets across America using biodiesel. Today, a simple Google search on the word "biodiesel" returns web site results in the tens of thousands. In a span of less than ten years, biodiesel has gone from being virtually unknown in the U.S. to a buzzword used by presidential candidates, rock stars, and energy experts.

Despite the recent biodiesel buzz, we lack media coverage of biodiesel's full potential. The fact that biodiesel can be made from sources such as used cooking oil makes for novel stories, but we have not yet seen hard-hitting news stories in the *Economist*, *Scientific American*, or *National Geographic* about the potential for biodiesel to change our energy landscape. We await serious political debates on *Larry King Live* and *C-SPAN* on exactly how the nation should embrace biodiesel as well as the critical conversations on *Oprah* and *Donahue* on how biodiesel can reduce dangerous diesel school bus emissions–a known contributor to childhood asthma. This is the type of media coverage that has resulted in hundreds of millions of dollars in research and development funds for other alternative fuels, such as hydrogen. It is my hope that this book will play a pivotal role in bringing biodiesel this type of media coverage, leading to a groundswell of national support.

America must stand up and face its Mid East petroleum dependence. We must ask ourselves, "What, exactly, is the 'main course' that is going to fuel the growing energy appetite of our country?" As this book illustrates, the "main course" isn't oil, it isn't hydrogen, it isn't natural gas, and it isn't even synthetic fuels. Instead, the "real meal" for Americans will be a new mix of clean renewable energy resources–resources that don't run out.

Writing *Biodiesel America* was a surreal experience. Each time I sat with my editorial team to discuss what might happen next in the energy world, it did. A number of sections of this book had to be revised immediately before publication because things we had predicted had already come to pass. King Fahd of Saudi Arabia died (not that we had wished him to do so, but his demise was as imminent as that of the House of Saud itself). China made bold moves to capture an American oil company. When that failed they entered discussions with Venezuela, prompting Pat Robertson, host of *The 700 Club*, to recommend that the United States assassinate leftist Venezuelan president Hugo Chavez. Naturally, global oil prices shot through the roof.

Hurricane Katrina, although unforeseen, pummeled the delicate, Gulf-based oil and gas industries, bringing almost 50% of America's oil and gas production to a standstill in less than 24 hours. As *Fox News's* Geraldo Rivera donned a raincoat and stood squarely in front of a Beaumont oil derrick, 5 million motorists lined the outbound highways from Houston to escape Hurricane Rita (I was one of them), and cars lined up at empty gas stations stretched for miles, America got its first inkling that the security of a large portion of its domestic energy infrastructure is paper-thin. Following the hurricanes were reports in the *LA Times* and on *CNN* that oil company profits were the highest they had been in decades.

But the real icing on the energy cake of late 2005 was the passage of a long awaited energy bill, which after recent events only seemed sensible. The bill-turned-law even contains small incentives for biodiesel, ethanol, wind, and solar. But the majority of its $14.5 billion in tax breaks will go to the oil, gas, nuclear, and coal industries. Passage of the law did little to hinder oil prices from their continued climb, this time to over $60 a barrel.

With the exception of Pat Robertson's comments, the hurricanes, and Geraldo's choice of reporting locations, a similar series of events had been outlined in the first manuscript for *Biodiesel America*. But my team and I were not predicting the future. We were merely reading the writing on the wall: America is at an energy crossroads, and if we are to survive and flourish in a post-cheap-oil world, fundamental change to our nation is imminent.

My motivation for writing *Biodiesel America* was simple: to clarify America's need for immediate energy security and to show how biodiesel fits into the mix of energy resources that will soon fuel our country. It was to empower Americans to support and adopt biodiesel and other important renewable energy resources. As such, this book pulls back the curtain of misinformation covering the history of oil, making sense of the energy crisis of the 1970s and giving an accurate snapshot of our current energy insecurity. It delves into the world of Dr. Rudolf Diesel, the man who invented the diesel engine and designed it to run on vegetable oil over 100 years ago. *Biodiesel America* details the entire gamut of alternative energy resources and explains how hydrogen, hybrids, methane, and biodiesel fit together.

The book also explores the social, economic, and political ramifications of biodiesel. Imagine a nation that has a booming farm business, millions of new, high-wage jobs, a healthy economy providing money to social services, schools, and community infrastructure, and a complete independence from foreign sources of energy. Sound like America in the 1950s? No. That is the America of tomorrow. And this book shows us how to get there. By laying the groundwork for new types of energy, this book provides information critical to a new course of action for our nation. If taken seriously, such action could deliver us from oil dependence and revitalize our country.

On an individual level, you stand to benefit from this new "American Energy Revolution." With the information in this book, you will be better prepared to invest in profitable energy stocks, companies, and enterprises. This book will help you understand how to increase your energy security, the energy security of your family, and of your community. It will also teach you how to protect yourself and your loved ones from the negative health effects of diesel exhaust. But most of all, this book offers you a way to begin benefiting from the upcoming changes in America's energy infrastructure. Not twenty-five years from now. Not even a decade from now. But right now.

CHAPTER 1

America's Crude History

"Drill for oil? You mean drill into the ground to try to find oil?"
An enlistee for the first drilling project in 1859

Oil: In the time that it takes Earth to travel around the sun once, humanity extracts 30 billion barrels of it from the crust of this planet. In fact, every time Earth rotates, our society burns over 3 billion gallons of it. From the time you wake up until you're in your car heading to work, 130 million gallons of it will be transformed into heat and pollution. In the time it took you to read this paragraph, we will have obliterated over 100,000 gallons of it. Once used, it is gone forever. It can never again be formed or replaced.

We call this precious substance "black gold," or "crude," and for now, it's everywhere. Oil forms the basis for pesticides, fertilizers, and agricultural inputs. It fuels the machines that plant, harvest, and process our food. It fuels the transportation industry that carries our food to the stores. It even encases our food in a form we call "plastic."

It is in almost everything we touch, from hair spray to keyboards to the clothes we wear to the chairs we sit on. It is the foundation for manufacturing all modern technology, from circuit boards to telecommunications wiring. Roads are made from it. It fuels the cars we drive to work. It keeps our lights on. It cools our houses in summer and warms them in winter. It carries our water inside pipes.

Oil has allowed us to make quantum leaps in lifestyles and quality of life. Modern medicine couldn't function without it. It has given us compounds to repair teeth, replace bones and joints, and build synthetic hearts. It engulfs us, protects us, and sustains us.

Oil allows us the freedom of mobility. Cars, buses, trucks, trains, boats, and planes all run on it. It moves every good, every commodity with which we come in contact. It is the basis for all commerce and all trade.

Touch something. Go ahead. Reach out and touch something-anything. Now think. Could it have come to you without oil? Even the book you are reading was transported to you with oil. It's inescapable. And for now, we are swimming in a sea of it. But it hasn't always been that way and it won't be that way forever.

New data suggests that our current oil-laden path will be short-lived. And as a result, new technologies like the ones discussed in this book will soon alter the way we interact with energy. On the surface, this book is simply about a fuel called "biodiesel." But as you will see, it's really about much more. This book is a journey through time, science, technology, agriculture, and the mechanisms that move the world you thought you knew. It's a journey of understanding and a journey of truth.

Are you ready? Let's begin that journey.

In the Beginning

When you think about the origins of fossil fuel, you might picture scenes from an old black and white dinosaur movie or from the more recent film, *Jurassic Park*. Regardless of the mental imagery, one thing remains certain: we hold a common belief that fossil fuel comes from dinosaurs. But that's not true.

The truth is that the oil, gas, and coal to which the term "fossil fuel" refers are not made from giant dinosaurs. The main source for oil was a group of water-borne microscopic organisms called algae.[1]

If you've ever cleaned a pool or had the misfortune to slip on an old brick pathway, you know algae are oily. To perform photosynthesis, algae maximize their exposure to sunlight by floating close to the surface of water. To do this, algae internally produce a form of oil both to store energy and to buoy themselves up.

The algae that lived millions of years ago contained chains of carbon atoms called *n-paraffins*.[2] Just as dinosaur bones allow us to identify the type of dinosaur from which they came, n-paraffins are chemical links between algae and the fossil oil we use today.

Since ancient algae turned into oil, you might wonder why your swimming pool doesn't turn into oil if left unattended. While we can dream of making millions of dollars growing oil in our backyards, the development of fossil fuels occurred in rare geological circumstances over such an extensive period of time that we won't see the creation of any substantial quantities of fossil fuel in our lifetime.

So how did oil form? And, more importantly, why does it matter to us? To answer the first question, we must look at the geological history of the planet. To answer the second, we need only look to the prices at our nearest service station. If no more oil is being formed and no more is being discovered, then we will pay an increasingly high price for this precious substance.

Hot Stuff

Algal life proliferates in the presence of nutrition, heat, and carbon dioxide—conditions that are amplified during periods of global warming. From about 270 million years ago to about 10 million years ago, there were approximately four periods of natural global warming that resulted in intense algal growth. After the algal blooms died, their remains rained down onto ocean floors, forming the basis for the petroleum oil we use today. The *organic theory* of oil states that the formation of oil from organic life occurred as a result of these intense proliferations of microscopic, floating sea-creatures.

The organic material settled to the bottom of oceans and lakes. In rare cases, when the geological conditions were right, these organic sediments were buried in mud, silt, and sand. Deep underground, the organic sediments were baked at temperatures of up to 400 degrees Fahrenheit. Over millions of years, the sediments were transformed to rock. When temperature and pressure were in the proper ranges, this rock became the *source rock* for oil.

Oil escaped from this source rock and migrated through cracks and fissures into *reservoir rock*—porous rock such as sandstone. But only when the reservoir rock was trapped inside another membrane of impermeable rock did fossil fuel accumulate in large enough quantities to drill. Thus, the oil and gas that we drill today is actually stored in sandstone and other porous rocks trapped inside hard rock membranes, deep beneath the surface of the planet.

A Fly in the Ointment

While the majority of geologists agree that oil was formed by microscopic organic life forms that died millions of years ago, the *theory of inorganic oil formation* states something very different.

The inorganic theory is based on a hypothesis from Russian scientists that oil comes from a potentially limitless, primordial material deep in the earth.

The primary American proponent of the inorganic theory of oil development was the late Professor Thomas Gold of Cornell University, author of the book *The Deep Hot Biosphere*. Gold believed that oil and gas are constantly generated by microbes deep beneath the earth's surface and are not the result of decaying organic plant matter. The proof he offered for this theory is the existence of oil in *basement rock*, rock that was never near the surface of the earth and therefore not exposed to algae and protozoa.[3]

Gold got a chance to test his theory with a superdeep well drilled in Siljan, Sweden, in 1998. Despite the international excitement caused by Gold's "endless oil" theory, the data of his experiment were less concrete. The well, which was drilled four miles into basement rock, yielded 80 barrels of oil before the project was abandoned.[4] Inorganic theorists claim that this provides evidence that oil is not a fossil fuel at all, but most geologists agree on an alternative explanation.

According to U.S. Geological Survey research geologist Gregory Ulminshek, the reason oil can be found in basement rock is that sometimes basement rock is lifted up as a result of geological movements. Sedimentary rock containing oil then falls down into the gaps in the basement rock, leaving oil deposits. "Geology is an empirical science," says Ulminshek, "and we are sure that all the oil and gas that has been found in 150 years of exploration is of a biological nature."[5]

Ulminshek's words are echoed by other geologists who concur that oil did not, as Gold had hypothesized, come upward from some great primordial substance inside the planet. There has yet to be any solid proof, either from Dr. Gold's camp or from any other institution, on the theory of inorganic oil formation. What has been proven, however, is that there is an undeniable connection between organic life that existed millions of years ago and the oil we use today.

Let There Be Light

Oil is made up of strings of hydrogen and carbon called *hydrocarbons*. Be it in plant tissue or some form of oil, nature uses hydrocarbon bonds to store the energy of sunlight. When they are burned, hydrocarbons give off heat and light. There are multiple sources of naturally occurring hydrocarbon-based oils, including liquid petroleum, vegetable oil, and animal fat.

Long before Thomas Edison turned on his first light switch, the new world was using oil lamps for light.[6] But these lamps weren't fueled by the kind of oil we use today. Instead, the majority of these lamps were fueled by whale oil. As the new world became settled, the need for cheap lamp fuel increased and whales were hunted in great numbers for their blubber. The sperm whale, *physeter macrocephalus*, was the focus of the nineteenth century American whaling industry.

Sperm whales are renowned for the spermaceti oil found in their heads; this oil is an exceptional lamp fuel and machinery lubricant. An average male sperm whale weighs about 80,000 pounds.[7] In the mid-1800s, a large sperm whale could yield 85 barrels of oil valued at about $3,000. By comparison, the average farm at that time cost about $2,500.[8]

As the United States and Europe entered the Industrial Revolution, the need for whale oil became acute. In 1848, with the invention of the exploding harpoon, the whale industry itself exploded. From 1816 to 1855, gross receipts from the whale industry grew twelvefold, and whales became the staple fuel not only for lamps, but also for processing wool, leather, soap, and paint.[9] Whale oils also permeated the cosmetic, medicinal, and chemical industries. With the increase in industrial manufacturing, whale oil became a critical component of machine lubrication.

Within the span of forty years, whale products became the backbone of a rapidly growing industrial society. But whaling was a risky business. As the whaling industry increased the rate of whale harvesting, ships had to travel further out to sea to hunt the remaining whales. Eventually, expensive steamships were built and outfitted for arduous hunts, some of which lasted years. Not even the might of these vessels could sustain the dying whale industry. And in 1871, the entire Arctic fleet of 34 whaling ships was lost in an ice storm, costing two million dollars and raising insurance premiums for whalers to prohibitive heights. According to Karl Brandt, author of *Whale Oil, An Economic Analysis,* "almost every other industry promised steadier yields and involved less risk."[10]

Like the petroleum industry that would soon emerge, whaling was a boom and bust enterprise. The very nature of whaling destroyed the whale population on which it relied. Added to the inherent problems of whaling were the discovery of gold in California and the development of the cotton textile industry, both of which drew laborers from the whaling vessels, leaving many of them empty at the docks. When petroleum was discovered in Titusville, Pennsylvania, in 1859, the migration of workers from ships to oil rigs was fast and furious. America was growing, and she needed a cheaper, more reliable form of energy.

Pennsylvania Black Gold

To say that oil was "discovered" in Pennsylvania in 1859 is inaccurate. For almost a thousand years in the land surrounding the Caspian Sea, oil had seeped to the surface into pools and was used for lighting and medicine. In America, black oil had bubbled to the surface of what is now known as Oil Creek in Northwest

Pennsylvania for centuries. The Seneca and other Native Americans skimmed oil from the surface of this and other oil rivers and springs. They used the oil for medicine, for dye, and for weatherproofing wigwams. Early European settlers learned the techniques from the Native Americans and followed suit, using cloth and wood to skim the oil.

In the mid-1850s demand for liquid energy was increasing. A New York attorney named George Bissell noticed "rock oil" advertised in Pennsylvania as a medicine. He knew the oil was flammable and wanted to explore the commercialization of it as an inexpensive illuminant. Bissell teamed up with Yale chemist Benjamin Silliman, Jr., who had been researching "rock oil." The two formed a company with investors that would come to be known as the Seneca Oil Company and in 1857 hired a man named Edwin L. Drake to manage their first drilling operation.

Almost two years later, Bissell and his group had found nothing. A letter was mailed to Drake instructing him to terminate the project. But on the afternoon of August 27, 1859, the drill bit, already sixty-nine feet deep, dropped into a crevice and slid down another six inches. Work was called off for the weekend. The following day, the project's blacksmith, "Uncle Billy," went to inspect the well. What he saw when he peered down into the drilling pipe would change history: dark liquid was floating on top of the water.

When Drake arrived on Monday, he found Uncle Billy and the workers had amassed tubs, washbasins, and barrels filled with oil. Later that same day, Drake received the termination letter that had been mailed by the Seneca investors. The drilling operation continued, and the Seneca Oil Company would spark an international energy shift toward oil.

The Birth of an Industry

During the 1850s the growing demand for cheap lighting and the declining whale population spurred the newly formed petroleum industry into action. Canadian horse exporter turned-doctor-turned geologist Abraham Gesner developed a process to refine lamp oil from asphalt. He named this new liquid *kerosene,* and he established the Kerosene Works company in New York to make the "coal oil." The design for an affordable oil lamp was imported from Eastern Europe, and in no time demand for oil as an illuminant increased.

The placement of early oil wells quickly determined the economic ups and downs of the oil industry itself. Oil wells were drilled close together, rapidly depleting the small oil pockets over which they were often built. Each time an oil field was discovered, many oil wells would be drilled and production would suddenly skyrocket, only to flatten out and eventually taper off completely as the oilfield "dried up." The wild swings in oil production quickly turned oil into a "boom and bust" business.

After the first discovery in Pennsylvania, oil sold for the extravagant price of $40 per barrel. One year later, with supply outpacing demand, the price per barrel sunk to just 10 cents. In some cases, oil was sold for as low as a penny per barrel. All hope of price stabilization was destroyed after several major oilfields were discovered in East Texas in 1930. Soon thereafter, martial law was declared and federal troops moved in to stop the unchecked oil production.

The Texas Railroad Commission was soon formed as a cartel to prevent overproduction and protect the domestic price of U.S. oil. But even with these measures in place, almost nothing could stop the gushing wells, and "hot oil" was smuggled out past armed troops at night. In the wake of the unpredictability of the oil industry, a new enterprise would arise. Its business practices would reshape American capitalism and form the foundation for the global businesses that would follow.

A New Standard

In 1870 a young, business-minded man by the name of John D. Rockefeller started a company, with three partners, called Standard Oil. Rockefeller embodies the ultimate rags-to-riches story. He began life as a poor farm boy without two pennies to rub together. By the time he was in his twenties, his small grocery company was grossing nearly half a million dollars a year. He was famous for being able to make deals based on borrowing money. A careful accountant and an aggressive businessman, Rockefeller kept his books balanced and his eyes on the prize.

Rockefeller had begun by investing $4,000 with his grocery partner into an oil drill. Soon there were two drills. Then three. From there, Standard Oil was born. Within ten years, the company had transformed the oil industry by "standardizing" production and creating a consistent and reliable industry. Daniel Yergin, author of the oil history book *The Prize*, explains Rockefeller's modus operandi: "The objective of Rockefeller's audacious and daring battle plan was, in his words, to end 'that cut-throat policy of making no profits' and 'make the oil business safe and profitable' — under his control." The first vertically integrated company and the first multinational, Standard Oil owned oil rigs, railroads, and retail outlets–everything from the means of production to the storefront. Despite Rockefeller's success, his conglomerate would soon be too big for even him to control.

By the late 1870s Pennsylvania oil companies made a stab at throwing off Rockefeller's tight grip by building an oil pipeline to go around his railroad system. Unsure of whether or not a pipeline would even work, these companies feared complete failure. But success was in the cards, and oil began flowing around Rockefeller's back. His empire would continue to grow, however, until a 1911 Supreme Court Ruling to break the "unreasonable monopoly" of Standard Oil — resulting in the creation of several different companies.

The largest remaining company was Standard Oil of New Jersey, which retained almost half of the net value of the conglomerate. It eventually became Exxon. The second largest of Standard's children was Standard Oil of New York with 9% of the total value. It eventually became Mobil. Ironically, 88 years later, these two companies would reunite—forming the largest oil conglomerate on Earth: ExxonMobil. Standard Oil of California eventually became Chevron. There were also sibling companies in Ohio and Indiana, which would morph into the American office of BP and Amoco, respectively. Continental Oil would become Conoco; Atlantic Oil would eventually be gobbled up by ARCO. At their height, these companies would grow into a family of seven large oil companies. But like the oil industry itself, they would eventually plateau and decline.

America Embraces Oil

Oil fueled the American Civil War and hurled the United States into the Industrial Age. Oil provided a cheap source of energy and lubrication and allowed for more rapid manufacturing of machinery. From 1860 to 1880, oil consumption in the United States grew fortyfold from 500,000 gallons to 20 million gallons. By 1920 oil production had grown again, to almost 450 million barrels.[11]

For the first 40 years, oil had been used primarily as an illuminant. In the first decade after 1900 however, Thomas Edison's light bulb and his electricity company took New York by storm, pushing the illumination market squarely toward electricity. Fortunately for the oil industry, the introduction of the gasoline-powered automobile would spur a new market for "rock oil." By the time Henry Ford rolled his first Model T off the production line on October 1, 1908, worldwide oil consumption had risen to 10 million barrels per year. In its first year of production, the Ford Motor Company assembled one million vehicles. The rise of the automobile and of other types of petroleum-powered machinery increased oil consumption again threefold, so that by the late 1930s, when Texas oil fields began pumping vast amounts of oil, worldwide oil consumption had risen to 2 billion barrels a year.[12]

World War I: The First Mechanized War

Fueled by oil, machinery changed the scale of warfare. World War I was expected to last only a few weeks or months. Instead, it lasted four years, illustrating the incredible power nations now had to sustain war. Oil had given armies a new resilience and a new power for destruction.

Oil fueled the vehicles of war, simplified transport of supplies, vastly increased the mobility of men and machines, and maintained the home front. Oil made nations strong, gave them points of vulnerability, determined strategy, and became part of the spoils.

Diesel-powered submarines gave Germany a distinct tactical advantage during WWI. Germany, well aware of the role that oil would play in battle, attempted to choke the supply of oil to Britain and France by sinking tankers. During a five-month period in 1917, Standard Oil of New Jersey lost six oil tankers to the German submarines. Walter "Boss" Teagle, the head of Standard Oil of New Jersey, described World War I as a petroleum war, making the point that, munitions aside, oil decided the war.[13]

Oil determined the outcome of skirmishes on land and on sea and also opened an entirely new arena for war: the sky. The Wright brothers made their first flight in 1903 fueled by petroleum. At the start of WWI in 1914, planes were considered good for sport. But the war inspired all manner of mechanical innovation. Consequently, airplane production increased radically. Europe produced more than 200,000 planes over the course of the war, while the United States, involved in the war for only a year and a half, produced 15,000 planes on its own. The incredible power and number of airborne fighting machines only increased the need for oil.

As the First World War came to a close, the scramble began for rights to Middle Eastern oil. Disputes broke out over oil rights in Iraq even before the first official discovery of oil was made there in 1927. Oil was no longer a commodity for a handful of entrepreneurs; it was a resource over which nations fought.

World War II: Oil Decides Victory

Oil, or rather the lack thereof, became the Achilles heel for the two major Axis powers. Neither Germany nor Japan had significant domestic oil resources. Before the outbreak of war, both Adolph Hitler and the Japanese military saw oil as the impetus to propel their civilizations into the post industrial age. It is no surprise, then, that securing oil became a priority in Hitler's "Grand Strategy," and a priority for Japan.

The United States was supplying 80% of Japan's oil as Hitler began amassing his armies. When Japan showed signs of alignment with the Third Reich in 1940, the United States froze all Japanese assets, effectively cutting their oil supply. Japan's desperation for fuel quickly became clear as the country conserved fuel and used the roots of hundreds of thousands of its precious pine trees to make aviation fuel.

Focused on the fossil fuel it needed to advance attacks, Japan captured the oil fields in Indonesia in 1941. Japan soon began producing Indonesian oil, but before long faced a new problem. In order to get oil from Indonesia back to the Far East, Japanese oil tankers would have to pass across the Pacific Rim—well within range of the U.S. Naval Fleet at Pearl Harbor, Hawaii.

On December 7, 1941, Japan attacked Pearl Harbor, and within a few hours destroyed the backbone of the U.S. Pacific Naval Fleet. Japan had redefined the rules of combat, but they didn't stop there. The United States soon felt the brunt of a new form of attack: Kamikaze fighters. The use of men as armed missiles, a tactic unthinkable to the United States, was in part motivated by Japan's fuel shortage. A plane that did not return to home base required only half as much fuel.

Despite its control of Indonesian oil fields, Japan would continue to experience fuel shortages throughout the war as American submarines punched holes in Japanese supply lines. Oil became the deciding factor in Japan's inability to maintain sustained attacks on multiple fronts.

Germany's invasion of European, Russian, and African fronts brought the need for both sides to travel farther, faster, with more munitions. "Mobile warfare" became the standard in WWII, and oil quickly replaced the horse as the centerpiece of military planning.

Unlike Japan, Germany got much of its oil from an unconventional source. A German chemical cartel, I. G. Farben, developed, among other things, synthetic oil production from coal. [14] I. G. Farben gave Germany the one thing it needed most: fuel. Like the Japanese with their Kamikaze attacks, Hitler conserved oil by using *blitzkrieg* attacks to overrun his enemies quickly, before the oil needed to fuel extended battles became a factor. Once Hitler moved his army into Russia, thus lengthening his supply lines, he acted to control Russian oil fields.

Oil Changes the Tide

Despite I. G. Farben's "coal fuel" and Japan's control of Indonesian oil, both Germany and Japan suffered from inadequate fuel supplies. The tide began to turn against the Axis powers after Nazi forces were defeated in North Africa because the British intercepted German fuel supplies crossing the Mediterranean. Meanwhile, the United States and England were systematically destroying Nazi coal-to-fuel processing facilities. Consequently, Germany's sophisticated airplanes were towed to runways by cows.

Even though the United States supplied 65% of the world's oil at the time, the Allied forces also faced setbacks due to oil supply disruptions. General Patton himself said, "If I could steal some gas I could win this war."[15] There is even speculation that if Patton had the oil he needed, he could have ended the war nine months sooner. Japanese and Nazi forces were, however, overrun by the well-oiled Allied Forces, who closed the theater of war by bombing Hiroshima, Nagasaki, Dresden, and Hamburg.

1950-1960: A Different Kind of Boom

Oil had fueled our armies and helped America and her allies win both World Wars. By the time the Second World War ended, oil production was skyrocketing, and with no war to fuel, oil was literally gushing into the world markets. With oil flowing freely and soldiers returning home, America had reason to celebrate.

Cheap energy paved the way for a higher standard of living for a relatively young American population, resulting in the "Baby Boom" of the 1950s. As this large population of children became young adults in the sixties, they further changed America with lifestyles based on what seemed like a limitless supply of oil and plastic products. With money in their pockets and the freedom to go anywhere, young Americans developed new ways to eat, new places to meet, new music, new hairstyles, and even new uses for the automobile.

At their core, four of the seven huge oil corporations that survived the World Wars were still children of Standard Oil. The new oil boom would soon send all oil company profits soaring and give the seven largest petroleum companies unprecedented global economic dominance. The "Seven Sisters," as they were called, (Exxon,

Chevron, Texaco, Shell, BP, Mobil, and Gulf), knew that the cheapest, most accessible oil on the planet was concentrated in the Middle East. Seeing billions in potential near-term profits, Middle Eastern governments began to demand 50% of the profits made from oil in 1950, shortly after the close of the Second World War.

The governments of oil exporting countries, however, had no power to set oil prices. Instead, the Seven Sisters set the price of oil, and determined what 50% of their revenues actually meant in terms of payments to the producing governments. Producing countries would count on oil selling at a certain price, only to have that price slashed as oil companies undercut competitors. Oil exporting governments became increasingly uneasy with the 50/50 agreement. Fluctuating oil prices caused economic destabilization of the exporting countries, making their age-old struggles for power even more difficult.

The situation came to a head in 1960, when worldwide oil production began to outpace demand, creating a buyers' market. To remain competitive, Western companies, led by Standard Oil of New Jersey, again cut the price of oil without consulting the producing countries.[16] Tensions from producing governments turned to outrage. Threatened by the possibility that exporting countries would nationalize their oil fields and altogether cut out their Western partners, oil companies attempted a series of apologies. Shell even raised the price of oil by a few cents. But the damage had already been done.

The Rise of OPEC

Until 1960 both oil exporting governments and oil companies had pushed for increasing production to increase revenue. Juan Pablo Pérez Alfonzo, the Venezuelan oil minister, had spent time in America studying the Texas Railroad Commission and wanted to find a way to maximize profits from Venezuelan oil sales while minimizing foreign intervention.[17] The 1960 price cut provided the motivation Pérez Alfonzo needed to bring exporting countries together. Alfonzo joined with Sheikh Abdullah Tariki, Saudi Arabia's Minister of Petroleum, and representatives from Iraq, Iran, and Kuwait, to form a consortium called the Organization of the Petroleum Exporting Countries (OPEC). At the time these five founding members of OPEC produced over 80% of the world's oil exports. The twofold purpose of OPEC was (and still is) to: 1) Set limits to production that all members agree upon, and 2) Defend the price of oil.[18]

OPEC works on the basis that each country has a fixed quantity of proven oil reserves. All the oil reserves of all the OPEC countries are added together, and each OPEC nation represents a percentage of the total. Each year OPEC sets a total output, and each country's individual output is decided by their percentage. In this way, OPEC maintains relatively stable oil prices and maintains a steady flow of cash to producing governments.

At first OPEC did not pose a threat to the United States, even though U.S. oil consumption had risen tenfold from 1930 to 1970. But in 1970 the United States reached its all-time high in domestic oil production at 11.3 million barrels per day. For the first time ever, in March of 1971 the Texas Railroad Commission allowed 100% U.S. production, eliminating any excess production capacity that could be used in times of crisis.

And so it was that every day thereafter the United States would produce less oil and would become more dependent on the oil-producing governments of the Middle East.

America Hits Its Peak

The U.S. oil production peak was no surprise to geologists, who had known with some certainty since the mid-1950s that the United States would hit its peak in the 1970s. In 1956 M. King Hubbert, a geophysicist for Shell Oil, announced that production of American petroleum started at zero, would one day end at zero, and somewhere in-between would hit a peak. Based on the *ultimate recoverable reserves* (URR)[19] and a bell curve, Hubbert estimated that the date of *peak oil* production in the United States would occur close to 1970. As predicted, U.S. oil production peaked at 11.3 million barrels per day in 1970.[20] From the peak of production onward, the United States would produce less oil every year.

While Hubbert predicted the peak oil production of the United States with accuracy, his work was derided by the international oil community. "Hubbert's Peak," as it was called, unveiled a truth that

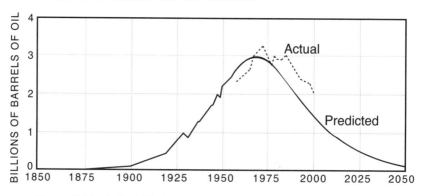

Hubbert's Peak
Actual vs. Predicted U.S. Oil Production

Source: *Hubbert's Peak, The Impending World Oil Shortage*

The solid line represents U.S. oil production up to 1956 and Dr. Hubbert's prediction for future U.S. oil production; the dotted line shows actual U.S. oil production after 1956. The dips in the dotted line, not predicted by Hubbert, correspond to the oil shocks of the 1970s.

few people in the oil business were willing to accept: just as the United States experienced a peak in oil production, so too would the planet experience peak production. If Hubbert's science was accurate, the oil industry itself would have to prepare for a peak in worldwide oil production, followed by a permanent decline. In a business that relies on a limitless supply of a limited resource, Hubbert's predictions continue to elicit debate.

The end of over one hundred years of surplus oil in the United States also marked the end of our nation's vast security margin of excess production capacity. By 1973 oil imports into the United States had risen to 6 million barrels of oil per day.[21] The worldwide security margin of oil production is arguably the most important factor in determining the economics and politics surrounding oil. By closely monitoring security margins rather than reserves, we can foresee when demand will outpace production and can extrapolate when potential energy shortages may occur. As the United States would learn three years after it hit peak production, the loss of its security margin spelled trouble.

1973-1978: The Oil Shocks

On October 6, 1973, the date of the Jewish holy day Yom Kippur, Egypt and Syria attacked Israel, and America watched in horror as other Arab nations rallied around the attack. The blow against Israel triggered a domino effect of hatred from the Arab world toward countries that supported Israel, and the OPEC nations stopped oil exports to, among other countries, the United States of America.

In one fell swoop, OPEC paralyzed the United States. "The Arab Oil Embargo," as it was called, stopped the entire U.S. economy by pushing U.S. gas prices up 40% and creating public panic. Lines at many American gas stations stretched for miles.

Luckily for the United States, there was still oil in Alaska and the North Sea. Production on those fields began pumping oil back into the veins of America, and the United States reestablished a small security margin. Peace was also reestablished in the Middle East, but even that didn't last for long.

In 1979 the United States was again off guard when oil supplies were suddenly constricted, leaving the nation reeling. The events leading up to the '79 shock are a testament to the danger of American dependence on Mid East energy supplies.

For more than 100 years, Britain had troops in the Persian Gulf. In 1971 the British pulled out, leaving a military vacuum. After America's support for Israel in the 1973 Yom Kippur War, the United States was viewed an enemy of the Arab world. Fearing retaliation, Congress was hesitant to send U.S. forces to stabilize the Middle East.

The United States called on the Shah of Iran to safeguard the region and its oil. Filled with delusions of grandeur, the Shah rapidly spent money building his private army and preparing to police the region. Using the pre-OPEC model of revenue generation, he quickly forced increased oil production across the region.

Oil began flowing freely, and OPEC's grip on price controls began to slip. The Shah lined the pockets of everyone around him, including multinational companies, national Iranian leaders, and the military. But the majority of Iranian people rarely saw the benefits of their own natural resources, and the Shah's popularity among them declined. Iran's oil income rose to $30 billion a year, and the Shah and a small group of elite hoarded most of the oil revenue.[22] Meanwhile, the overproduction of oil brought on by the Shah's mismanagement again pushed oil prices down in the late 1970s. Lacking its once-steady supply of foreign dollars, Iran experienced a substantial deficit. Fed up with the economic roller coaster, the people of Iran took action.

Strikes in the oil fields left Iranian oil production, which had been at five million barrels per day, at a standstill.[23] A diverse group of clergy, merchants, and militia united in a successful coup d'etat, toppling the Shah's regime. Ayatollah Khomeini returned from exile and took control of Iran. His open hatred of the West exacerbated the already tense situation. With nobody at the helm of the Middle East, and with Western influence toppled, the price of oil spiraled out of control.

1976-1980: Crisis in Confidence

With oil at $40 a barrel, many Americans believed that we had entered a permanent oil shortage. Recognizing what he called a "crisis in confidence" in America's ability to provide consistent energy to its own population, President Jimmy Carter attempted a course correction for the United States. Like Nixon before him, Carter believed the only way the United States could ever achieve independence from the Middle East was for Americans to rise to a position of energy independence. Unlike Nixon, however, Carter was intent on letting the American public know exactly how he felt about the energy situation.

Carter, a mild-mannered peanut farmer from Georgia, turned heads when in 1979, during his nationally televised "Crisis in Confidence Speech," he wore a sweater to symbolize the simple ways Americans could conserve energy. In his speech Carter said: "In little more than two decades we've gone from a position of energy independence to one in which almost half the oil we use comes from foreign countries." Carter was as displeased with the results of the shift toward Mid East oil as most Americans. "This intolerable dependence on foreign oil," he said, "threatens our economic independence and the very security of our nation."[24]

The efforts of Presidents Nixon and Carter, as well as their administrations' efforts, led to landmark successes in increasing the energy efficiency and the energy independence of the United States. U.S. oil consumption dropped by 8% and gasoline consumption dropped by 5% during the first year of Carter's plan. The plan allocated $227 billion for mass transit and alternative energy, paving the way for the development of new bus, rail, and carpool systems. Thus in many cities gasoline consumption declined further. The plan quadrupled solar energy funding and created the Solar Energy and Energy Conservation Bank, giving solar research and development a much-needed boost. Ethanol production skyrocketed to 500 million gallons a year, reducing U.S. gasoline consumption at that time by nearly 10%.[25]

During the late 1970s, the U.S. government became interested in the increased production of domestic energy of any type. Under Carter's plan, coal and natural gas production increased substantially and $22 billion was allocated into the development of synthetic fuels from both. Oil exploration increased, resulting in new deepwater discoveries in the Gulf of Mexico, soon to be a tremendous resource.

Carter's energy program revitalized the U.S. economy by increasing efficiency. After only four years, the United States had reduced its oil imports by an impressive 25%. and the energy efficiency of the American economy had improved so much that it took 3½% less energy to produce a constant dollar of GNP than it did in January 1977.[26] Despite Carter's warnings that his plan needed support to continue, the economy was already showing signs of bouncing back and much of the impetus created under his administration was soon lost.

CHAPTER 2

The End of Cheap Oil

"The Stone Age did not end for lack of stone, and the oil age will end long before the world runs out of oil."

Sheikh Zaki Yamani, former Saudi Arabian oil minister

The majority of the world's daily oil supply flows from a surprisingly small number of oil fields. In fact, over 20% of the world's daily oil comes from just fourteen giant oil fields. These "oil giants," which have fueled the rise of nations and ushered in the industrial age, are an average of forty-four years old. While new fields found in the last few decades will never produce more than 250,000 barrels per day, the largest of the giants–the Ghawar field in Saudi Arabia–still produces over 500,000 barrels per day.[1]

Early oil explorers, or *wildcatters*, relied on hunches, best guesses, or local rumors to decide where to drill for oil. At the beginning of the oil exploration era, sophisticated equipment was unnecessary to find the massive underground stores of oil. Today, seismic equipment, deep bore drills, satellite mapping, Global Positioning

Systems, and 3-D imaging allow explorers to find even the smallest pockets of oil.

Better technology has not, however led to substantial increases in the amount of oil being discovered. "We can find a needle in a haystack," says fifty-year veteran petroleum geologist Colin Campbell, "but it is still a needle."[2] While worldwide oil discovery in the 1960s had reached as high as 55 billion barrels per year, discovery in the 1980s ranged from a high of 41 billion barrels to a low of 19 billion barrels per year. Worldwide discovery is now down to 7 billion barrels per year and falling. Today we discover less than one barrel of oil for every four barrels we use.[3]

According to the media, both production and discovery skyrocketed in the 1980s. The discrepancy between what was reported and what was actually found has to do with *reported oil reserves*.

Responding to the climate of scarcity created by the previous decade's oil shocks, oil-producing countries made grandiose reassessments in their reported reserves in the 1980s. Between 1985 and 1990, six of the eleven members of OPEC (including Saudi Arabia) increased their reserves by at least 42%–with no justification of significant discoveries. The combined OPEC increase in reported reserves totaled 287 billion barrels–roughly one third of all of the oil that has been produced to date on Earth. Under OPEC, oil-producing nations have much to gain from increased reserves–namely, increased production and increased profits.[4] Using these spurious statistics, the ongoing worldwide "oil discovery plot" shot upward and the future of oil discovery looked bright. Meanwhile, oil consumption was increasing and the actual yearly rate of oil discovery was declining.

During the past decade, however, the silence enshrouding the discovery decline has lifted as graphs depicting accurate oil discovery appeared in *Scientific American* and *The Oil and Gas Journal*. The media is only now beginning to cover the pivotal news that geologists around the world have known since the mid-1980s: that

World Oil Reserves and Discoveries

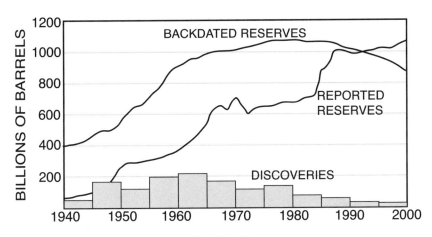

Source: Scientific American, March 1998

The way reserves are reported gives the illusion that more oil is continually being discovered, while properly backdating the revised reserves to the date the oil field was discovered shows a more accurate picture of oil discoveries.

90% of all conventional oil on the planet has already been discovered.[5] Since we can only produce the oil that has been discovered, we know that production must eventually follow discovery downward toward zero. What is less obvious, however, is that this downward trend has already begun within the largest and oldest oil field on Earth, and the decline of this field may point to the beginning of the decline of worldwide oil production altogether.

The Elephants

According to ExxonMobil, the largest oil discoveries were made in 1937, 1948, 1960, 1975, and 1985. During these periods of intense discovery, geologists identified 1,311 potential oil reservoirs on Planet Earth. Some of those reservoirs have been divided into multiple fields, resulting in over four thousand oil fields with almost one million individual wells today.

World Oil Discovery
According to ExxonMobil

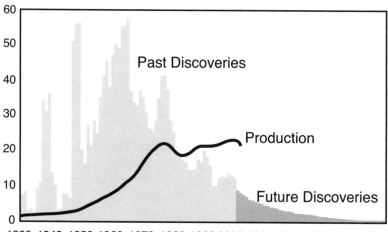

Source: Oil & Gas Journal, June 2003

But these large numbers provide a false sense of security. Almost half of the 82.5 million barrels of oil we produced each day in 2004 came from just 3% of these oil fields. Almost 70% of our daily oil supply comes from oil fields discovered prior to 1970.[6] These super giants, as they are now called, were once known as "the Elephants." The largest of the Elephants is Ghawar, discovered in 1948 in Saudi Arabia.

Saudi Arabia was formerly the largest of the *swing producers*. A swing producer refers to any country that has excess production capacity (also know as a *security margin*). Historically, swing producers acted like savings accounts in the world oil-supply bank. When demand for oil rose, the swing producers opened their oil taps, releasing more oil onto the world markets and staving off major price hikes. Today, Saudi Arabia, which produces 25% of the world's oil, is thought to be producing to the limit of its capacity.

Like the United States, Saudi Arabia is investing little into the construction of new refineries because of zero potential for a positive return on investment.

While Saudi Arabia originally reported its *Ultimate Recoverable Reserves* (URR) to be 170 billion barrels of oil in 1989, its URR increased to 258 billion barrels in 1990, adding almost 90 billion barrels of potentially recoverable oil.[7] According to many geologists, this revision was based on Saudi Arabia's desire to retain its status as the largest oil-exporting nation under OPEC, rather than on actual discoveries of new oil.

Since Saudi Arabia claimed it had more oil than was previously thought, the country was allowed to produce more oil under OPEC, taking the lion's share of world oil production and the majority of the profits. During the Gulf Wars of the 1990s and until 2002, Saudi Arabia produced a total of 35 billion barrels of oil, exceeding its previous quota and raking in billions in U.S. dollars. Today, Saudi Arabia still claims it has 258 billion barrels of oil–the same quantity it had in 1990. Meanwhile, the Saudis claim no new oil discoveries.

Why did Saudi Arabia increase its URR without substantiating discoveries? Why didn't Saudi Arabia subtract the 35 billion barrels of oil it produced in the 1990s from its total reserves? And, more importantly, how much oil does the world's number one exporter really have?

An Elephant Falls in the Desert

The largest of the Elephants is the Ghawar field. Located in the east-central region of Saudi Arabia along the Persian Gulf, the field has produced 55-65% of all Saudi Arabia's oil from 1951 through 2004.[8] In 2004, the Ghawar field produced 5.5% of the planet's

Middle East - Persian Gulf Region

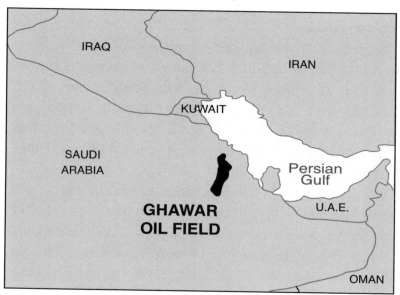

Source: Simmons and Co., *The World's Giant Oilfields*

daily total of 82.5 million barrels of oil. Thus, Ghawar's production has tremendous influence on the United States and the rest of the world.

While there had been whispers at energy conferences that Ghawar was faltering, hard data was, until recently, nonexistent. Things changed after the September 11th attacks, when Saudi Arabia opened its doors to the Western media in an attempt to look less like a breeding ground for terror and more like America's well-intentioned oil-producing neighbor. New information has since begun to flow. Perhaps the most disturbing piece of new data on Ghawar comes from Saudi Arabia's own oil company, Saudi Aramco. According to an article published by the New York Times, Saudi Aramco claims that the rate of decline of production in the Ghawar field is about 8% per year.[9] Using the *Rule of 72* (an equation used to determine how long it will take for something that is growing to double, or something that is declining to be cut in half),[10] we can deduce that the available oil in the field will be cut in half within ten years.[11] Such a rapid rate of decline spells certain death for the Ghawar field and certain death for Saudi Arabia's production of "cheap" oil.

Desperate Measures

When approximately half the oil in an oil field has been extracted, the pressure in the field begins to drop. Steam and/or water may be injected into the oil field to push the remaining oil out. Injection keeps the pressure in the field high and stabilizes production. Injection, however, is a losing battle. The more oil that leaves the field, the more water must be injected. As the field fills with water, a mix of water and oil flows out of the producing well. The percentage of water at these wells is called the *water cut*. As the water cut increases and the oil layer thins, the quality of oil declines. The lighter, more valuable layers of oil are the first to go.

Unbeknownst to many in the Western world, wellhead pressures are dropping and water injection is increasing across the entire Ghawar field. Of the 3,400 oil wells drilled into Ghawar, most of the wells in the eastern part of the field are no longer pumping oil *out*. Instead, Saudi Aramco uses these wells to pump *in* approximately 7 million barrels of water each day. By comparison, 5 million barrels of oil are being produced in Ghawar each day.[12]

Ghawar's water cut is between 35-55%. Onsite engineers report the water cut as being much higher in some locations. For example, in the southern end of Ghawar, in the Haradh field, 500,000 barrels of water are injected each day to extract only 300,000 barrels of oil. As most fields require no water injection, or, at most, some steam injection, Ghawar's heavy water injection indicates that the end of the largest oil field on the planet may be close.[13]

Much of the recent information available on Ghawar comes from

Matt Simmons of Simmons and Company International. Simmons is not a typical whistle-blower. He is, instead, in the business of making money from oil. His company, Simmons and Company International, is an independent investment bank that specializes in the energy industry. The company has handled $62.8 billion in transactions, including 385 mergers and acquisitions valued at $49.3 billion.[14] Simmons' clients include the World Bank, the U.S. Government, Halliburton, Chase Manhattan Bank, Merrill Lynch Asset Management, Petro-Canada, The Dow Chemical Company, Fisk Corporation, and Janus Capital. Simmons has also acted as an energy advisor on an energy task force commissioned by Vice President Dick Cheney.

According to Simmons, Ghawar peaked in 1990 at just over 6.5 million barrels per day.[15] He explains that once production peaks in an oil field, it becomes increasingly more difficult to extract the oil that is left in that field. This is particularly true with Ghawar, due to its vast physical area. Simmons believes that even though Ghawar may still contain billions of barrels of oil, much of the field will soon be abandoned due to low output pressures. When referring to the Ghawar field in his company's report, *The World's Giant Oilfields*, Simmons writes, "...this ultra-giant field is now in its early stages of decline."

Ghawar's production dropped from 6.5 million barrels of oil per day in 1990 to 4.5 million barrels of oil per day in 2004, indicating that it has peaked and is now on the downward slope of production. In the words of National Iranian Oil Company's senior official, Ali Mortexa Sasam Bakhtiari: "The big risk to Saudi Arabia is that Ghawar's rate of decline increases to an alarming point. That will set bells ringing all over the oil world because Ghawar underpins Saudi output and Saudi undergirds worldwide production."[16]

Ladies and gentlemen, ring your bells.

Oil, Oil, Everywhere

In a recent article for the *Wall Street Journal* entitled "Oil, Oil, Everywhere," Peter Huber and Mark Mills lay out a plan to save America from its energy crisis. The duo, who are also authors of the recent book *The Bottomless Well*, center their argument not on a transition to non fossil fuels, but rather on a transition to oil produced from ancient *tar sands*.

Tar sands, or oil sands, are a combination of clay, sand, water, and bitumen—a thick, sticky form of crude oil. Tar sands deposits are found all over the world, with the largest deposits found in Venezuela and Alberta, Canada. The deposits were created as conventional oil seeped from deep belowground to the surface, where it was degraded into tar by water and bacteria.

"In sum," write Huber and Mills, "it costs under $5 per barrel to pump oil out from under the sand in Iraq, and about $15 to melt it out of the sand in Alberta. So why don't we just learn to love hockey and shop Canadian?"[17] The answer is simple: the extraction of oil from tar sands is extremely expensive and requires more energy than it yields in oil. Huber and Mills fail to address the economic ramifications of increasing the production cost of oil threefold (from five dollars a barrel to fifteen dollars a barrel). They also fail to address the tremendous resources needed to produce usable oil from the tar sands.

The oil content in tar sands is relatively low–ranging from 1% to 20%. Thus, two tons of sand must be mined to produce a single barrel of oil.[18] According to Sonia Shah, author of the book *Crude*, the extraction of oil from tar sands consumes vast quantities of otherwise usable energy resources. "The trouble is," says Shah, "mining oil from tar sands burns up to 1/5 of Canada's natural gas and emits no less than 6 times more carbon dioxide than producing a barrel of conventional oil, requires 6 times more fresh water than the oil it renders and leaves behind vast lakes of waste water."[19]

Oil companies ignored tar sands as a potential source of petroleum until very recently, as the price of petroleum reached record highs in the fall of 2004. Now, oil companies including ExxonMobil, Chevron/Texaco, and Royal Dutch Shell are investing in oil sands extraction in Alberta. The $5 billion Athabasca Oil Sands Project, launched by Shell and ChevronTexaco in 2004, yields roughly 155,000 barrels of oil per day. Meanwhile, similar projects in Venezuela's Orinoco basin yield roughly 500,000 barrels a day.[20] By comparison, the world currently consumes more than 80 million barrels of oil per day.

Huber and Mills deviate from the thinking of the Department of Energy, the National Renewable Energy Laboratory, The Rocky Mountain Institute, and other proponents of high tech, high efficiency solutions to a shrinking national oil supply by asserting that our "energy supply is infinite" and that "the 'waste' of energy is a virtue, not a vice."[21] Ignoring the political and economic reality of depleted domestic oil supplies, the two authors focus their argument on a trapped oil reserve–the only cost for which is a nearly endless supply of energy and resources with which to process it.[22]

Oil's Downward Slide

Estimates for the total amount of oil that existed prior to production range from 1.5 trillion barrels to 3 trillion barrels. The majority of geologists peg the total world endowment somewhere close to 2 trillion barrels of *conventional* oil–oil extracted through conventional drilling as opposed to oil contained in tar sands. Consuming the first trillion barrels of oil took approximately 150 years. Undoubtedly we will consume the majority of the next trillion barrels faster. How much faster will depend on the rate of oil consumption worldwide.

Currently the world consumes approximately 31 billion barrels of oil per year. Divided into one trillion barrels, this would afford

us roughly thirty-two more years of oil. However, this oversimpli-
fication does not take into account the annual increase in world oil
consumption, as well as the political, economic, and technological
barriers to extracting, refining, and consuming the second trillion
barrels of conventional oil.

The Energy Information Administration predicts that worldwide
oil consumption would increase from 28.4 billion barrels a year in
2002 to 43 billion barrels per year by 2025.[23] We use the word *would*
because oil consumption would increase by that much if that were
possible–that is, if the oil reserves and production facilities necessary to provide the end product existed. However, they do not. Few
new refineries are being constructed because no new oil is being
created, and no substantial oil reserves are being discovered. Thus,
with no chance of recouping their investment, no bank or financier
will underwrite the billions of dollars needed for new facilities construction.

To quench the growing worldwide thirst for oil, *more* oil, not
less, would have to be extracted. While it is possible to push some
of the larger oil fields into short-term increased production, the
effect of peak production is ultimate: the world's largest oil fields,
the backbone of our oil supply, will show substantial declines in
production.

It's important for us to be aware that just because production of
oil will decline, demand will not. In fact, our rate of consumption is
increasing. One factor contributing to an increase in worldwide oil
consumption is China. China's oil demand is growing at 10-13% per
year.[24] China now manufactures about 250,000 new cars per month,
for example.

The supply pattern of the oil that sustains us is changing. In
2003 and 2004 in the United States, especially in California, we
experienced fuel shortages due to demand overshooting supply.
The reason cited for West Coast fuel shortages is that there is not

enough refining capacity to meet demand. We must keep in mind that no new refineries have been built in the United States for three decades.[25]

In short, the petroleum oil production system we have in place to carry our society forward does not inspire confidence. Worldwide demand for oil will double within twenty years. No new refineries are being built because there are no substantial quantities of new oil being discovered. The United States passed peak production in 1970, as was accurately predicted. We rely increasingly on two large oil fields in the Middle East to stabilize the growing demand for oil. But according to the physical geology of the planet, we will soon hit (and may have already hit) peak production.

The Cost of Doing Business

The price we pay at the pump for gasoline is only a fraction of the cost we as a nation pay for oil. According to the U.S. Department of Energy, supply disruptions and oil shocks have cost the United States more than $3.4 trillion over the last thirty years. And the transfer of wealth to oil-producing countries over the past thirty years has significantly increased our trade deficit by sending $1.16 trillion abroad. [26]   The U.S. Department of Energy estimates that each $1 billion of trade deficit costs America 27,000 jobs, citing oil imports as a significant cause of unemployment.[27] This is consistent with estimates from the National Defense Council Foundation (NDCF), which cites a loss of 828,400 jobs in the U.S. due to dependence on foreign oil. Finally, the NDCF estimates that we are losing $159.9 billion in GNP annually through oil imports.[28] With peak world oil production on the horizon, it is difficult, if not impossible, to calculate the substantial cost to the U.S. economy that upcoming oil constraints will have.

Today the eleven members of OPEC–Algeria, Indonesia, Iran,

Iraq, Kuwait, Libya, Nigeria, Qatar, Saudi Arabia, the United Arab Emirates, and Venezuela–produce about 40% of world oil and claim to hold more than three-quarters of the world's total proven crude oil reserves.[29] In essence, these nations hold the balance of global economic and political power.

According to Colin Campbell, veteran geologist, author, researcher, and leading advocate of the theory of Peak Oil, world oil production will be inextricably tied to the politics surrounding these countries. In his book *The Coming Oil Crisis*, Campbell explains that due to their disproportionately large oil endowments and their control over the world oil market, the Middle East oil producers "will be holding the world at ransom."[30]

Our reliance on Middle Eastern governments and their oil forces the United States and the rest of the West into compromise. To get the oil we need, we must do business with OPEC. In light of the history of oil and the unstable future this resource provides our society, we, as Americans, must ask ourselves: Is the price break we receive on foreign energy worth the sacrifice of our national sovereignty?

Oiling the Chain

An economy that lacks the basic ingredient for production–energy–will flounder. If the economy is starved of energy long enough, it will shrink, just as a person starved of food weakens and shrivels. As proof of this theory, economists point to the loss of money in the United States economy caused by petroleum imports.

The United States spends approximately $97 billion each year on oil imports. Although Canada, Mexico, Venezuela, and Nigeria currently make up the bulk of oil exports to the United States, we still import roughly 36% of our total imported oil from the Middle East. Historically, our expenditures on foreign oil are tied directly to events in the Middle East.

U.S. Expenditures on Imported Oil

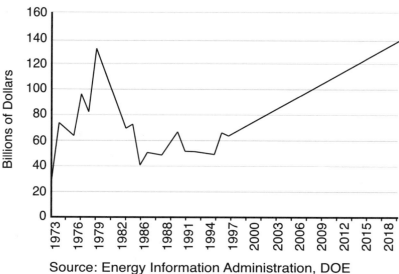

Source: Energy Information Administration, DOE

After the 1973 oil shock, U.S. expenditures on foreign oil rose sharply, from approximately $20 billion dollars to over $35 billion dollars per year. After the 1979 oil shock, yearly expenditures again rose from approximately $40 billion per year to over $65 billion per year. U.S. oil expenditures dropped during the 1980s as America pumped the remainder of our "cheap" oil from Texas and Alaska, and inexpensive North Sea oil hit the worldwide markets. According to the Energy Information Administration, which is operated by the U.S. Department of Energy, our expenditures on foreign oil began steadily increasing again in 1998, spiking at over $90 billion per year in 2000. In 2003, expenditures were at $97 billion per year and climbing.[31]

U.S. Congressman and Texas rancher Mac Thornberry says oil imports are wreaking havoc on our economy. In the Capitol Hill newspaper, *Roll Call*, Thornberry, who serves on the Armed Services Committee and the Permanent Select Committee on Intelligence, says that over 50,000 U.S. jobs have been lost since the early 1980s due to decreased oil production. "U.S. oil output now stands at 6.36 million barrels per day," adds Thornberry, "the lowest level since 1954."[32] As Thornberry accurately points out, the rise in expenditures on foreign oil corresponds to a decrease in domestic oil production and a loss of American jobs.

The Department of Energy also cites job loss as a result of oil imports, but rather than direct loss of jobs in the oil industry, the DOE cites overall job loss represented by the trade deficit. A *trade deficit* is the result of a nation importing goods of greater value than the goods it exports. The trade deficit in the United States is caused largely by the increasing quantity and price of our primary import: *oil.*

In 2005 the trade deficit stood at $617.1 billion, with oil imports accounting for approximately $100 billion.[33] As the United States imports more oil at a higher price, the trade deficit increases. Since the Department of Energy estimates that every $1 billion in trade deficit is equivalent to the loss of approximately 27,000 jobs, the $100 billion-worth of oil imported into the United States each year is equivalent to the loss of approximately 2.7 million jobs.

In the strictest sense of economics, these potential jobs would be required to produce the energy needed for our nation. This assumes that the jobs would be domestic in nature because the energy to run the economy would be domestic. But since the energy represented by the trade deficit is *foreign* in nature, so are the jobs. Instead of hiring people in our country to produce energy, we are hiring people in other countries to procure our energy.

Shock Value

While the cost of oil imports to the United States economy–both in lost cash and lost jobs–is substantial, it is dwarfed by the cost of the oil shocks. The National Defense Council Foundation (NDCF), a nonpartisan, nonprofit think tank, spent a year analyzing the hidden costs of petroleum. Their analysis of the 1973, 1979, and 1991 oil shocks puts the combined costs of these shocks at between $2.3 trillion and $2.5 trillion. By comparison, Oak Ridge National Laboratories, the Department of Energy's largest science and research laboratory, estimates the cost of the oil shocks at $4 trillion.

In the case of the United States, we import approximately 60% of our oil and will soon, according to our own Department of Energy, import 80% of our oil. Our primary and most expensive import is oil. In essence, valuable cash, which would normally be recycled back into our economy—creating jobs, paving roads, paying for healthcare and education—is vanishing. Oil, the energy resource critical to running our economic machine, is coming to us at a greater price each year.

The economic energy forecast for the United States looks grim. Our nation is caught in a cycle in which the oil we import will always be more expensive than the commodities we export. As an economy, we have a negative balance of trade. The United States is in the red. It's clear how we got into this position, but how do we get out?

The Changing Faces of the Seven Sisters

Judging by the merger frenzy of the Seven Sisters oil companies, oil depletion is taking its toll on the business of oil production. Shrinking oil reserves have resulted in the seven companies cannibalizing themselves. According to Campbell, "They merge and buy their own stock because all they can do is downsize…If things were fine and growing demand really could be met there would be expansion in these companies and room for everyone."[34]

Today four of the original seven oil companies remain. Chevron bought Gulf and then merged with Texaco; BP bought Amoco. Shell bought a number of smaller companies, including Enterprise, which holds North Sea oil reserves. And Exxon merged with Mobil. Thus, the large companies that remain today are: BP, Shell, ExxonMobil, and Chevron-Texaco.

Besides cutting their oil exploration budgets, which now average 5% as opposed to 30% in the 1960s, these companies are changing their images. BP has initiated a stock buyback program and has admitted that it will make no efforts to increase oil production. Instead, it says, production is expected to decline. Meanwhile, BP and Shell are both playing the environmental field. While some environmental organizations see their handiwork as *greenwashing* (the practice of appearing green without actually changing corporate practices), it appears that at least two of the four remaining sisters are beginning to put their money where their mouths are.

In 1995, when Lord John Browne became CEO of British Petroleum, BP was a medium-sized company with dwindling North Sea reserves. The largest producer of North Sea oil, BP pumped 2 million barrels per day from the region in the 1980s. By the late 1990s, production had declined to one million barrels per day. Browne, unfettered by BP's apparent decline, began an aggressive marketing and merger campaign. In 1999 he headed BP's merger with Amoco in a deal worth $140 billion. Next came BP's purchase of Atlantic Richfield Co. (ARCO) for $27 billion.[35]

BP Solar bought the solar panel manufacturer Solarex for $45 million, transforming BP Solar overnight into one of the largest renewable energy companies in the world. Following suit, Shell began an aggressive solar investment campaign, dedicating $500 million to renewable energy research and development over the next ten years.[36]

Despite opposition even from within BP itself, BP's Browne has been blazing the trail toward a new image for his company. BP is working with the Pew Center for Global Climate Change, seeking advice from the non governmental organization Environmental

Defense, and has pulled out of a group known for its lobbying for drilling in the Arctic National Wildlife Refuge. Browne and BP are also working with the United Nations International Governmental Panel on Climate Change to stabilize greenhouse gases.

Taking its green effort one step further, BP officially changed both its name and its logo in the one hundred countries in which it operates. BP's new name is "Beyond Petroleum." And its new logo, reminiscent of a sunflower, has replaced the old BP shield at service stations across the United States and around the world. BP is also installing solar panels on some of its service stations with the goal of providing between 10% and 15% of each station's power needs.[37]

While the majority of BP's revenue still results from annual sales of 3.5 billion barrels of oil and gas, its image shift and aggressive "green" campaign have brought substantial increases in a form of green that makes shareholders happy – profits. Browne has transformed the company into the second largest oil company in the world, with $174 billion in gross annual revenue. BP now operates 15,500 service stations in the United States and a total of 26,500 service stations worldwide.[38] The company is actively involved in the solar and hydrogen industries. BP is even selling biodiesel at select service stations in the Midwestern United States.

An Industry Evolves

Looking back over the history of oil in the United States, three points are clear:

1) Oil, or an equivalent energy source, is critical to the survival of our nation;

2) The business of oil production is becoming unstable because of decreasing worldwide oil reserves; and

3) America's energy security depends on a rapid and aggressive transition away from foreign oil sources and overconsumption of energy, and toward domestically produced energy and energy efficiency.

In short, the companies we have heretofore known as "oil companies," may be critical to moving America toward a sustainable energy future. In retrospect, these companies have been supplying an energy medium. And whether it is oil or another form of energy, the United States, and the rest of the world, will continue to demand energy.

Creating the level of energy infrastructure that will carry our nation well into the twenty-first century will require a substantial investment of capital and labor from both the public and private sectors. According to Herman Scheer, author of *The Solar Economy: Renewable Energy for a Sustainable Global Future*, the finance for the investments in renewable energy must come from the fossil energy business.[39] Companies like "Beyond Petroleum" may be doing just that. By laying the groundwork for large-scale investment and development of a renewable-energy-based economy, "oil companies" may soon transition to "energy companies." If the transition is to happen, it will soon place the energy companies in a position to fuel the future of our country, and possibly our planet.

Diesel: The Man and His Vision

"If at present the applicability of vegetable and animal oils to Diesel motors seems insignificant, it may in time reach an importance equal to that of liquid fuels and tar oil."

Rudolf Diesel, Inventor of the diesel engine (b.1858 – d.1913)

I n April 2002 something unusual occurred at the annual Volkswagen stockholders meeting in Hamburg, Germany. Volkswagen Chairman Ferdinand Piech arrived at the meeting in a black aerodynamic vehicle he had driven from VW headquarters in Wolfsburg. On the drive the car, which had been developed in complete secrecy for three years, averaged 317 miles per gallon–the highest fuel efficiency ever achieved by a four-wheeled passenger automobile. The vehicle in question wasn't a hybrid or a hydrogen car. It was a diesel.

For some time, Volkswagen's engineering team had been working on the design for a "3-Liter" car–a car that could achieve a rate of efficiency, in European terms, of three liters of fuel consumed for 100 kilometers of travel. This translates to about 80 miles per gallon. Hoping to reach a milestone for the automotive industry, Volkswagen decided to take the challenge one step further and develop a vehicle capable of traveling 100 kilometers on one single liter of fuel – roughly 250 miles per gallon. Not only did they hit the mark, they set a new world record.[1]

While the Volkswagen engineers had to make many design innovations in their "1-Liter Concept Car," they could not compromise in two areas: safety and fuel efficiency. The choice of a carbon fiber body was a natural one, since carbon fiber is stronger than steel and lighter than aluminum. But the engine was another story. No available engine could perform to Volkswagen's lofty specifications. They decided to base their prototype engine on the most efficient technology available: diesel. They started from the drawing board and redesigned the diesel engine from the ground up. What they achieved is a new world standard for efficiency, cleanliness, and power (the prototype accelerated to 60 miles per hour effortlessly). In many ways, Volkswagen was continuing the dreams of an engineer whose ideas on efficiency had been dormant for almost a century.

Rudolf Christian Karl Diesel (1858-1913) and his engine shaped our society. Diesel engines were revolutionary: they were far more efficient than the steam and gasoline engines of their time; they were incredibly durable and powerful. Today, diesel engines have become the backbone of the worldwide transportation infrastructure that moves food, goods, and energy supplies. Without diesel engines, our society would not function. Diesel vehicles seen in European showrooms now push the 80-mile-per-gallon mark, and prototype diesel vehicles consistently demonstrate between 80-300 miles per gallon.[2] Almost 100 years after their development, diesels continue to excel. As Rudolf Diesel himself believed before his mysterious death, the diesel engine has not yet reached its full potential.

Diesel's Early Years

Rudolf Christian Karl Diesel was born in France in 1858, one year before Edwin L. Drake struck oil in Pennsylvania. His father, Theodor, was a struggling leather worker and shoemaker who had emigrated from the city of Augsburg in the province of Bavaria. He met his wife, Elise, a fellow native of Augsburg, in Paris. She came from a wealthier merchant family; together they had three children: Louise, Rudolf, and Emma. Truly part of multiple cultures, young Rudolf learned three languages. At home he spoke German, at school French, and with his mother who had been a governess in London, English. As a child, Diesel was fascinated with science and known for his curiosity. He once opened up the gas jets in his family's apartment, nearly blowing up the entire building.

By the time young Rudolf finished elementary school in 1870, France was about to declare war on Prussia. With the onset of war, the Diesels and all other foreigners were forced to leave Paris. They relocated to England, where Rudolf's father earned a meager wage of one pound per week. Rudolf acquired a deep fear of poverty from his youth – a fear that would stay with him for life. Thanks to the generosity of his father's cousin, Rudolf was able to move back to Augsburg to attend a three-year technical high school.

By the time he turned fourteen, Diesel had decided to become an engineer. As a child, he had already been distinguished as an exceptional student, receiving a medal for superior performance from his elementary school, the Société pour l'Instruction Élémentaire. Not only was Diesel first in his class, but he was also the youngest student ever to graduate from the Royal Technical High School, and he graduated with the highest grades ever achieved. His performance was rewarded with a scholarship to the Munich Technical University. There, Diesel befriended Lucien Vogel, a man with whom he would later work closely. Diesel continued to excel in academics and on finishing his final examinations in 1880 once again received the highest scores in the history of the school.

Diesel's mental agility was proven by his scholastic achievements, and he began working immediately for Sulzer Engine Works in Switzerland, where he learned how to build refrigeration machines and steam engines. In 1880 he was assigned to a position in Paris, where he supervised the establishment of an ammonia-based refrigeration plant. He was soon promoted to manage the sales and installations of ice machines throughout France and Belgium. Meanwhile he spent his spare time working on his own ammonia engine and a new version of the ice machine.

Building the Black Mistress

Diesel began construction of his engine at a time when the engineering and scientific communities in Europe, and particularly in Germany, were making great strides. Diesel studied the advances in internal combustion discovered by Nicolaus August Otto, Eugen Langen, Gottlieb Daimler, and Wilhelm Maybach, and based his ideas on their technologies. However, the fundamental principles of Diesel's engine were extremely different. As a student Diesel had been fascinated by the concept of *compression ignition*. In one of his science classes, he had watched a demonstration of how early Southeast Asian people created fire. In the Malayan fire piston, a small piece of tinder was placed in a hollow bamboo shoot that was capped at one end. A tight-fitting wooden rod was then shoved into the bamboo cylinder at high velocity. The makeshift piston compressed the air inside the bamboo cylinder, heating the air and igniting the tinder. This compression ignition is a basic principle of the diesel engine.

Diesel's engine required a perfectly fitting piston and cylinder operating at extremely high pressure. The tight tolerances made manufacturing difficult. Diesel and Vogel built an engine based on Diesel's modified design of an internal combustion engine. At first the "Black Mistress," as Diesel called his engine, did not work. After analysis, it became clear that Diesel's design called for a larger piston so the pressure from compression would be higher. A new piston was manufactured and installed. The engine rotated smoothly at three hundred revolutions per minute, but Diesel was reluctant to attempt ignition.

The myth that Diesel's first engine exploded is untrue. On August 10, 1893, encouraged by Vogel, Diesel attempted a first combustion test. After the piston was raised up to the compression position, a small charge of gasoline was sprayed into the cylinder. Combustion was instantaneous, and the force of the piston rising back up inside the cylinder shot the indicator gauge on top of the engine up to 80 atmospheres, at which time the indicator gauge itself exploded, throwing metal and glass shards across Diesel's shop and narrowly missing Diesel and Vogel. While the indicator gauge shattered, Diesel's engine was unharmed, and its performance was proof that his theory of heat combustion worked.

Diesel and Vogel faced a secondary setback: they needed a consistent fuel delivery system. It took five years to develop the needed fuel injection technology, and by 1897 Diesel had made so many changes to his engine that he had to apply for new patents. Once patented and tested, the diesel engine was poised for acceptance into the engine market.

Diesel believed that the steam engine, the mainstay of industry production, was outdated, inefficient, and in need of succession. But he wasn't the only inventor propelling the world toward internal combustion. While the diesel engine provided raw power to move massive objects, Nicolaus August Otto's gasoline engine (a.k.a. "The Otto"), which used a spark to ignite its fuel, was fast spinning and capable of rapid acceleration. Both Otto and Diesel found themselves working for a new conglomerate called Maschinenfabrik Augsburg-Nürnberg (M.A.N.). This company was responsible for incubating the development of both engines.

The introduction of Diesel's engine for heavy-duty applications and of Otto's engine for light-duty work permanently shifted society. According to Morton Grosser, author of *Diesel: The Man and the Engine*, these engines formed the basis for a vast expansion of the first Industrial Revolution. Grosser explains that the steam engine was an evolution of the available technology. The internal combustion engine, however, represented a quantum leap forward. Internal combustion engines could operate independently of weather and water flow. The new engines were far more dependable and as a result, they broke down infrequently. "The change," says Grosser, "was correctly called an Industrial Revolution."

Thus, like his contemporaries Alexander Graham Bell, Thomas Edison, the Wright Brothers, and Nicola Tesla, Rudolf Diesel played an important role in shaping our society. The diesel engine soon outpaced the steam engine in every capacity. It was smaller, lighter, substantially more efficient, used a myriad of fuel sources including vegetable oil, and was extremely reliable. By 1898 diesel engines were being manufactured and shipped across Europe and into Russia.

Diesel Visits America

The man who bought the exclusive rights to the diesel engine for North America was none other than Adolphus Busch, the same man who also brought Busch Beer to life. Despite his success in the brewery market, Busch's diesel engine franchise struggled to find its feet, and Diesel soon found himself crossing the Atlantic to help launch his engine in the United States.

Diesel traveled across America with his wife and took detailed notes of his journey. He was taken with the vastness of America and the seemingly limitless supply of resources. He was also impressed by the generosity he received from strangers and admirers during his trip. At the conclusion of his visit to America, Diesel was convinced that his engine would be poorly received in the United States because of the large supply of fuel and raw materials and the lack of cultural attention to efficiency.

After his visit, Diesel predicted that air pollution would become an acute problem for America and would eventually be a factor in determining the design of engines for the U.S. market. He also claimed that the diesel locomotive would gain very slow acceptance, but once it was accepted, it would be more widely used in the United States than in any other country.

Diesel encouraged Americans to work from the basis of efficiency, rather than from the basis of limitless resources. He commented repeatedly on the American business model of looking at the initial cost of an engine, rather than both the initial cost and the operational cost. "The word 'efficiency,' which is the basis of every contract in Europe," said Diesel, "is unknown to a vast portion of Americans."[3] In one visit, Rudolf Diesel successfully predicted what would take Americans almost 100 years to learn: pollution and waste are not unfortunate by-products of industrialization but rather signs of poor engineering, and our industries, to be sustainable, would have to become efficient and clean.

Diesel's observations about his engine's slow emergence into the American market were also correct. Because of their heavier castings and the accuracy of the machining necessary for their construction, American diesel engines continued to be about three times more expensive per unit of power than their gasoline counterparts.[4] It was not until the introduction of diesel engines into locomotives that Rudolf Diesel's invention truly found acceptance in the United States.

Diesel's Mysterious Death

Rudolf Diesel spent money as if it would never run out. Perhaps as a means to cover his childhood fears of poverty, he built a lavish house, kept many servants, and lived in great comfort. But Diesel's spending habits pushed him to work continuously, even after his engine was being successfully manufactured and distributed around the globe. Compounding his stress were numerous lawsuits against him, all of which claimed that he had "stolen" the idea for his engine. Among those suing Diesel were Nicolaus August Otto and Eugen Langen of Otto & Cie, who held patents on the gasoline engine. These inventors were extremely adversarial towards Diesel and other engine inventors. Otto & Cie's patents and legal actions were seen as a stranglehold on the development of the internal combustion engine.

Keen to expand its empire, Germany declared war on France and Russia soon after the onset of World War I. Not long thereafter Britain entered the war against Germany, and the stage was set for the world's first mechanized war. Diesel was a pacifist, and the role his engine played in warfare disturbed him. He had business ties and friends on both sides of what was quickly becoming a world-wide conflict. His divided allegiance may have cost him his life.

Rudolf Diesel, whose engines were being installed in the German U-boat submarines (Unterseebooten), was a good friend of the English inventor Sir Charles Parsons, creator of the Parsons Turbine, the most efficient steam engine yet invented. Parsons' turbines were being installed in five *Queen Elizabeth* battleships – the fastest, most powerful warships in the world. Diesel was also a consultant to the British Diesel Company, which was investigating the use of diesel engines in their naval vessels. The Prussians, soon to be unified as "Germans," knew that their diesel engines gave them superior naval abilities and that if Diesel collaborated with the English, the Germans would lose a distinct tactical advantage.

Parsons and Diesel planned to meet on October 1, 1913, to discuss plans to use the diesel engine in the British Naval fleet. As the journey neared, Diesel's behavior became quite erratic. Diesel sent his wife and servants away and called his eldest son, Rudolf, Jr., to his home. He led his son through the house, showing him the function of each of his keys as well as the location of important papers. When his wife and servants returned to the house, they found many papers had been burned.

On September 28, 1913, Diesel wrote to Rudolf, Jr., complaining of increased headaches, insomnia, and heart pain. He then gave his wife an overnight bag and insisted she not open it. The next afternoon, September 29, Diesel boarded the cross-channel steamship *Dresden* at Antwerp. He ate dinner with George Carels, a friend, and retired for the evening. The next morning Diesel was nowhere to be found. Carels reported Diesel's absence to the officer in command and learned that a petty officer had discovered Diesel's hat and coat neatly folded under the stern railing. Upon further investigation, Diesel's notebook was found on his bedside table with a cross inscribed under the date September 29th.

Eleven days later, on October 10, the Belgian steamer *Coertsen* sighted a body floating at sea. The crew took from the body a coin purse, a medicine kit, and a spectacle case. Eugen Diesel, Rudolf's son, identified them all as belonging to his father. Martha Diesel, Rudolf's wife, would find twenty thousand marks in cash in the overnight bag her husband had given her. A financial audit of Diesel's banking revealed all accounts closed and a substantial sum owed on loans.

Rudolf Diesel's death was presumed a suicide by the Germans. But English newspapers reported possible foul play by the Germans or French. While we may never know the exact circumstances of Diesel's death, we can be certain that Diesel was acutely aware of the role his engine was about to play in a war the scale of which had never been seen. As a young boy, he had shared his childhood among three cultures that would now use his invention to shed each other's blood. As a Christian and a scientist, Diesel faced the unthinkable: he had struggled through a lifetime of physical pain, had been recognized as a brilliant inventor, had devoted his entire career to the betterment of humanity through his invention, and now, in the blink of an eye, the very people whose lives he had attempted to improve were creating war machines powered by his engine. Whether he took his own life or was assassinated, Diesel stood at the precipice of a new era for humanity. Neither he nor his invention will ever be forgotten.

Powered by Peanut Oil

Before his death, Rudolf Diesel was an active supporter of vegetable oil as a fuel for his engine. In 1900 at the World's Fair in Paris, the Otto Company displayed a small diesel engine running on peanut oil. The diesel engine was not modified in any way to use vegetable oil. The engine operated so well that few people were aware of its fuel. The French government was particularly interested in the diesel engine for use in the African colonies. Since the colonies had access to large quantities of ground nuts (cashews, peanuts, and jatropha), the French government reasoned they could "grow" their own fuel source and have power without importing coal or oil.

Diesel foresaw his engine as a key component to the industrialization and prosperity of agrarian communities not endowed with fossil fuel. He spoke about "growing" fuel using the sun's energy as the main input. He was also skeptical about the long-term viability of fossil fuel itself. Diesel reasoned that by using vegetable oil as a fuel, people could be free from dependency on oil. "Motive power can be produced," he said in 1911, "even when our total store of solid and liquid fuel will be exhausted."[5] Sixty years before the first international oil shock, Rudolf Diesel accurately predicted that his engine would be instrumental in a society facing fossil fuel supply restrictions.

Rudolf Diesel believed the resources of petroleum in countries such as Africa and America were low. He understood that if industrialization was to occur internationally, his engine would be a key element in energy systems independent of oil and coal. It is safe to say that the fuel and the engines that evolved from Diesel's original vegetable-oil-fueled diesel engines, *biodiesel* and *turbodiesel engines*, stand to make a significant contribution to a society with a greater demand for energy than there is supply.

Diesel's Dream Machine

Diesel based his engine theory on a short essay by Sadi Carnot called *Reflections on the Motive Power of Fire (Reflexions sur la puissance motrice de feu)*. Carnot emphasized the first law of thermodynamics: *Heat and mechanical energy are never created or destroyed; instead they only change form.* The critical challenge for Diesel was transforming heat into mechanical energy efficiently. Diesel wanted to build an engine that converted the maximum amount of heat (in this case, the burning of a fuel source) to mechanical energy (movement of the piston).

As Carnot correctly pointed out, the more efficient the design, the less heat is lost. Thus, the hotter the temperature in the cylinder at the end of the power stroke, the more energy wasted as exhaust. Diesel based his engine design on Carnot's three ideal conditions for an efficient heat engine:

1) The temperature in the cylinder at the beginning of the power stroke must be as high as possible.
2) The temperature of the exhaust gas in the cylinder should be as cool as possible at the end of the power stroke.
3) The cooling of the exhaust gas should occur instantaneously as the gas increases in volume so that no heat is lost to the cylinder walls.[6]

While many designers attempted to follow these principles, none was more dedicated or came closer to perfecting them than Rudolf Diesel and the diesel engine. In fact, Carnot's principles themselves became known as "the original Diesel cycle."[7]

How the Diesel Engine Works

The diesel engine works by *compression ignition*. Compression ignition is based on the principle that the temperature of a gas increases with pressure. The air in the cylinder/combustion chamber is compressed and its temperature rises above the flash point of the fuel. Fuel is then injected into the combustion chamber and ignites almost instantly. No spark is needed.

The *spark ignition* engine, on the other hand, uses an electrically generated spark to ignite a mixture of air and gasoline. The diesel engine needs no spark plugs, no ignition coil, no distributor, and no carburetor. Most diesel engines contain *glow plugs*, small electric heaters that help heat the air inside the cylinders so the engine can start. Diesel engines are generally more reliable than gasoline engines because they do not have electrical ignition components.

The virtue of the diesel engine can also be its vice. Since a diesel engine uses compression to ignite its fuel, the engine must have a fuel that only ignites under very high pressure. While the hydrocarbon chains that make gasoline are between seven and ten carbon groups long, diesel fuel is composed mostly of hydrocarbons that are fifteen carbons long.[8] The longer chains in diesel fuel make it more difficult to burn than gasoline. Because of the poor "atomization" of the spray in older diesel engines, the fuel spray droplet size was large (think garden hose) as opposed to more modern diesel engines, where the spray is very fine (think hair spray). The poor injection technology in older diesel engines results in the emissions of partially burned fuel in the form of soot. The black soot common to older diesels can be reduced by using biodiesel or by making a diesel engine burn fuel more efficiently.

Turbochargers and Intercoolers

The addition of modern components can make diesel engines burn fuel as cleanly as gasoline engines. Modern diesels often come with *turbochargers* and *intercoolers*. A turbocharger uses otherwise wasted exhaust gas pressure to compress air going into the *combustion chamber*, the volume inside each cylinder where air and fuel mix and explode. Forcing more air into the combustion chamber ensures more complete combustion of the fuel and can significantly increase the power of diesel engines.

An *intercooler* is a network of thin metal fins that cools air coming out of a turbocharger. As exhaust gases spin a turbocharger, the turbocharger becomes hot and heats the air going into the engine. Since hot air takes up more space, the turbocharger has to work to force air into the engine. To increase the efficiency of the turbocharger, air can be routed through an intercooler. In the same way a radiator cools water, an intercooler cools the turbocharged air using the cool air coming toward the vehicle or by circulating water through its fins. Cooling air brings oxygen molecules closer together and makes air denser. (In other words, dense air takes up the same amount of space, but has more oxygen in it.) The more oxygen that is forced into a combustion chamber, the more complete the combustion will be. Thus the addition of an intercooler and a turbocharger to a diesel engine greatly improves fuel combustion.

The Fuel System

The basic parts of the diesel fuel system are the fuel tank, the injector pump, and the injectors. The injector pump pulls fuel from the fuel tank and forces it through the injectors into the combustion chamber.

There are two ways to inject the fuel into a diesel engine. The first method is to inject the fuel directly into the cylinder; the second is to inject the fuel into a *prechamber,* where it partially combusts before entering the cylinder. These methods are called *direct injection* and *indirect injection.*

Older diesel engines commonly use indirect injection. The purpose of indirect injection was to mix the fuel and air in the prechamber by swirling them together. In more modern engines this is accomplished through high fuel-injection pressures, which create a highly atomized spray (again think hairspray) and a turbulent air/fuel mix (think cyclone). Most new diesels use direct injection or turbo direct injection (TDI). While the old indirect injection engines are tough, the newer TDI engines are quiet, clean, and more efficient.

The First Hybrids

As Diesel himself predicted, the diesel engine was slow to catch on in America. Twenty-six years after Diesel's death, in November 1939, General Motors launched No. 103–a diesel-powered locomotive. A yearlong, 83,890-mile odyssey through America proved that the diesel locomotive was superior to the steam locomotive that preceded it. Diesel engines were embraced by U.S. railroads and rapidly replaced steam locomotives as a means of moving America's trains.[9]

Engineers soon determined that the most efficient use of the diesel engine was in combination with an electric motor. The two engines together formed a diesel-electric *hybrid.* The hybrid design couples a diesel engine operating at constant speed with an electrical generator that powers electric motors that propel the vehicle–in this case, a train. Diesel-electric trains were more efficient than straight diesel locomotives, which had themselves shown a substantial efficiency gain over steam engine locomotives. The diesel-electric hybrid design was soon adopted for use in submarines, where limited fuel supply was a tactical consideration.

Passenger Diesels Get Off to a Rough Start

While diesel engines proliferated in the agriculture, transportation, and manufacturing industries, their use in consumer automobiles was all but unheard of until the 1980s. Mercedes Benz and Volkswagen both offered diesels in the 1970s, but the cars seemed a strange breed when compared with their fuel-thirsty muscle-car cousins. With the introduction of fuel injection on many gasoline-powered vehicles and an increasing demand for horsepower, efficiency took a back seat as American car companies hammered out lines of big, fast, heavy, gasoline-powered cars.

After the oil shocks of the 1970s, American automobile engineers began to look seriously at efficiency. Not to be outdone by their European counterparts, who were producing 4-cylinder diesel cars, engineers at GM created the first 350-cubic-inch V-8 diesel engine. It was first offered in the 1978 Oldsmobile "Ninety-Eight," a car with the aerodynamics, drag coefficient, and style of a metal brick. Even this rectangular vehicle, fitted with a diesel engine, achieved a 25% increase in fuel economy over its gasoline counterpart.[10] This was not surprising considering the EPA highway mileage for a 1978 Ninety-Eight was only 27 miles per gallon. In contrast, the diesel-powered Volkswagen Rabbit had already achieved 45 miles per gallon.

According to Morton Grosser, author of Diesel's biography, Oldsmobile entered the U.S. diesel market with an engine consistent with American tradition. The V-8 was large, quiet, and favored acceleration over fuel economy. "If cars can be said to have national characteristics," says Grosser, "Oldsmobile's entry in the diesel market must be as American as apple pie." Oldsmobile went on to make many popular diesels, then stopped. Their diesel production line included the Oldsmobile Cutlass Supreme diesel, the Oldsmobile Delta 88 Royal diesel, the Oldsmobile Ninety-Eight Regency, and the Oldsmobile Toronado.

The famed GM 350 diesel engine also found its way into trucks, boats, and construction equipment. Unfortunately for GM, inadequate product testing on their first diesel engines did not reveal important flaws; many U.S. customers were dismayed when their GM diesel automobiles had severe problems during the first 50,000 miles, such as cracked heads, cracked blocks, and stuck pistons. In addition to mechanical problems, American diesels became infamous for black exhaust. GM's entry-level diesel cars belched black smoke, creating a stigma for diesel power. When oil began flowing again from Texas, the North Sea, and Alaska, and the price of U.S. gasoline dropped, diesels became only a bad memory for American consumers.

Eventually, GM successfully redesigned their big 5.7-liter diesel V-8. Ford followed suit with 7.1- and 7.3-liter diesels, and Dodge worked with the engine manufacturing company Cummins to create a line of diesel-powered Dodge trucks, now famed for their reliability. By the end of the 1980s, American heavy-duty vehicle manufacturers had finally embraced the diesel engine for its power and longevity. But the damage had been done, and the word "diesel" would be considered synonymous with "dirty" for American car buyers. From the late 1970s onward, the fuel efficiency of American consumer vehicles decreased, while the fuel efficiency of European consumer vehicles increased without loss of comfort, speed, or power.

Modern Hybrid Diesels

In 1993 seven federal agencies and America's big three automakers began a research and development program called the Partnership for a New Generation of Vehicles (PNGV). The goal of the program was to create family sedans that achieved three times the fuel efficiency of similar vehicles while maintaining performance, safety, and comfort. In 2000 General Motors, Ford, and

DaimlerChrysler each unveiled a unique PNGV concept car. To the surprise of many, all three vehicles were diesel-electric hybrids. Ford presented their Prodigy diesel-electric hybrid, capable of 70 miles per gallon. DaimlerChrysler created the Dodge ESX4 diesel-electric hybrid family sedan, capable of 72 miles per gallon. Not to be outdone, General Motors introduced the diesel-electric Precept at 79.6 miles per gallon (almost identical to the fuel economy of Volkswagen's non hybrid diesel Lupo and Audi's non hybrid diesel A2, both of which are now for sale in Europe).

While America's Big Three did not initiate production of their prototypes, the PNGV program showed that diesel-electric hybrids represented the most efficient liquid-fueled vehicle technology available. Since then, diesel-electric buses have found their way into city fleets in New York City, Los Angeles, Seattle, Portland, and Philadelphia. Studies show that these buses have lower nitrogen oxide and particulate emissions than similar buses with Compressed Natural Gas (CNG) engines.[11] Per mile traveled, the diesel-electric buses are the cleanest on the market today.

Federal Express has a contract with Eaton Corporation to build the world's largest hybrid diesel-electric truck fleet–completely replacing all 30,000 of its medium-weight delivery trucks with diesel-electric hybrids. The move will cut the emissions of FedEx's medium duty trucks by 90% while increasing their fuel efficiency by 50%.[12] Nissan, Toyota, and Mercedes Benz have all since unveiled plans for diesel-electric hybrid passenger vehicles.

While Toyota made an auspicious entrance into the new U.S. hybrid vehicle market with the introduction of its Prius in 1999, we in America await the introduction by a commercial auto manufacturer of a diesel-electric hybrid consumer vehicle. With considerable media buzz around the diesel-electric prototype of the new Mercedes R-Class, there are signs that we may soon see diesel-electrics in the United States. And with conventional diesel vehicles already achieving higher fuel efficiency than gasoline-electric hybrids, there is an opportunity for diesel-electric hybrids to flourish in a market driven by increasing fuel prices.

The New Breed of Diesels

A new breed of diesels is hitting showrooms around the world. These new diesel vehicles incorporate lightweight alloy construction, direct-injected engines, rapid acceleration, and ultra low emissions. The vehicles also deliver something that prototype engineers and car companies alike have been promising for three decades: double, triple, and in some cases, even quadruple the fuel efficiency of similar vehicles on the road today. Finally, all of these automobiles are compatible with *biodiesel*, the vegetable-oil-based fuel we discuss in great detail in this book.

In the following section we review the Jeep Liberty CRD which is sold primarily in the United States, Volkswagen's TDI line including the New Beetle, Golf, Jetta, and Passat which are sold internationally, and the Audi A2 which is sold primarily in Europe.

The Jeep Liberty CRD

Jeep, a company that was founded to address the American military's need for rugged automobiles, made its start supplying vehicles in World War I. Original Willys Jeeps can still be seen at car shows, on the road, and climbing through rivers and over hills. Almost every part for the original Willys is available today from catalog companies. Considering that this vehicle was first produced in 1940, Jeep's ability to create a car with future utility is unsurpassed.

Jeep's initial entry into the U.S. diesel market was in the 1980s, when it offered a limited number of Cherokees with four-cylinder diesel engines made by Renault. These diesel Jeeps were well received, but soon after their introduction Renault pulled out of the U.S. market and Jeep stopped producing diesels for the United States. Jeep did, however, continue to offer a diesel version of some of its vehicles in overseas markets.

When asked why DaimlerChrysler decided to offer the Jeep Liberty with a diesel engine, Robert Lee, vice president of Chrysler's Powertrain Product Engineering, the team responsible for the design, product engineering, and approval of all power trains and their components within Chrysler Group, explained that the diesel engine offers a combination of better fuel economy and reduced carbon dioxide emissions. "The benefit of fuel economy adds considerable customer value, whereas the reduced CO_2 emissions of a new diesel engine add social value for each and every one of us," says Lee.

In 2005 Jeep began offering customers in the United States a Common Rail Diesel (CRD) engine in its Liberty model SUV. The CRD is a powerful, cleaner-running, quieter diesel engine. The *common rail* eliminates the many fuel-injection lines leading out of the injection pump. Instead, there is just one fuel conduit, or rail, that leads from the injector pump to the injectors. Rather than the injector pump selecting a specific injector to fuel, the injector pump simply maintains a high pressure (24,000 psi) in the common fuel rail. The injectors are electronically opened, releasing fuel into the cylinders. The new common rail system allows the Liberty CRD power plant to deliver the fuel consumption of a four-cylinder while still providing the acceleration of a V-6 and the torque of a V-8.

The Liberty CRD is 25% more efficient than the four-cylinder gasoline Liberty. Thanks to the increase in torque, the Jeep Liberty CRD can tow an impressive 5,000 lbs., more than double a four-cylinder gasoline Liberty and equal to the V-6 model. With a 20.5-gallon fuel tank and 22-mpg city and 27-mpg highway (compared to the gasoline Liberty four-cylinder at 20/24 and Liberty V-6 at 17/22), the driving range is close to 500 miles. [13]

The Volkswagen TDI Line: New Beetle, Golf, Jetta, and Passat

Since its inception, Volkswagen, which means "the people's car," has inspired a level of customer loyalty uncommon in the auto industry. Despite the company's beginnings as an extension of Germany's Third Reich, its cars have achieved an almost zealous following in the United States and beyond. Volkswagen clubs sprouted up soon after U.S. sales of their air-cooled Beetle and Transporter vans started in the mid-1950s. By the 1970s, the VW Beetle had found its way to just about every corner of the planet and had even become a central character in the popular Herbie movie series. Today, Volkswagen operates 35 manufacturing facilities in 15 countries and is Europe's largest passenger-car producer.[14]

Volkswagen began selling diesel-powered Rabbits, Jettas, and pickup trucks in the United States and Canada in 1977. These vehicles were typical of the lightweight, simple designs of Volkswagen. Diesel VWs also carried a huge bonus to drivers feeling the bite of the early oil shocks: they got between 45 and 55 miles per gallon. These early diesel Volkswagens were powered by a 1.6-liter, 4-cylinder naturally-aspirated diesel engine. A turbocharged version of the engine was carried over into Volkswagen's Golf and Jetta.

Noting the success of its original diesel vehicles among fuel-conscious consumers, Volkswagen redesigned its diesel engine and in 1996 released its 1.9-liter turbo direct injection (TDI) diesel engine in the Golf and Jetta. The new TDI engine was quiet, was a snappy performer, and still sipped fuel at around 50 miles per gallon. In Europe, the introduction of the TDI Golf prompted a "diesel craze" in which young drivers began to modify their TDIs, achieving high levels of performance and efficiency. European diesels soon hit the racetrack and European car manufacturers including BMW, Peugeot, Renault, SAAB, Seat, and Volvo began offering vehicles with TDI engines. Over the next decade, Volkswagen further refined its TDI engine for better performance, lower noise, lower emissions, and lower maintenance.

In January 2004, Volkswagen announced it had begun a research venture with agricultural conglomerate Archer Daniels Midland (ADM) to investigate the use of biodiesel in its TDI engines sold in the U.S.[15] While Volkswagen TDIs in Europe are certified to run on any blend of biodiesel including 100% biodiesel (B100), the collaboration of the automaker with the United States' largest soybean processor marked the first glimmer of hope that VW might extend its endorsement of biodiesel stateside. On National Agriculture Day, March 17, 2005, Volkswagen announced official warranty support for a mixture of 5% biodiesel and 95% diesel fuel (B5.) Volkswagen and ADM are now cooperatively assessing the potential of warranty support for a 20% biodiesel blend (B20.)[16] While they wait for the official corporate stamp of approval, Volkswagen TDI drivers across the United States (myself included) run their vehicles on biodiesel blends as high as 100% (B100) with no ill effects.

Volkswagen currently offers its 1.9-liter TDI engine to US customers in its New Beetle, Golf, and Jetta and offers a 2.0-liter version of the TDI in the Passat. Power, handling, comfort, and safety are unaffected by the TDI engine. As a result, these vehicles operate with almost no noticeable difference from their gasoline-powered counterparts. While EPA fuel consumption estimates put the TDI version of all four vehicles at or below 45-miles per gallon, many drivers of the New Beetle report fuel efficiencies of over 55 miles per gallon with one report of 76 miles per gallon.[17] Volkswagen's TDI vehicles still enjoy some of the cultish appeal as their earlier vehicles. A cursory Internet search reveals TDI Web sites, newsletters, and chat groups, and a growing array of after-market TDI paraphernalia.

The Audi A2

The Audi A2 is the first modern diesel vehicle with a body made completely of aluminum. The A2 weighs 43% less than if it were made of steel and is 100% recyclable. The light but strong frame held up well in safety tests, receiving a four- out of five-star safety rating from the European New Car Assessment Program (EURONCAP).[18] In the words of Henry Ford, "I cannot imagine where the delusion that weight means strength came from."[19] Four airbags and "ribbed" energy-absorbing struts inside the doors and frame add to the A2's safety features. The car has the lowest drag coefficient of any production automobile, giving it the best aerodynamics on the market.[20] The A2 requires oil service only once every 31,000 miles. Most importantly, the A2 goes almost 80 miles per gallon or 2.99 liters per 100 kilometers.[21]

Almost 80% of the A2's power is available just above idle speed, from 1,300 RPMs upwards. This makes the Audi A2's performance akin to a sports car because the engine has high torque at low RPM. Step on the accelerator and the car scoots. The A2's modern, ultra-efficient turbodiesel direct-injection engine is the first diesel engine to have a light-alloy cylinder head as well as an engine block made entirely from aluminum. This saves about 32 pounds of weight compared with a conventional cast-iron engine block. Weighing in at only 220 pounds, the 1.2-liter TDI engine is one of the lightest passenger-car diesel engines currently manufactured.[22]

Similar to the Volkswagen Lupo, the Audi A2 has a manual transmission with no clutch. A separate switch on the instrument panel activates the fuel-saving "Eco" mode. In this mode, the shifting points are reached earlier. By means of a start/stop function, the engine cuts out if the vehicle remains stationary for a few seconds and the driver is depressing the brake petal. As soon as the brake pedal is released, the engine starts again automatically without delay. The engine start/stop function is combined with an "intelligent" energy-saving clutch to give the car an operating efficiency of between 78 and 100 miles per gallon. Its 5-gallon tank gives the car a range of about 416 miles. At the time of writing, Audi has no plans to release the A2 in the United States.[23]

Diesel Vehicle Sales: A Rising Trend?

After the poor acceptance of diesel automobiles by American consumers in the 1980s, major U.S. manufacturers stopped making diesel vehicles, and their sales plummeted. With the introduction of the Ford, Chevy, and Dodge diesel pickup trucks, U.S. diesel sales began to climb again in the late 1990s. Today there is minimal support from the auto industry for diesels in America. Volkswagen currently offers diesel engines in the Tuareg, New Beetle, Jetta, Golf, and Passat. Mercedes offers a diesel sedan and now sells its well-known Sprinter vans in the United States under the Dodge name. Meanwhile Jeep is entering the U.S. diesel market, and a handful of European manufacturers are awaiting legislative decisions to determine whether they can begin exporting diesel cars to the United States.

While the United States has seen a recent increase in diesel vehicle sales due to rising fuel prices and the need for more fuel-efficient cars, Europe's diesel sales have been steadily increasing for a decade. All major car markets in Europe have recorded a consistent yearly increase in the sale of diesels in the last 5-10 years.

Toyota, Nissan, Isuzu, Kia, Saab, Volvo, Peugeot, Renault, BMW, Volkswagen, DaimlerChrysler, Seat, Jaguar, and even Ford sell a wide range of diesel cars, trucks, sports utility vehicles, and heavy duty vehicles overseas. Many of these vehicles get over 50 miles per gallon; a growing number achieve 70-80 miles per gallon. Diesel sales for 2003 alone in most of the major Western European markets showed a record increase of 3.2% and accounted for 44%

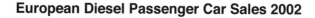

European Diesel Passenger Car Sales 2002

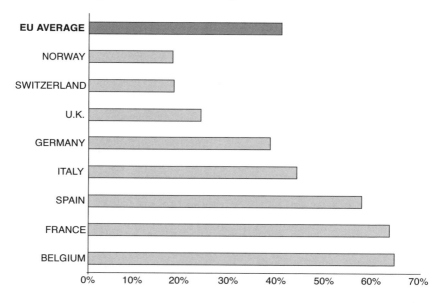

of the total vehicles sold.[24] With the new "Euro IV" limits that are in effect as of January 1, 2005, diesels must emit even fewer particulates and lower nitrogen oxide emissions (a.k.a NO_x). But even stricter emissions requirements have not hampered the sales of diesels in the European car market; European diesel engine manufacturers are undaunted.

Interestingly, while European diesel sales continue to climb, the overall car market in Europe is actually *shrinking*. During the period from 1998-2003, the European car market shrunk by 1 million vehicles and is still falling at the rate of 1.4% per year. This is due in part to better public transportation and to the rising fuel and operating costs of automobiles in Europe. In cities such as London, drivers must pay a daily fee just to drive within city limits. Despite the shrinking market, in 2003, 6.3 million diesel vehicles were sold – nearly double the number of diesels sold only five years earlier in

1998.[25] In 2002, diesels accounted for 38% of Germany's passenger car sales, 63.2% of France's, 57.3% of Spain's, and 23.5% of the United Kingdom's. If they are going to drive, Europeans want to do it as efficiently as possible: by driving diesels.

While the United States still enjoys low fuel prices relative to Europe, U.S. diesel sales have already begun an upward trend. With prototype diesels reaching over 250 miles per gallon and hybrid diesels already in production for buses, we can be assured that the U.S. consumer diesels are on the verge of a sharp increase in market share.

CHAPTER 4

Alternative Fuels 101

"The fuel of the future is going to come from fruit like that sumach out by the road, or from apples, weeds, sawdust – almost anything. There is fuel in every bit of vegetable matter."
Henry Ford, founder, The Ford Motor Company (b.1863 - d.1947)

Biodiesel is one of many energy technologies that will, in the near future, allow America to stabilize its economy, reduce the flow of valuable cash to foreign nations, create more jobs, clean its environment, and secure its homeland. Biodiesel is an important feature of this new technology landscape, but not the only fuel or the only technology that will power us into the 21st century.

Today, Americans consume more energy than the citizens of any other nation. The staple of our national energy diet for the better part of 150 years has been a "limitless" supply of oil. While the oil shocks of the 1970s ushered in a brief period of conservation, during which wasteful energy practices were curbed in the public sector, these events were a blip on the radar of progress. "To be healthy our economy must grow. To grow, we must consume. And to consume we need energy," economists seemed to tell us. So after the oil shocks America found more energy, and America went about the business of growing.

And grow we did. America itself grew from approximately 205 million people in 1970 to just under 300 million today.[1] We grew wealthier, too. Our per capita expenditures more than doubled from $7,926 in 1960 to $17,403 in 1990.[2] As the consumer market ballooned, so too did the amount of energy it took to make the goods we bought. Consequently our national energy consumption increased, underscoring the need for imported oil, which doubled from around 6 million barrels per day in 1973 to over 12 million barrels per day today.[3] The growth in our energy use has put the United States in a precarious position. If the United States suddenly had to supply its own oil with no foreign imports and no new discoveries, our country would consume its entire reserves in four years.

Less than 5% of America's energy presently comes from *renewable* sources of energy–sources that are fueled by the sun, wind, and hydropower, and are therefore not based on limited natural resources. Considering that even nuclear energy is based on the limited availability of uranium, the United States has based a great deal of its economic wellbeing on energy supplies with finite life spans.

That could soon change, however. Due to the rising cost of non-renewable energies and the decreasing cost of renewable energies and renewable energy technologies, the renewable energy market is growing. In the pages that follow, we explore the framework of energy that powers the United States. We look at the interplay of conventional and alternative energies today and the possibilities for a future in which America supplies its energy needs through domestic fuels and technologies like biodiesel.

The Three Principles of Good Energy

According to the first law of thermodynamics, energy is neither created nor destroyed; it merely changes form. Thus, no society "creates" energy. We merely change energy into forms that are more usable than others. Oil is a good example. It was formed millions of years ago, when the sun's energy gave microorganisms the fuel for life. Oil is essentially stored solar energy. Energy has changed forms, but it has not been created by us–or even by the microorganisms. The microorganisms themselves only transformed the sun's photonic energy into chemical energy in the form of bonded hydrogen and carbon. Millions of years later, as we burn those hydrocarbons in engines, we change the bonded energy once again–to heat.

Because energy is neither created nor destroyed, fuels like biodiesel, hydrogen, propane, natural gas, and petroleum itself are called *energy carriers*. These gases and liquids provide us with a means to "carry" energy and to fuel machinery. Batteries are also energy carriers, as they quite literally carry electrical energy from one place to another. *Energy sources,* on the other hand, include the sun and the atoms that make up our universe. To assess energy carriers and their associated energy technologies, we use three important measures. They are:

I. Energy Balance Ratio

Regardless of the "source" of energy or which energy carrier we choose, it takes energy to manufacture the liquid and gaseous energy carriers we use today. There is no free lunch. Even with the freest energy known to man, the energy that streams from the sun (one day of which is enough to fuel the entire United States for a year and a half), the energy needed to build solar panels must be subtracted from the energy they will produce.[4] The ratio of how much energy it takes to create an energy carrier versus how much energy that carrier will contain is called an *energy balance ratio*. An energy balance ratio of less than 1.0 indicates that it takes more energy to produce an energy carrier than the carrier contains.

II. The Cost of Externalities

The external costs, or *externalities*, associated with a type of energy carrier or energy technology are the costs not paid by the owner or operator of that energy technology, but paid instead by society. For example, we pay one price at the pump for fuel. But what is the external cost for doing business with Saudi Arabia and Iraq? The external cost of the pollution created? The external cost of domestic job loss? The Office of Technology Assessment includes the following in its "partial" list of externalities: air emissions such as sulfur dioxide, nitrogen oxides, carbon dioxide, particulates, and air toxins; waste generation such as toxic waste, solid waste, liquid radiation, electromagnetic fields, and runoff from mining, processing, and fuel storage; and human impacts such as death, illness, accidents, cancer, respiratory illness, and poisoning.

III. Ease of Integration with Existing Infrastructure

Perhaps the single most important factor in determining the near-term potential of energy technologies is how well a given energy technology fits into our modern, multi-trillion-dollar energy infrastructure. In the United States alone there are approximately 170,000 gas stations, 138 million passenger cars, 28 million heavy-duty diesel vehicles, and oil and liquid fuel pipelines that traverse approximately 150,000 miles, as well as 20,500 diesel-electric locomotives that move goods over 200,000 miles of train tracks.[5] America's electrical grid is also well developed, bringing electricity to approximately 107 million residences and 4.4 million commercial buildings.[6] Any alternative energy that does not slip easily into America's existing energy infrastructure is unlikely to gain acceptance in our highly developed energy market.

Energy Efficiency

Eliminating or minimizing wasteful practices could save America billions of dollars and reduce our dependence on foreign oil by billions of barrels of oil every year.

In 2003 the Alliance to Save Energy found that an overwhelming majority of consumers – 92%– agree that business, government, and consumers have an equal responsibility to reduce energy use.[7]

A number of studies conclude that private businesses can make money through energy efficiency while saving the nation's valuable cash reserves from flowing into overseas pockets. Since moving from theory into reality is not always as simple as it sounds, here are some useful energy saving tips:

1) Our dependence on foreign oil could be almost eliminated over the next 20 years if average fuel economies jumped from the current national average of 25 miles per gallon to 45 miles per gallon. When you purchase a new vehicle, consider buying a hybrid, a turbodiesel, or a smaller, more efficient family sedan instead of a Sport Utility Vehicle.[8]

2) We waste up to 2 billion gallons of gasoline per year due to poorly inflated tires. Keep your car's tires inflated to their rated pressure, which is always printed on the side of the tire.[9]

3) Keep your vehicle well tuned. A poorly tuned vehicle wastes up to 10% of its fuel and produces more emissions.[10]

4) When you shop for new appliances, including light bulbs for your home, make sure they carry the ENERGY STAR logo. Every home in America that switches its five

most used light bulbs to ENERGY STAR bulbs saves around $60. If every home in the nation did this, it would save America $6 billion annually.[11]

5) Plug home electronics, such as TVs and VCRs, into power strips and turn the power strips off when equipment is not in use. "Ghost loads" from electronic devices use 5 percent of our domestic energy and cost consumers more than $3 billion annually.[12]

6) Look in the back of this book for more references and ideas on saving energy and money. You might be surprised at how much you can increase your disposable income by cutting the fat from your monthly energy diet.

Six Engines that Move Our World

I. Gasoline

The gasoline engine is the mainstay for personal transport in the United States and much of the West. It relies on an explosive, flammable fuel created through the distillation of crude oil. The engine works by compressing a mixture of gasoline and air, and then igniting that mixture with a spark generated by a spark plug. The resulting explosion forces a piston down and generates the motion needed to turn a crankshaft. The disadvantage of gasoline engines is that, when burning fossil fuel, they produce approximately twenty pounds of carbon dioxide per gallon of fuel burned, as well as a myriad of other emissions.[13] At around 28% efficiency, they are less efficient than the diesel engine or electric motor. Most gasoline engines can be modified to run on a cleaner-burning alcohol fuel called *ethanol*, as well as natural gas (a.k.a. *methane*) and hydrogen.

II. Diesel

Similar to gasoline engines, diesel engines use a fuel made from the refining process of oil. However, diesel fuel is substantially heavier than gasoline. Instead of compressing a mixture of fuel and air, the diesel engine compresses only air. A powerful injector then sprays fuel into the super-compressed air, initiating instantaneous combustion and pushing the cylinder down. While traditionally dirtier than gasoline engines due to the soot, sulfur dioxide, and carcinogens they emit, diesel engines are more efficient than gasoline engines and typically operate at around 42% efficiency. All diesel engines can run on the cleaner-burning alternative, vegetable oil-based biodiesel, with no or minor modifications.

III. Electric

The first vehicle manufactured in the United States was powered by an electric motor. An electric motor functions on a completely different principle than either of the two common "combustion" engines. In a typical electric motor, a central shaft is wrapped in magnets. The shaft is inserted into a housing of tightly wound copper wire. When electricity is applied to the wire windings, a magnetic electrical field is generated, forcing the magnets to move away from the wire. Since the shaft is suspended inside the wire coils by fixed bearings, the electrical field forces the shaft to turn rapidly.

The electric motor is extremely efficient; up to 80% of electrical energy is converted into motion. All electric motors must be powered by an electrical energy source such as a power line or by an electrical storage device such as a battery or ultra-capacitor. In the case of a *fuel cell* car (discussed later in this chapter), an electric car is powered by electricity generated by a fuel cell that is, in turn, fueled with hydrogen, methanol, or gasoline. Despite their high efficiency, electrical vehicles have long suffered from short driving ranges due to battery or fuel cell limitations.

IV. Gasoline-Electric Hybrids

Gasoline-electric hybrids recently entered the U.S. market with the Honda Insight, the Toyota Prius, and Ford's new Escape SUV. These vehicles do not have to be "plugged in" to charge, and they offer higher efficiencies than similar non hybrid models. The term "hybrid vehicle" refers to a vehicle with at least two sources of motive power. Thus, a *hybrid electric vehicle* (HEV) indicates that one of the sources of power is electric. A *gasoline-electric hybrid vehicle* (GHEV) contains both a gasoline engine and an electric motor. GHEVs use the gasoline engine to generate power for the electric motor, and in some cases, also to power the vehicle. Unlike strictly electric vehicles, GHEVs generate all of their needed electricity onboard and never need to be recharged. The electric motor, which is the primary source of motive power for the vehicle, draws its power from a generator that is coupled to the gasoline motor. GHEVs also contain an energy storage device, such as batteries or a super capacitor, that provides a "buffer" for times when the electric motor needs more electricity than the gasoline motor and generator can supply. Combining the gasoline engine with an electric motor gives a GHEV higher efficiency than a regular gasoline-powered vehicle and a greater driving distance between fill-ups. GHEVs in the United States have achieved fuel efficiencies between 40 and 65 miles per gallon.

V. Diesel-Electric Hybrids

Long before the Prius hit showroom floors, diesel-electric hybrids were powering their way across America's heartland–and across much of the planet. Diesel-electric engines have been used in train locomotives since 1925 and are now crossing over into other markets. The combination of the diesel engine's high thermal efficiency with the electric motor creates a power train capable of achieving the highest efficiency of a vehicle using combustion technology–up to 60%.

VI. The Air Car

A relatively simple vehicle technology is now in production in Africa and is catching on in developing countries. The *air car* is powered by compressed air that flows into a pneumatic cylinder. The compressed air moves the cylinder, which in turn compresses a fluid (as do most pneumatic cylinders). The compressed fluid then pushes the cylinder back to its starting position. Air Car inventor Guy Negre claims the production vehicles have a range of over 180 miles at 35mph and a top speed of 65mph. Like an electric vehicle, the air car relies on an energy carrier (the compressed air) that must be "charged" (or in this case, compressed) using an external source of electricity. The big difference is that the air car requires no large batteries (saving owners from having to replace the batteries every five years), and it can be charged using a relatively simple air compressor. The air car is considerably lighter than an equivalent electric vehicle and costs far less to produce. As an emerging technology for urban environments, the air car offers a low-pollution, high-efficiency alternative to combustion, electric, and hybrid vehicles. In addition, its single tailpipe emission–air–leaves the local environment unchanged.[14]

The Fossil-Based Alternatives:
Natural Gas (Methane), Propane, Methanol, Hydrogen, and Gas to Liquid Fuel

The use of the term *alternative fuel* has become so broad in recent years that it's hard to tell which fuels are alternatives to petroleum and which ones have adopted the "alternative" label for marketing purposes. No matter how they are labeled, all *fossil fuels* are based on a limited supply of prehistoric resources, which in one form or another are trapped in Earth's crust. The following fossil fuels are sold as alternatives to gasoline and conventional oil. While they may offer some relief from tightening worldwide oil supplies, these fuels are only useful as long as we can reliably extract and/or import them.

I. Natural Gas (Methane)

Natural gas is predominantly methane with small amounts of other volatile and inert gases. Methane, designated CH_4, is a versatile gaseous compound that, when burned in air, releases only water, carbon dioxide, limited nitrogen oxides and particulates, and energy.[15] (Methane from fossil sources must be distinguished from that derived from organic sources; see below on Renewables, II.) Natural gas is used to heat homes, as well as for stoves and ovens, for industry, and for electricity generation. When used as a vehicle fuel, natural gas is stored under high pressure in tanks and is called Compressed Natural Gas (CNG).

Natural gas is usually found in conjunction with oil deposits during drilling, but it can also be found by itself, especially in veins of coal deposits. For decades, most natural gas was considered an undesirable byproduct of oil refining and was often burned at the source of oil extraction. (If you've ever noticed fires over oil derricks, these fires are burning natural gas.) As demand for natural gas has increased, both in the United States and in the rest of the world, great effort has been expended to capture and transport this ever-more-valuable fuel source.

Calling natural gas "natural" is similar to calling oil or coal "natural." Indeed, all three are products of nature and are therefore natural. However, all three are also fossil-based resources and are therefore limited. Natural gas is usually marketed as an alternative fuel. But despite its versatility, natural gas has challenges as a vehicle fuel.

Natural gas requires unique fueling infrastructure and unique vehicle modifications. Fueling vehicles with natural gas requires a compression refueling station. These compression stations are typically designed to handle rapid fueling, which occurs during a period of time comparable to conventional liquid fueling and/or timed fueling, that can occur overnight or over several hours. Fuel prices at such stations vary, but are generally higher than prices at conventional liquid fuel stations because of the compression equipment and compressed fuel storage required. Additionally, operations and maintenance costs of these stations can be higher due to electrical demands from the compressors and required maintenance of the equipment.[16]

Despite the fact that most of these technological problems can be overcome, natural gas faces a much larger problem as a fuel mainstay: it is in increasing demand but its supply is limited. An overwhelming 95% of all new power plants built in the U.S. in the last four years are fueled with natural gas. Natural gas now supplies 20% of America's electricity and accounts for one fourth of

Proven World Natural Gas Reserves

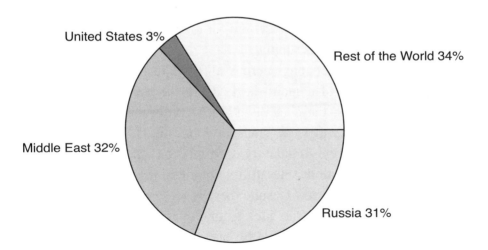

Source: Oil & Gas Journal, December 23, 2002

the total energy consumed in the United States.[17] To meet the growing demand for natural gas, supplies will have to double every 20 years.[18] But natural gas discoveries are slipping behind demand. In 2001, for the first time ever, more natural gas was used than discovered. Just as oil peaked in the United States in the 1970s, America's natural gas has likely reached its peak.[19]

II. Liquefied Natural Gas (LNG)

Like any gas, natural gas becomes denser as it is compressed. When cryogenically frozen, natural gas turns into a liquid. Liquefied Natural Gas (LNG) consists mainly of methane (CH_4) that has been cooled to -260° Fahrenheit. Liquefying natural gas provides a means of transporting the fuel long distances by ship, train, or truck. When natural gas is liquefied, its volume at atmospheric pressure is reduced by a factor of 610.[20]

To move LNG between countries, the fuel is pumped into massive, often bubble-shaped, heavily insulated tanks that sit in double-hulled ships. When an LNG ship reaches its destination, the LNG is moved into stationary, heavily insulated tanks. The LNG is then sent to *regasifiers,* which turn the liquid back into gas. Natural gas then enters the pipeline system for distribution to customers as part of their natural gas supply.

As a part of safety engineering, all LNG facilities are designed to prevent fires and contain the LNG in the event of a spill. In the United States, these facilities must conform to standards set by the U.S. Department of Transportation, the U.S. Coast Guard, the Federal Energy Regulatory Commission, the National Fire Protection Association, state utility commissions, port authorities, and other local agencies. Despite these assurances, there is a growing resistance to LNG facilities among concerned citizens due to fears that LNG facilities could be easy targets for terrorist attacks. The construction of several LNG facilities has been halted or abandoned due to legal action from citizens' groups.

Despite the concerns about safety, the combination of higher natural gas prices, lower LNG costs, and rising natural gas demand has set the stage for increased global LNG trade. Consequently, liquefied natural gas (LNG) is expected to play an increasingly important role in the natural gas industry and global energy markets over the next decade.

III. Propane (LPG)

Also known as Liquefied Petroleum Gas (LPG), propane is produced as a byproduct of natural gas and crude oil processing. More than 200,000 propane vehicles and 4,000 propane fueling stations exist in the United States. Propane is relatively clean burning when compared with gasoline or diesel fuel. However, the high cost and limited quantities of this fuel, which is used mostly for rural heating and stoves and barbecue grills, points to a low growth potential for propane as an alternative vehicle fuel.[21]

IV. Methanol

Methanol, the simplest alcohol, was first made by distilling wood and was therefore called wood alcohol. Today, virtually all methanol is made from conventional natural gas, although some small-scale systems have been developed to make methanol from hog manure or landfills. Methanol saw brief use as an alternative fuel in the late 1970s and continues to enjoy very limited support as an alternative fuel. Methanol has never reached commercial success as a stand-alone fuel for a number of reasons.

First, methanol in its pure form can act as a colorless nerve poison. It is absorbed easily by skin, eyes, and lungs and can cause toxicity. Second, methanol is extremely flammable and burns with a colorless flame, making it difficult to safely transport and handle. Third, methanol contains fewer BTUs per gallon and is more corrosive than other fuels. Fourth, methanol in the United States has been used to produce the fuel additive MTBE (methyl tertiary butyl ether), which leaks from gasoline storage tanks into groundwater and has been linked to cancer. Fifth, methanol production is tied to the price and availability of natural gas. Recent upswings in the price of natural gas have had a deleterious effect on the U.S. methanol industry. According to Julian Darley, author of *High Noon for Natural Gas,* by 2001 about half the methanol industry and a third of the ammonia-producing industries in the United States had shut down, due to natural gas prices more than doubling.[22]

Today methanol is used in many commercially available solvents. Some products that contain methanol include: windshield wiper fluids and deicers, antifreeze, glass cleaner, canned heat, paints, varnishes, and paint thinners and removers. Methanol is also used in the manufacturing of biodiesel. In addition, methanol is still used in performance racecars and track cars where extremely high-octane fuel is required. A company called Methanex that operates plants in Canada, New Zealand, and Chile produces most of the methanol consumed in the United States.[23]

V. Hydrogen

The push toward hydrogen began with NASA, which has used liquid hydrogen as a fuel to launch shuttles and rockets into orbit for over two decades. NASA has also used liquid hydrogen as a fuel onboard the shuttle and on the new international space station. Surprisingly, however, the billions of dollars of government and private support for hydrogen and fuel cell technology has yet to result in one commercially available hydrogen passenger vehicle.

A fuel cell transforms hydrogen into electricity through an electrochemical conversion. Hydrogen flows into a fuel cell and the fuel cell produces electricity. Since fuel cells create electricity, they can be used to power electric vehicles. A fuel cell's 80% efficiency coupled with an electric motor and inverter's 80% efficiency yields a total fuel-to-mechanical-vehicle efficiency of 64%. However, the majority of energy is lost, not in the vehicle but rather in the process of manufacturing hydrogen.

Hydrogen is the most plentiful element in the universe and together with carbon, forms the basis for all life on earth. Hydrogen is also the simplest element; a hydrogen atom consists of only one proton and one electron. Despite hydrogen's remarkable qualities, it does not occur alone in nature. Instead, it is always bonded with other elements, such as oxygen in water (H_2O) or with carbon in methane (CH_4).

To separate hydrogen from other elements, one of two methods is used: the hydrogen can be stripped away from natural gas or another compound by intense heat in a process called *reforming*, or it can be stripped from water by passing a current into the water in a process known as *electrolysis*. According to the U.S. Department of Energy, 95% of the hydrogen made today is manufactured by reforming natural gas, oil, or coal.[24] Manufacturing hydrogen from any source is expensive and results in a fuel with an *energy balance ratio* of less than one. In other words, the energy it takes to produce hydrogen is greater than the usable energy of the finished hydrogen fuel.[25] Hydrogen "is expensive and energy-intensive to liquefy," says Joseph J. Romm, author of *The Hype About Hydrogen*. "Moreover," he states, "a gallon of liquid hydrogen has only about one-quarter the energy of a gallon of gasoline."[26]

Another option for integrating fuel cells into vehicles involves using methanol as a fuel that could be distributed at gas stations and turned into hydrogen on board vehicles. But creating methanol adds yet another point of energy loss, as well as its own host of pitfalls. (See Section IV., above.) Another possibility is that reforming hydrogen from natural gas will act as a "bridge technology" until hydrogen can be produced from water with solar electricity and wind power. While this solution is theoretically clean, it does not account for the decreasing supply of natural gas and the current national electricity production deficit. Under these circumstances, it seems unrealistic that the United States could allocate the trillions of dollars necessary to completely redevelop both its transportation infrastructure and its electrical generation to accommodate hydrogen vehicles. Consequently, the U.S. Department of Energy's Energy Information Administration predicts that in 2025 there will be a negligible number of fuel cell vehicles sold in the United States.[27]

Despite hydrogen's inability to make positive near-term returns on investment as a vehicle fuel, hydrogen and fuel cells may one day play an important role in our energy diet. One key to the success of the hydrogen industry could be in electricity generation, where, coupled with renewable energy technologies like solar and wind, hydrogen and fuel cells could see growth as integral parts of stationary renewable electricity power plants.

VI. Gas to Liquid Fuel (GTL) or Fischer Tropsch (FT)

As Germany neared the First World War, its engineers struggled to find alternative sources of fuel for its rapidly mechanizing army. In 1923 Franz Fischer and Hans Tropsch discovered a process for transforming coal into liquid fuel. The "Fischer-Tropsch process" reforms natural gas, coal, or *biomass* (biological products such as straw and wood) into a mixture of carbon monoxide and hydrogen. These gases are reacted to form long-chain hydrocarbons like diesel fuel.[28] The "FT diesel," as it is called, has a high *cetane* (a measure of the combustibility of diesel fuel) and low sulfur content. While FT diesel can theoretically be used directly as a diesel fuel, it is almost entirely used as a blend stock to increase the value of low-quality diesel fuel. Currently, two companies operate GTL plants. Shell operates a plant in Bintulu, Malaysia, that uses natural gas as a feedstock to produce low-sulfur diesel fuel. Sasol operates a plant in South Africa that uses coal as a feedstock to produce a multitude of petroleum products.[29] Today more than 50 million barrels of GTL or FT fuels are produced worldwide, but with large GTL plants under construction in the Persian Gulf region, that number is expected to increase. GTL fuel is likely to see increased growth as fossil fuel prices rise.

The Renewables:
Biomass, Methane (from digestion), Ethanol, and Biodiesel

Unlike fossil-based alternative fuels, renewable fuels offer concrete options for long-term, sustainable domestic energy production. Widely misunderstood (and in most cases underestimated), these fuels represent a formidable technological and economic leap toward energy independence.

I. Biomass

Biomass refers to a large group of forestry and agricultural products, as well as biodegradable industrial and municipal waste. Biomass includes things that can be grown each year such as: grassy components (straw, pellets), tree components (sawdust, wood chips, wood pellets, various nuts and fruits), other plant materials (corn, soybeans, sunflowers, and their oils, stalks, and residue), and animal-based materials (oils, animal manure or its gases, carcasses, etc.). Biomass can be used as a solid fuel, or converted into liquid or gaseous forms, for the production of electric power, heat, chemicals, or fuels.

By integrating several biomass conversion processes, multiple energy products can be made in one facility, called a *biorefinery*. Similar to petroleum refineries, which produce multiple fuels and products from one or more types of petroleum, biorefineries produce fuels, heat, electricity, and chemical products from naturally grown substances.

Biomass can generally be stored and used when needed, and it can be used in many applications, including heat, electricity, and liquid fuel. Biomass can provide a constant supply of energy, independent of oil imports. By developing biomass, we improve our trade balance, increase national employment, support rural communities, reduce greenhouse gas emissions, fortify our electricity grid, and strengthen our national security.

II. Methane
(from Digestion or Degradation of Organic Material)

No discussion of alternative energy is complete without the story about the pig farmer who shoveled manure into the back of his truck, where a Rube-Goldberg device created the fuel that allowed him to travel down the road. Indeed, stories such as this about ingenious ways to use methane abound.

In addition to extracting natural gas from the earth's crust, natural gas can be made from organic substances and can be an effective fuel for generators and other stationary applications. While technically the same as natural gas from fossil sources, organically produced natural gas is often referred to as "methane." Methane has been used for centuries as a fuel. Thousands of years ago the Chinese used methane gas produced from sewage as a cooking fuel. Today, methane generated by garbage dumps and by dairy, cattle, and pig farms accounts for over 20% of the methane lost to the atmosphere, where the gas is twenty-two times more effective as a global warming agent than carbon dioxide.

Organic solids are converted to methane in a device called a digester, which is essentially an oxygenless breeding ground for bacteria. The anaerobic bacteria "eat" the solids and emit almost pure methane. This methane can be further purified and used to power electrical generators or used as a heating fuel for buildings and homes. Each year enough methane could be generated from waste sources in the United States to displace approximately 260 million barrels of oil, or 4% of the U.S.'s annual energy demand.[30]

III. Ethanol

Ethanol is an alcohol made through the fermentation of sugars, which are typically derived from starches such as corn, potatoes, and grain. As a fuel, ethanol burns cleanly. It is nontoxic and drinkable. Ethanol is also *renewable*, meaning it can be grown again and again. Considering its many uses and the ease with which it is made, it may seem odd that ethanol fuel has had such a rocky history in the United States.

Ethanol first reached commercial success in the late 1800s in Germany, when the government created a series of loans and tax incentives for farmers to build and operate cooperative distilleries. Farmers participating in the program brought their excess potatoes to distilleries, which in turn gave them a portion of alcohol as well as most of the fermentation by-product (the spent mash). No money changed hands, and the farmers took home the mash to feed animals and fertilize their land. The alcohol provided heat, light, and power. Both the mash and the alcohol could be turned into cash–the mash by creating meat and the alcohol for sale as a commodity. By 1900, the program had made significant contributions to the German agricultural economy.

In 1906 President Teddy Roosevelt spearheaded legislation to lift alcohol taxes for industrial use and simplify paperwork for farmers to build their own stills in the United States. The "Rough Rider" spurred a rush of activity across the Midwest, and at least one automaker took note. Henry Ford designed his 1908 Model T to use both ethanol and gasoline. Convinced that ethanol would pave the way to the future, Ford built a large ethanol plant in the Midwest and formed a partnership with Standard Oil to sell ethanol fuel at gas stations. By 1920 ethanol accounted for 25% of Standard Oil's sales in the Midwest.[31]

Threatened by the success of the farmer-run fuel, Standard Oil soon began undercutting the price of ethanol by selling gasoline below cost. Prohibition was then enacted and effectively ceased legal ethanol production in the United States. Henry Ford was forced to close his ethanol plant but continued to produce cars that were compatible with ethanol or gasoline until 1931 – two years before Prohibition was lifted.

During the Prohibition years, from 1920 to 1933, America lost 200,000 farms, reducing the total number of farms to 6.2 million.[32] The potential income loss from the stoppage of ethanol production was in the millions. When the law was finally lifted and ethanol production again ramped up in 1933, it was evident that Standard Oil had no intention of sharing the fuel market with farmers. (By 1935, the number of farms in America had increased to 7 million, the highest number in history.)[33] In fact, one Standard Oil radio advertisement warned that national gasohol legislation would "make alcoholics out of America's 22 million motor cars."[34]

The oil shocks of the 1970s and the removal of lead as an octane booster in gasoline forced policy makers to reconsider ethanol as a "gasoline extender" and an "octane enhancer." By the late 1970s, ethanol production was again on the rise due to a mandate for cleaner-burning fuels and a tax credit for ethanol blended into gasoline. Ethanol plants sprang up across the Midwest and the alcohol began flowing again into America's gasoline supply–sometimes as an additive and sometimes at high concentration. Unfortunately for the ethanol industry, technical and quality issues gave rise to public backlash against ethanol.

A number of factors led to ethanol's decline. First, ethanol fuel has a propensity to attract water. Combined with water, ethanol can create problems with combustion as well as corrosion of fuel system components. Without proper care in handling and storage, much of the ethanol supply was easily contaminated with water in the 1970s.

Second, cars had changed considerably since Henry Ford's Model T. More complex carburetion and fuel injection on automobiles meant cars needed a way to automatically increase the fuel side of their fuel-to-air ratio in order to burn ethanol effectively. At high concentrations, ethanol tends to burn "hot" in engines not properly adjusted for ethanol, causing some engines to overheat. Third, some fuel blenders unknowingly (or deceivingly) blended 10% methanol rather than 10% ethanol into gasoline supplies, leading to severe engine problems. By the end of the 1970s, ethanol received a strong slap on the wrist, both from consumers and from the fuels industry.

Despite these setbacks, ethanol production has been steadily increasing since the 1980s. In 2003 alone, the United States produced 2.81 billion gallons of ethanol.[35] The fuel ethanol industry now contributes 143,000 jobs to the U.S. economy and adds $8.9 billion to the Gross Domestic Product of the United States.[36] Since all vehicles sold in the United States today are compatible with up to 10% ethanol, most of the ethanol produced today goes directly into gasoline to increase its octane and extend gasoline supplies. [37] While some motorists continue to distrust ethanol fuel, millions of cars across the country are now running on a percentage of ethanol with no unwanted side effects.

Ethanol's energy balance ratio has long been questioned by the fuels industry. However, as Dr. Hosein Shapouri, Senior Agricultural Economist at the U.S. Department of Agriculture, explains in a recent paper published by the American Society of Agricultural Engineers, the energy balance ratio of corn ethanol has been increasing over time due to the increased efficiency of ethanol production and of farm production. On the low end, Shapouri says the energy balance ratio of ethanol is one unit of energy input to 1.34 units of energy in the finished ethanol.[38]

In other words, the energy balance ratio of the energy put into corn-based ethanol vs. the energy in the final product shows a *posi-*

tive energy gain of at least 34%. Corn ethanol has also formed the basis for a new technology called *cellulostic ethanol production* that allows efficient production of ethanol from the leftover straw from crop production as well as any agricultural waste product. As in Brazil, where ethanol fuel accounts for up to 30% of the nation's fuel production, the United States has the potential to displace a substantial quantity of the oil it imports by increasing its production of ethanol.

IV. Biodiesel

According to the Department of Energy, biodiesel is the fastest growing alternative fuel in America today. Biodiesel has five qualities that make it an ideal fuel for the transportation industry. First, biodiesel is made from any type of vegetable oil, so its source crop can be grown in any region of the United States. Second, biodiesel is renewable: it can be grown year after year, regardless of fossil oil supplies. Third, biodiesel is compatible with any diesel engine. No or little modification is needed to use biodiesel in a diesel engine. Since diesel engines are the backbone of our transportation and agriculture, one of every three gallons of fuel consumed in the United States is diesel fuel. Fourth, biodiesel reduces a host of emissions, including a near total reduction of carbon dioxide and sulfur dioxide, as well as substantial reductions in carcinogenic aromatics and ozone-forming particle emissions. Fifth, biodiesel's energy balance ratio is approximately 1:3, or 300%, meaning for every one unit of energy that goes into making the fuel, three units of energy are present in the final fuel. This is because, with biodiesel, crops create the energetic hydrocarbon chains that are the basis for the fuel. These crops are fueled primarily by solar energy. Thus, biodiesel is a "liquid solar fuel."

Biodiesel isn't perfect, though. It does not perform as well as diesel in cold weather and can "gel." Care must be taken in transporting and storing biodiesel because it is a cleansing agent and tends to dislodge dirt and sludge. The use of biodiesel can also lead to an increase in emissions of nitrogen oxides (NO_x), emissions that were, until recently, thought to be a primary contributor to smog-forming ozone. In the energy market, though, these challenges are overshadowed by biodiesel's high utility. Due to its ease of integration into existing infrastructures, the simplicity of manufacturing the fuel, and its favorable energy balance ratio, biodiesel is poised to become a major force in the American energy market.

Alternative Electricity

While not technically part of our liquid fuel mix, electricity generation is the basis for powering at least two and possibly three of the engines that we outlined in the beginning of this chapter: electric vehicles, air cars, and hydrogen fuel cell vehicles. Since these vehicles all have exceptionally low tailpipe emissions, it is important to note where the "fuel" to power them actually comes from. Today in the United States, coal accounts for 51% of our electricity generation, natural gas accounts for 20% of our power generation, nuclear accounts for 20%, hydropower accounts for 7%, and geothermal, solar, wind, and other smaller generating facilities account for the remaining 6%.[39] Despite the fact that more than 70% of our electricity generation comes from fossil fuel, there is great potential for the United States to generate the majority of its electricity through renewable energy. Since non-fossil sources of electricity generation have the greatest growth potential, we outline them here.

I. Nuclear

Few technologies in America's history have created more controversy than the generation of power through nuclear fission. Today there are 104 nuclear power plants in the United States, generating 764 billion kilowatt-hours of electricity–enough to power some 773,000 households. But nuclear energy requires uranium–an expensive and limited resource–and produces a significant amount of hazardous waste. Nuclear power plants, too, are expensive to build and maintain, and pose at the very least a perceived health and safety risk to those who live in nearby communities. Despite their risks, nuclear power plants generate nearly 20% of the total U.S. electricity supply.[40]

Nuclear energy is created through a chain reaction called fission, which splits atoms–usually those of uranium–into smaller pieces. The reaction generates heat, which in turn creates steam. The steam turns a turbine that is coupled with a generator to generate electricity.

Aside from the steam rising from their large cooling towers, nuclear power plants emit little else into the atmosphere. Nuclear power is often extolled as a "clean" source of energy because–unlike fossil fuels–it produces zero carbon and greenhouse gases. But nuclear power plants produce hazardous by-products, such as depleted uranium, plutonium, and other radioactive materials. Depleted uranium, a highly toxic substance, has a half-life of 4.5 billion years, meaning the area in which it is stored becomes permanently contaminated.

These by-products of the fission reaction present a difficult problem: where do you put them? Nuclear waste is typically stored in cooling pools within the reactors. Once the pools reach capacity, the nuclear waste is moved to another site. The waste is put into reinforced casks and entombed in concrete bunkers, usually located close to the reactor site.[41]

In 2002 the U.S. Department of Energy began construction on the nation's first permanent site for storing nuclear waste generated by power plants and nuclear defense testing. The Yucca Mountain Deep Geological Repository in Nevada will store waste in reinforced casks 1,500 feet underground, and is due to be completed in 2010. But some residents of nearby Las Vegas–roughly 100 miles from Yucca Mountain–are opposed to the construction, since no one can guarantee them that the highly toxic nuclear waste won't leak.[42]

The problem of how and where to store radioactive nuclear waste adds to the considerably high cost of nuclear energy. When nuclear energy was first introduced as a means to augment the post-war energy boom of the 1950s, TV and print ads heralded atomic energy as "Power Too Cheap to Meter."[43] In practice, however, nuclear energy has proven more expensive to produce than coal, oil, or natural gas, according to several economic studies, including one conducted in 2003 by the Massachusetts Institute of Technology (MIT).[44]

Nuclear power plants cost $3 to $5 billion to build, and have limited life spans: reactors must be "decommissioned," or permanently taken offline, after 25 years. Like fossil fuel, nuclear power is also dependent on a limited and expensive resource: uranium. Found primarily in areas of the desert southwest, Australia, and Brazil, uranium is a precious radioactive metal that is costly to mine.

The World Nuclear Association estimates that demand for uranium will outpace supply by the year 2013 as existing inventories decline and as countries such as Russia and China begin to rely more heavily on nuclear power. Commercial stockpiles of uranium dropped 50% between 1985 and 2003, according to MIT's 2003 study.[45]

The ever-present threat of radiation leaks has also dampened consumers' enthusiasm for nuclear power. The largest nuclear accident in U.S. history occurred on March 28, 1979, at a nuclear power facility known as Three Mile Island near Harrisburg, Pennsylvania. The accident occurred when one of the plant's reactors–which had only been online for three months–suffered a partial core meltdown. The accident took more than a decade to clean up at a cost of nearly $1 billion, and resulted in a federal ban on new power plant construction. More than 100 tons of radioactive material was eventually removed from the site.[46]

While no deaths or injuries were ever officially tied to the Three Mile Island accident, in 1997 epidemiologists at the University of

North Carolina who studied cancer rates within a ten-mile radius of the site found a two-to tenfold increase in the number of diagnosed cases. While the UNC findings contradict the findings of an earlier study by researchers at Columbia University, Steven Wing, who coauthored the 1997 UNC study, says there is a direct correlation between the radiation released by the accident and increased cancer rates. "The cancer findings, along with studies of animals, plants and chromosomal damage in the Three Mile Island area residents, all point to much higher radiation levels than were previously reported," says Wing.[47]

II. Geothermal

Geothermal (Earth heat) energy is cheap, clean, and efficient, and offers a way to grow America's electricity production. Currently, the United States produces about 2,800 megawatts of geothermal electricity–less than 1% of total U.S. electricity consumption.

Today's geothermal technology produces electricity from steam and from hot water; the two basic types of geothermal power plants are called steam and binary. Steam plants use steam reaching temperatures over 300° Fahrenheit. The Geysers steam plants in northern California are the largest single producer of geothermal electricity in the world. The steam either comes directly from the earth, or the very hot, high-pressure water is depressurized to produce steam. The steam then turns turbines, which drive generators that generate electricity. The only significant emission from these plants is water vapor. Miniscule amounts of carbon dioxide, nitrogen oxides (NO_x), and sulfur are also emitted, but at a rate roughly 50 times lower than traditional fossil-fuel power plants. Energy produced this way currently costs between 4 and 6 cents per kilowatt-hour (kWh) and is on a par with other sources of electricity generation.

Binary plants use water ranging in temperature from 100° to 300° Fahrenheit. The hot water is passed through a heat exchanger, where it heats a secondary fluid with a lower boiling point. The secondary fluid vaporizes, which turns the turbines, which drive the generators. The secondary fluid is then condensed and moved back into the heat exchanger. Meanwhile, the hot water is also condensed and returned to the reservoir. Because binary plants are self-contained, they create no emissions. Since lower temperature geothermal water is more common, binary plants are also more common and offer the greatest growth potential for geothermal electricity.

Researchers at the Department of Energy's National Renewable Energy Laboratory (NREL) in Golden, Colorado are working on new technologies to improve heat-exchange efficiency, lower the equipment-damaging effects of the partially corrosive geothermal fluid, and improve condensing capability. Research is also under way on geothermal technology that would generate electricity from the heat of the deep, hot, dry rock formations of Earth's crust, and possibly the even deeper, almost unlimited energy in Earth's magma.

III. Hydro

As the name suggests, *hydropower* simply means power from water. Hydropower accounts for less than 1% of America's electricity generation and about 17% of the world's electricity generation. While hydropower has been used for centuries to power grain mills and sawmills, the current generation of hydropower facilities ranges from large-scale installations like that at Hoover Dam to small-scale hydro turbines that can be installed in creeks and rivers. Regardless of the scale, well-planned hydro-generation sites are designed to use as much of the flowing water as possible with minimal damage to the local ecosystem.

Hydroelectricity generation can be divided into four sizes: micro-, mini-, small-, and large-scale. Individuals and small communities use micro- and mini-scale units. Such small-scale hydroelectric development requires comparatively little physical space and causes little damage to the local ecosystem. These small-scale hydro systems capture the energy of flowing water without the need for dams and feed their electricity directly into a grid or, for off-grid homes, into a battery storage bank.

Large-scale hydro requires the construction of dams and reservoirs, which store potential energy in the form of water. When energy demand spikes, these dams can increase their electricity output by allowing more water to flow. The disadvantage of large-scale hydroelectric facilities is that if a plant is operated at peak capacity for long periods of time, its reservoir or dam can run low. Environmental damage resulting from reservoir flooding, sedimentation, and destruction of fish and wildlife habitats are also concerns. The physical limitations of our country limit the potential for growth in this relatively high yield, low emissions form of power generation.

IV. Solar

While there are several types of large-scale solar power installations, the most typical technology used to create electricity from the sun's radiation is called the *photovoltaic* (PV) cell. Also known as solar cells, photovoltaic cells are converters. Without any moving parts, noise, pollution, radiation, or maintenance, they take the energy from sunlight and convert that energy into electricity. A typical solar cell consists of a glass cover to seal the cell, an anti reflective layer to maximize incoming sunlight, layers of silicon, and a front and back electrical contact. The electric current stimulated by sunlight is collected on the front contact and travels through a circuit to the back contact.

Similar to hydrogen and fuel cells, the use of photovoltaics was first introduced by NASA in the 1950s as a means to power satellites. Since then PV technology has increased from less than 5% efficiency to 15% efficiency for commercially available cells. Higher technology cells, like those used by NASA today, can be up to 20% efficient. The increase in solar cell efficiency has meant

U.S. Solar Radiation and PV Production Potential

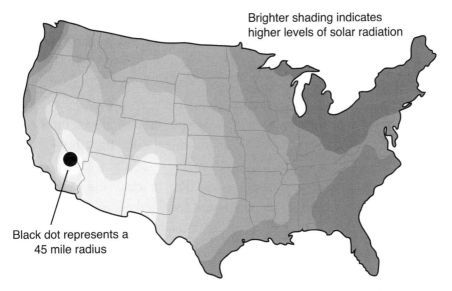

Brighter shading indicates
higher levels of solar radiation

Black dot represents a
45 mile radius

Source: Energy Information Administration and Renovus Energy

a decrease in cost. Today most of the cost of a solar cell is in the manufacturing of the silicon. Despite the high short-term cost of solar electricity, costs for solar-produced power must be amortized over a much longer period than other types of electricity. Solar cells are guaranteed for 20 years and, unless they are physically damaged, will last up to 50 years.

The economics of solar present a situation different from many other types of energy generation. If a substantial one-time investment were made into large-scale solar facilities, could the cost then be absorbed over 20, 30, or even 50 years? If so, solar quickly becomes economically feasible. But aside from the U.S. government, what bank or lending institution would provide a 50-year, multi-billion-dollar loan at a reasonable interest rate? Herein lies the fundamental roadblock to solar technology: the speed of the return on investment.[48]

In an area equivalent to a 45-mile radius (6,600 square miles), the United States could produce 100% of its daily 10 billion kilowatt hours electricity demand using photovoltaic panels.[49] This scenario presents what has been up until recently a secondary roadblock to solar: solar electrical facilities only produce power when the sun shines, or rather during the day. However, fuel cell technology provides a way around this technological barrier.

If solar facilities were coupled with large-scale electrolysis to make hydrogen gas from water during the daylight hours, the hydrogen could be fed back through fuel cells at night, allowing for a constant output of electricity. In addition, much of the water used for the electrolysis could be recaptured from the exhaust of the fuel cells and recycled, thus lessening the demand of these "solar power facilities" for clean water. While the investment capital needed to build large-scale solar facilities may still be some years away, the technology for large-scale solar electricity generation exists today. It is only a matter of time before this relatively inexpensive and clean electricity generation technology becomes a mainstay for American energy production.

V. Wind

Wind energy technology has progressed far beyond the small machines that pumped water and powered direct current (DC) appliances in the 1930s and 1940s, to become one of the fastest-growing electricity sources in the United States. Today's generation of wind turbines are quiet, sleek multi megawatt power plants that power thousands of homes. The cost of electricity from these machines has fallen by 80% over the past 30 years and continues to fall annually. Current prices range from 4 to 6 cents per kWh and are in many cases competitive with coal, nuclear, and natural gas.

Wind turbines today are based on a three-blade design. The wind turns the blades, which spin a shaft, which connects to a generator that produces electricity. Utility-scale turbines range in size from

50 to 750 kilowatts. Single small turbines (below 50 kilowatts) are used for homes, telecommunications dishes, or water pumping.

Wind power plants now operate in 32 states with a total generating capacity of 6,374 megawatts (MW) of power, and make up less than 1% of total U.S. electrical generation. However, that percentage is likely to skyrocket in the short-term due to the falling cost of wind power and the ability of individual landowners to sell electricity back to the grid in many states. In 2003 alone, American wind generating capacity increased by more than 30%.

The wind farms that have been built to date primarily take advantage of what is known as Class 6 wind, which has an average speed of 20 miles per hour or more. The United States also has substantial Class 5 (17-20 mph) and Class 4 (15-17 mph) wind resources. Class 4 wind resources are more common and are located closer to towns and cities on land and offshore, making them easier and more economical to develop.

The National Renewable Energy Laboratory (NREL) estimates that the United States could potentially meet its entire electricity demand with wind power. Taking into account economic feasibility, however, NREL proposes that 20% of the nation's electricity could be produced using 0.6% of the land in the lower 48 states. But even this land would still be usable for cattle grazing, agriculture, and farm operations, because "less than 5% of this land would be occupied by wind turbines, electrical equipment, and access roads."

Before wind energy in the United States truly takes flight, it must overcome a substantial hurdle: wind energy is not constant. Even in the higher classes of wind power there are peak times and low times. Several methods exist to stabilize wind power. Among them are the production of hydrogen and the pumping of water into a dam.

During times of great wind energy, wind turbines often turn their blades away from the wind, thus slowing the generators and tapering the amount of electricity they produce. However, this potential excess electricity could be put into generating hydrogen from water. The Department of Energy has sketched plans to create hydrogen storage capacity inside the tall towers that support the turbines themselves. During times of low wind-production, hydrogen could be fed back through a system of fuel cells to augment the electricity produced by the turbines. This stationary application of hydrogen production and fuel cell technology would allow a near constant output from large-scale wind farms. The system could also be designed in such a way as to recycle much of the water emitted by the fuel cells, reducing the need for clean water as an input.

Despite wind energy's potential to quickly increase the nation's energy security, there is a substantial push against wind energy by individuals and citizen action groups who claim that wind turbines kill birds and that they deface naturally beautiful areas.

According to studies done by the Department of Energy, birds avoid colliding with wind turbines in most cases; and contrary to popular belief, night migrating birds rarely collide with wind turbines. (Perhaps this is due to the immense height of the turbines, which generally stand 200-300 feet off the ground and have an average blade span of 60-75 feet.)

Low bird mortality is also reported at most European wind power sites (such as those in Denmark, which produce 20% of that nation's power). With each new wind installation, bird mortality studies are done to ensure that the effect on the avian population is minimal. Even by killing thousands of birds annually (which would require the construction of thousands of new wind turbines), it is unlikely that any quantity of wind turbines could compete with the following: collisions with glass windows, which kill 100 to 900 million birds annually; collisions with electric transmission lines, which kill 174 million birds per year; house cats, which kill 100 million birds each year; vehicles, which kill 50 to 100 million birds each year; poisoning from agricultural pesticides, which kills 67 million birds each year; and hunters, who legally harvest 100 million birds per year.[50]

As to the physical appearance of wind turbines, the old adage that "beauty is in the eye of the beholder" could not be more appropriate. Given the choice of a wind turbine or a coal or nuclear power plant in their backyards, most Americans will opt for a wind turbine. Polls conducted by NREL in Texas showed that customers were concerned about the environment, and that they preferred renewable energy and energy efficiency resource options over fossil-fuel alternatives. After residents were polled in town halls and meeting centers, more than a terawatt of new renewable electricity generation was developed in Texas. As residents began to discuss their thoughts and feelings on energy, the wind energy industry in Texas began to boom. During 2001 alone, 916 megawatts of new wind energy capacity came online.[51]

Whether to power a new generation of vehicles or to maintain current energy supplies, America will soon need to build new power generation facilities. Regardless of the emotions that surround them, wind turbines are currently the cheapest, cleanest, most sustainable, and most available technology to satisfy our near-term national appetite for electricity.

CHAPTER 5

Farming Fuel

"Good farmers are not just people who dig in the dirt. They are the stewards of healthy soil, many of them unrecognized or even dismissed by those who can't comprehend why anyone would want to do such hard work so far away from a Starbucks."

George B. Pyle, The Land Institute

A s dawn breaks and sunlight splashes across America's heartland, one group of men and women is already hard at work. Farmers arguably form the foundation of the economic security, political might, and nutritional wealth that make America a global leader.

Influenced by the well-known image of Grant Wood's 1930 painting, *American Gothic*, many of us hold the belief that somewhere in the vast landscape that fills the middle of the country there is a group of somewhat stoic, salt-of-the-earth men and women dressed in overalls standing in front of wooden barns, farm implements ready at their sides. But farming in the U.S. has changed dramatically since the 1930s, as have farmers themselves. Farms have become larger, more mechanized, and more oriented toward far-flung markets. And as a result, farmers must now be versed in everything from fertilizers to the price of soybeans in Argentina.

In 1940 there were 6 million farms in the U.S., averaging 166 acres in size. By the late 1990s there were 2.2 million farms averaging 470 acres each. Farm employment fell from 12.5 million in 1930 to 1.2 million in the 1990s, even as the total U.S. population more than doubled. Today's farmers are highly skilled workers trained to use state-of-the-art plows, tillers, and harvesters. Computers are used to track farm operations, and biotechnology is used to manufacture seeds and fertilizers that can produce fast-growing crops. In short, farming has become a careful balancing act for the 2% of Americans who grow food for the rest of us.[1]

The farm sector of the U.S. economy has suffered three decades of setbacks. As a result, hundreds of thousands of farms have been lost. The liberalization of trade laws, the elimination of critical farm subsidies, and the consolidation of farms have worsened what many are now calling a "farming crisis." According to economists, a healthy domestic farm sector is critical to our nation's economic well-being. Biodiesel offers a means to revitalize the U.S. farming economy, by bringing jobs back to the Midwest and flowing valuable cash back into rural America.

Biodiesel can be made from a number of common crops like soybeans, many of which are already grown in America. Processing biodiesel into fuel employs people both on the farm and in localized crushing, processing, and transport industries. From the moment a seed is planted until the time that the vegetable-oil-derived fuel reaches the fuel tanks of vehicles, dollars that would normally be sent overseas to procure oil are cycled through the U.S. economy, keeping domestic business and industries healthy and strong. On the consumption end, biodiesel has the potential to offer Americans a real choice at the gas pump: fuel from the Mid East or fuel from the Midwest.

Today's Old MacDonald

Farming today combines hard physical labor, land management, and financial planning with a number of intangible benefits. Such benefits include working close to the land and living in a relatively clean environment – reasons some farmers endure the considerable stress associated with their profession. At an average age of 55 years old with an average of 15 years or more invested into their farms, most farmers employ fewer than thirty people. Despite advances in modern machinery, farming is difficult, tiring work demanding critical decision-making skills and long hours. The most important factor determining a farm's success is also the most difficult: long-term planning. Predicting crop yields and profits is easy to do on paper, but the reality of each season brings changes in weather, disease, commodity prices, and domestic subsidy and tariff policy.

Over the past three decades, there has been a trend away from small, diversified farms. Today most farmers specialize in just one to four crops. Farmers choose the crops they grow based on the local climate, the soil, the crops common to their region, and the international commodities market, or the market for their crops overseas. Each crop requires different equipment, different maintenance, and different personnel. Over the course of the year, a farmer must make tough decisions on problems specific to each crop, such as pest infestation, drought, rainfall, and disease.

During the planting, growing, and harvesting seasons, most farmers and their crews work from sunup to sundown. Even in the winter months, farmers dedicate themselves to the maintenance of equipment, machinery, and facilities. From replacing the drive shaft of a combine in the icy cold of North Dakota to changing a tractor transmission in the muggy Georgia heat, farmers must work with heavy machinery under adverse conditions. As a result, farmers have one of the highest injury rates of any profession and on average spend one week during their first three years recovering from injury.

As crops are harvested, farmers act as their own sales agents and manage the storage, transport, and sale of their crops. On the whole, farmers see low returns for their investment of time. The same farm may experience a windfall profit of tens of thousands of dollars one year and a severe loss the next, even though the farmer has changed little and done his or her best to predict crop yields. Thus, in addition to being a physically active crop expert, a land manager, and a sales agent, a farmer must also be dedicated enough to accept profit or loss for the year and begin work again at daybreak.

A Time for Change

Over the past century, there has been a transition from the small 100- to 200-acre farms to farms that span thousands of acres and gross hundreds of thousands of dollars per year. The greatest change, however, has occurred during the last 40 years. During this time a new breed of large mechanized farms emerged to produce the majority of U.S. agricultural products. While in many cases more profitable and stable than their smaller counterparts, these farms and the people who operate them are tied into a corporate production system ruled by unpredictable international markets.

American farming reached its heyday in 1935, when roughly 7 million farms across the nation were counted by the U.S. census. At that time, the average farm size was about 175 acres. [2] Since then the number of farms in the United States has dropped to just under 2 million and the average size has expanded to just under 500 acres. Of those roughly 2 million farms in the U.S., three-quarters generate minimal ($50,000 or less) or negative net incomes.[3] These smaller farms are considered "part-time or recreational ventures."

Size and Number of U.S. Farms 1850-2000

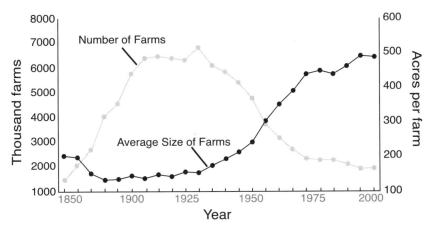

Source: U.S. Department of Agriculture, U.S. Census Bureau

The trend toward bigger farms continues today. For example, between 1994 and 1997, more than 42,000 farms with revenues of less than $250,000 per year disappeared, a decline of about 10%. Meanwhile, during this three-year period, nearly 20,000 farms with revenues in excess of $250,000 per year were added to the economy, an increase of about 17%. Thus, the U.S. experienced a net loss of about 22,000 farms between 1994 and 1997 alone. But what is most notable is not just the loss of farms (and jobs, and community, and lifestyle), but rather the consolidation of smaller farms into larger ones. This transformation from small-scale to large-scale agriculture is changing the face of the American farm.

The complexity and competitiveness of modern farming leaves little room for farmers who aren't bringing home big bacon. The USDA estimates that the farming consolidation trend will continue

Breakdown of Number of Farms According to Income:

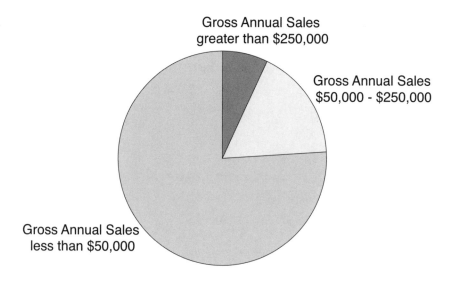

Source: U.S. Department of Agriculture

during the 2002-2012 period. As the size of farms grows, so too do the costs of additional land, machinery, seed, and chemicals. Farmers with liquid assets find it easier to grow and expand, while cash-poor farmers face a more difficult path. Added to the financial burden of small-scale farming is the reality that larger, more productive farms can better withstand adverse climactic changes and price fluctuations in operating costs for livestock, feed, seed, and fuel. Due to the fact that most subsidy programs are tied to farming output, larger farms also receive the lion's share of government payments and subsidies.

The Great Subsidy Debate

Many people believe that *biofuels* like biodiesel and ethanol are based on subsidies that take money from taxpayers and line the pockets of wealthy farmers. The truth is that subsidies play an important role our current economy. During times when market forces alone do not foster growth in an industry or when market forces have been modified in favor of a competitor, subsidies can provide an effective means for the U.S. government to give certain industries a "push" in the right direction.

So what is a subsidy and, more specifically, how do agricultural subsidies relate to biofuels? According to the University of Montana, "a subsidy is basically a payment from the government to producers or distributors in a given industry to prevent the decline of that industry." Subsidies take the form of grants, loans, and tax reductions. Farmer subsidies are given for a number of reasons, including disaster relief, trade assistance, land grants, commodity grants (paying for production that the market cannot absorb), and conservation monies (money paid farmers to refrain from growing).

U.S. farm subsidies were originally enacted to ensure that the American food supply remains constant regardless of market swings or environmental conditions. Without these important monetary buffers in place, farm production would swing from great highs to great lows. Supermarkets would have bread one week and no bread the next. Since food is the basic foundation of society, a disruption in food supply would result in economic and possible social calamity. Just as petroleum subsidies ensure our oil supply remains constant during times of political turmoil in the Middle East, farm subsidies ensure that our food supply remains relatively unchanged regardless of economic or natural occurrences.

Of the approximately 2.1 million farms reflected in the 2002 Census of Agriculture, only 33% received government payments of any type. The vast majority of farms (two thirds) received no assistance whatsoever. On a broader scale, if we look at farm operations over the time period from 1995-2003, taxpayers spent $131 billion on farm subsidies, or an average of $14.6 billion annually. This seems expensive, but consider that the majority of subsidies go toward stabilizing farms affected by the export market. For the same period of time, farm exports yielded approximately $40 billion a year–a reasonable return on the public's investment.[4]

The majority of subsidy money goes toward large farms that grow crops that sell on both the domestic and international markets. Between 1995 and 2003, the top 10% of farms received 72% of government aid in the form of conservation, commodity, and disaster programs.[5] These farms and entities collected, on average, $34,000 annually. While subsidy opponents cite this expenditure as a travesty, it is important to consider the nature of farming before accusing farmers of receiving undue subsidies.

Unlike other forms of production, where a fixed quantity of inputs will yield a fixed quantity of outputs, farming is variable. Crop yields are dependent on natural forces. Drought, soil erosion, tornadoes, rain, warm periods, cold snaps, and freezes all affect crop output. Further playing havoc with farmers are market forces in which farm commodities are often bought and sold on futures markets *before* the crops are even harvested. A farmer can lose his or her shirt in a hurry if the cost of inputs exceeds the value of the finished crop due to nature's temperament and market forces, both of which are well beyond the farmer's control. Under opposite circumstances, a farmer can *overproduce* and be penalized for the surplus crop. In this regard, farming quickly becomes a gambling game in which the only way to profit is to bet before you grow.

The difficulty of farming is evident in the returns that farmers see each year. In 2002 the average American farm's gross income (including government monies) was $97,320, of which $19,032 was the average farm's net income, with the majority of American farms actually showing a loss in income at the end of the fiscal year. It's no wonder that farming is not even the primary source of income for most farming families. According to the Environmental Working Group (EWG), which maintains the largest online public database of farm subsidies in the world, large-scale farming without subsidies isn't just unprofitable; it's impossible. The EWG reports that "almost all of the income for the average farm household, 89%, came from off-farm sources, the jobs in town or elsewhere that make farm living pencil out for most Americans. It's not just that government subsidies aren't saving the family farm. Not even farming is."[6]

Bigger, But Not Necessarily Better

Farms have gotten bigger, but have they gotten better? Farms today produce more per person-hour worked than ever before. But self-employed farmers are being replaced with farm managers hired by large companies. While the percentage of farms owned by sole proprietors was roughly constant between 1978 and 1992 at about 85% of all farms, the percentage of total farm output of these farms declined from 62% to 54% during the same period. This is not to say these smaller farmers produced less than they had previously. Instead, due to production increases from larger corporate-owned farms, the proportion grown by owner-operator farms dropped.

Corporate control of the farm sector is becoming more apparent both upstream and downstream from farmers. On the upstream side, consolidation is taking place among seed and chemical suppliers. The number of companies supplying seed is shrinking and their size is increasing. Today Monsanto, Dupont, Dow, and Novartis supply 69% of the North American seed corn market and 47% of the commercial soybean seed market.[7] After DuPont's purchase of Pioneer Hi-Bred, one of the largest seed suppliers in the world, DuPont's CEO, Charles O. Holliday, referred to the new conglomerate in a company press release by saying, "This will be the most powerful agricultural technology force in the world."[8]

On the downstream side, grain distribution to the commodities markets, which has been controlled by a handful of companies since the 19th century, is becoming more concentrated. Recently, Cargill purchased Continental's grain storage unit, resulting in a single company controlling more than one-third of U.S. grain exports. The newly merged Cargill/Continental giant joins agricultural companies ADM and Zen Noh, which all together now control 81% of U.S. corn exports and 65% of U.S. soybean exports.[9]

The primary reason for the mergers is export market volatility. During periods of low export volume, large trading companies can absorb idle time, and during times of soaring export volumes, these companies have the resources to increase farm production. The result is that an ever-smaller group of farmers who control an ever-larger portion of arable land must raise or lower production–not according to slowly changing government regulations or relatively predicable domestic markets, but according to the corporations that run the international markets for their products.

In many ways, this relatively new consolidated corporate agricultural system has disconnected the reality of farming from the markets where food is sold. Although American agriculture has become more mechanized and farms have increased in size in recent years, one cannot simply turn a dial to increase or decrease farm production. Nature is indifferent to profit and loss. Crops must be planned, planted, and harvested on a yearly or biannual basis. Change in crop production is often much slower than market fluctuations.

It is no wonder, then, that the wild swings in the international commodity market demand–like those in the 1970s (from a peak of 70 million metric tons to a low of 36 million metric tons) and in the 1990s (from a peak of 70 million metric tons to a low of 40 million metric tons)–bankrupt farms, wreak havoc on America's agricultural sector, and destabilize the financial structure it supports. Bigger may be better, but as long as the production of large-scale U.S. agriculture feeds volatile export markets, it's not better for American farmers–and it's certainly not better for the American economy.[10]

Swing High, Swing Low

During the early 1970s, farming in the United States experienced a boom as grain and soy were exported to Russia and China by the shipload. The increased revenues from exports brought farmers a new level of income, and many farmers borrowed heavily to expand their farms, buying equipment and building new infrastructure. Between 1972 and 1974, for example, sales of John Deere and International Harvester jumped by billions of dollars.

But the late 1970s brought disaster to America's agricultural community as Asia, Russia, and South America jumped into the commodity export market, pulling down world commodity prices. Compounding American farmers' ills were problems resulting from the oil shocks. Double-digit inflation, high fuel prices, and high agricultural input prices left many farmers owing more than their farms were worth. These events resulted in a combined farm debt of $120 billion in 1978, up over 100% from the beginning of the decade–the interest on which consumed roughly 50% of farm income. By 1985 farm debt had again almost doubled to $215 billion, the interest on which was $20 billion annually.[11]

Despite the economic swings of the 1970s, farm output in the U.S. continued to climb. Between 1985 and 1996 U.S. agricultural exports more than doubled. But the increase in exports did not bring an increase in income. Due to the globalization of the commodities markets and the resulting decline in the prices of basic farm products, U.S. farm income has remained static or fallen since the 1970s. For example, in the years spanning 1978 to 1997, real grain prices fell by 50%.[12]

In 1996 the Omnibus Farm Bill offered farmers some relief in the form of a promise of increased markets for their products if they accepted a reduction in subsidies. The bill encouraged the government to promote agricultural exports in trade deals with Latin America and the World Trade Organization (WTO). In addition, the USDA would eliminate restrictions on U.S. farm planning decisions. In essence, the deal was simple: lower cash support from the government would be traded for potentially untapped markets for U.S. farm commodities. The bill sounded good to farmers and it sounded good to both parties in the Senate and House. Unfortunately for U.S. farmers, the government's ability to break international agricultural market barriers was not as good.

In the two years that followed the passage of the bill, the U.S. farm trade balance fell by more than $13 billion as agricultural prices bottomed out. U.S. corn prices fell 56% from 1996 to 1998. Wheat prices fell 46% over the same time period.[13] While the dip in price was offset somewhat by increased exports and, later, higher commodity prices, the 1996 Farm Bill lifted government protection for farmers and shifted the balance of agricultural power away from farmers. More than ever before, farmers were now dependent on market forces completely outside the borders and jurisdiction of the United States. Meanwhile, the patchwork quilt of Middle America was being torn apart one farm at a time.

NAFTA and GATT Take Their Toll

As its name suggests, the international commodity market relies on a global system of interconnected economies rather than one domestic or regional economy. Changes in export laws, changes in tariffs, or reduction of domestic agricultural support require careful planning based on a formidable understanding of these international economies as well as each nation's competitive potential. However, close examination of the situation in 1996 reveals that only a limited number of international markets could possibly be opened for U.S. agricultural exports. Thus, when enacted, the Farm Bill set in motion a domino effect, resulting in an agricultural economic crisis the ramifications of which we are only now beginning to grasp.

Added to the fallacy that international markets would open their doors to U.S. farm products were the strong farm subsidy programs in other countries that buffered overseas farmers, giving them the ability to "float" low agricultural prices to maintain market position. Between 1990 and 1998, the U.S. agricultural trade balance with Europe fell sharply: U.S. agricultural exports to Europe declined by about $2 billion, while U.S. agricultural imports from Europe increased by $3 billion.[14] During this time the European Union (EU) maintained high subsidies to European farmers. Despite the establishment of the General Agreement on Tariffs and Trade (GATT) in April of 1994, which was supposed to reduce agricultural subsidies, EU farm spending increased from $46 billion in 1995 to $55 billion in 1997. During the same period U.S. government payments to farmers were $7 billion – less than 13% of the total amount spent by the EU subsidizing its farmers. Meanwhile, growing resistance by the European population to major U.S. farm products, such as hormone-treated beef and genetically modified soybeans, largely blocked U.S. exports to one of the wealthiest potential agricultural markets.

Hopes that U.S. farmers would enjoy an export boom to Canada and Mexico were also dashed by events of the late 1990s. Under the 1994 North American Free Trade Act (NAFTA) and the 1989 U.S.-Canada Free Trade Agreement, the quantity of agricultural products traded substantially increased throughout North America. The net financial effect, however, has been a decline in U.S. agricultural trade surplus with Mexico and Canada. In effect, NAFTA radically altered the *nature* of trade between the U.S., Mexico, and Canada–further widening the gap between exports and imports.

Under NAFTA, U.S. farmers saw overall exports of corn and other feed grains (such as sorghum) to Mexico and Canada increase.

Meanwhile, U.S. imports of fruits, vegetables, wheat, barley, and cattle all increased even more, leading to a declining trade balance. For example, between 1990 and 1998, U.S. export of feed grains to Canada increased by 127%, but at the same time U.S. imports of wheat from Canada increased by 249%, growing from $79 million in 1990 to $278 million in 1998. Similarly, U.S. corn exports to Mexico increased by 47% during that period, while cattle and calf imports from Mexico skyrocketed by 1,280%.[15] In many ways, the U.S. began to supply low-grade, bulk feed and protein and began importing higher-grade produce and higher-grade grains–a trend that has continued to undermine the ability of our agricultural sector to stabilize the U.S. economy.

The Export Bubble Bursts

Temporary relief was on its way for U.S. farmers in the 1990s in the form of an increase in positive trade with Asia. From 1990 to 1996, the trade balance with Asia increased by $8 billion. But the influx of dollars into Asia from Japan and other nations did not last. Investments into Asia eventually dried up, taking with them another strong export market for U.S. agricultural products. Following the Thai financial crisis of 1997, the U.S. agricultural trade balance with Asia returned to its 1990 level. To make matters worse, the 1996 Farm Bill went into effect, eating away at subsidies and deregulating much of the U.S. commodity market.

In short, despite higher annual crop yields, higher overall output, and even higher exports, farmers have had a steady, and in many cases declining, aggregate income.

According to Robert E. Scott, a researcher and writer for the Economic Policy Institute in Washington D.C., liberalizing trade in the early 1990s was built "on the false foundation of a speculative bubble." Scott says that the increase in trade has "increased the volatility of farm incomes, but it has yet to improve their average level."[16]

The relatively slow increase in the growth of agricultural exports and the rapid increase in agricultural imports has put America into a situation that it had avoided for almost 50 years: the U.S. agricultural trade hangs somewhere between a surplus and a deficit. This should not be confused with actual farm output, which is increasing annually. Nor should this be confused with the value of exports, which has also been increasing. The agricultural trade deficit has been caused, more than anything else, by changes in consumer

U.S. Agricultural Trade
Fiscal years 2000-2005, year ending September 30

Item	2000	2001	2002	2003	2004	Forecast Fiscal 2005 Aug.	Nov.
			Billion Dollars				
Exports	50.7	52.7	53.3	56.2	62.3	57.5	56.0
Imports	38.9	39.0	41.0	45.7	52.7	55.0	56.0
Balance	11.9	13.7	12.3	10.5	9.6	2.5	0.0

Reflects forecasts in the Nov. 12, 2004, *World Agricultural Supply and Demand Estimates* report.

Sources: U.S. Department of Agriculture and Bureau of Census, U.S. Department of Commerce.

habits. The value of food imports into the U.S. has been increasing faster than the value of our exports.

So what do U.S. consumers want that they're not getting from home soil? Wine, beer, fruits, vegetables, and beef, to name the leading imports. A weaker dollar has further raised the cost of imported agricultural goods.

It's clear that emerging soybean producers such as Brazil and Argentina (once importers) and the emergence of Russia as an exporter of wheat (once one of the largest wheat importers) have changed the world commodity markets. It's clear that the 1994 NAFTA and the 1996 Omnibus Farm Bill weakened the position of

U.S. farmers in a rapidly globalizing marketplace. It is now clear that the balance of agricultural trade is sliding into a deficit. What is unclear, however, is how this will affect America.

Debt and deficit are closely tied. As the total U.S. deficit increases, the United States' debt increases and its ability to make payments on its rising debt decreases. Since the late 1950s the United States' largest export (and one of its greatest sources of revenue) has been agricultural products. Even in the 1990s, the agriculture sector was able to reduce the total U.S. trade deficit by as much as 16%. From 1996 to 2004, however, agricultural imports into the U.S. have more than doubled, from $27.3 billion to $52.5 billion, while the value of exports increased by only 4%.[17] The problem with the elimination of America's leading source of trade revenue is that, in many ways, agriculture also underpins the economy. Without positive cash returns from agricultural exports, the United States faces severe economic implications.

Securing the Future

The effects of the 1996 "Freedom to Farm" bill were so deleterious to the U.S. agricultural community that in 2002, Congress passed the Farm Security and Rural Investment Act, which governs federal farm programs until 2008. The 2002 Farm Bill reversed many of the changes made in 1996. Included in the new legislation were critical provisions to ensure the success of U.S. farmers battling the yo-yo effects of the commodity markets. Namely, the 2002 bill provides for "counter-cyclical" payments to farmers when commodity prices fall below their target prices. The new legislation added an estimated $51.7 billion to all agricultural programs over the six-year life of the bill.

Interestingly, many of the bill's provisions are aimed at conservation of land and the return of vast tracts of farmed land to natural habitats and grasslands. These provisions reflect the growing efficiency in the U.S. agricultural sector. The government is literally thinking of ways to curb agricultural production. Meanwhile, the bill contains a number of provisions to stimulate the growth of energy products from crops. These provisions include an annual $1 million grant to educate government entities and the public about biodiesel; a mandatory expenditure of $1 million through the *Commodity Credit Corporation* (CCC), a government entity created to stabilize farm income, for testing bio-based products; competitive grant programs to build biorefineries to produce fuels; and a loan and grant program to help farmers purchase renewable energy systems.[18] These programs, while reflecting the need for a way to deal with America's agricultural surplus and the need to transition toward more carbohydrate energy sources, have not managed to curb the growing agricultural trade deficit.

In a November 2004 *Wall Street Journal* article, Sung Won Sohn, chief economist of banking behemoth Wells Fargo & Co., said: "It's very worrisome; we need agricultural trade surpluses more than ever because the nonagricultural deficit is ballooning." The article's author, Scott Kilman, added that the trade deficit is only sustained by foreign lenders willing to float the U.S. large loans. Many economists say this is unlikely to continue, and in Kilman's words, "the risks are growing for a market-rattling crash in the value of the dollar."[19]

Despite Congress's valid attempts at a course correction for the agricultural sector, the United States faces a serious agricultural trade problem. If we do not balance our imports and exports of agricultural goods, we will face severe economic impact. Given the importance of agriculture to the economy, it seems prudent to look toward biodiesel and other crop-based fuels to create strong domestic markets for agricultural goods and stabilize the American farm economy.

America's New Oilfields

At a cost of over $100 billion dollars annually, America spends more money on oil than any other imported commodity. According to the Department of Energy, the cost of imported petroleum will rise indefinitely. Agricultural product–namely soy, wheat, cotton, and rice–were once America's main source of foreign income. But worldwide prices for these commodities have dropped like lead paperweights, leaving farmers scrambling to produce more, faster, and with newer technologies. The rest of the world has caught on to U.S. agricultural production techniques. The result is a worldwide food "glut" and an all-time low in world commodity prices.

According to *The New American Farmer,* a USDA publication, many small-scale farmers are finding new markets for their food in the organics and cooperative markets.[20] However, small-scale farming in the United States continues to be a largely unprofitable endeavor. Meanwhile, despite advances in agricultural technology and new crop breeds with higher yields, large-scale farms are experiencing severe economic downturn due to the volatility of international commodities markets.

As the world prices of soybeans, corn, wheat, and rice flatten, a strong business case can be made for linking large-scale agriculture, not to food production for a worldwide market awash in grains and soybeans, but rather to a more stable market and one with increasing demand. In essence, the American agricultural sector is poised for a dramatic shift toward the production of a value-added commodity that is in increasing demand around the world and has a strong domestic market. An ideal commodity would have the ability to be consumed almost straight from the fields, eliminating international transport costs and eliminating unpredictable markets. That commodity just might be liquid fuel.

According to Alan Weber who, in addition to being one of

America's prominent biodiesel economists, participates in operating a 900-acre family farm in central Missouri, growing crops for fuel has the potential to help both small- and large-scale farmers. Weber explains that a biodiesel market will increase the demand for soybeans and other oilseeds. Regardless of the size of a farming operation, says Weber, farms growing fuel crops will see benefits. "If you're a soybean producer," says Weber, "you'll benefit from biodiesel demand. Whether you're raising 50 acres or 5,000."
Weber adds that biodiesel demand can help buoy sagging oilseed prices across the board. The soybean market has historically been driven by demand for meal. "If biodiesel takes off, we may move into an oil-driven market rather than a meal-driven market," explains Weber.

In 2004, U.S. soybean production was at 2.9 billion bushels. But at the close of the year, an excess of 133 million gallons of soybean oil had been produced. Biodiesel demand can help "soak up" much of the excess vegetable oil on the market, while stabilizing oilseed prices and giving farmers a much needed break from market swings.[21]

Concurring with Weber are a number of independent studies, including one by the Food and Agricultural Policy Research Institute (FAPRI), a project of the University of Missouri and Iowa State University.[22] The FAPRI study concluded that an increased soybean oil usage of 265 million gallons by 2010 would have the following effects on the U.S. farming industry:

- A 14% increase in the price of soybean oil;
- A 5% decrease in the price of soybean meal;
- An increase of $3.4 million to farm income.

Another study by AUS Consultants draws similar conclusions and adds that increased demand for biodiesel also results in lower loans and subsidies to farmers, increased price of other commodity crops, and no noticeable negative effects on the price or availability of food crops.[23] Overall, these studies show biodiesel provides a means to stabilize farm income and reduce farmers' dependence on government financial assistance.

The effects of increased biodiesel production will be felt beyond the agricultural community. Reduced soybean-meal prices will reduce input costs for livestock producers and can lead to increased exports of meat products, thus positively impacting the U.S. balance of trade. Increased biodiesel production will also lead to additional needs for oilseed crushing capacity, creating additional jobs and value-added activity for the economy.

Overall, biodiesel offers a bankable way to reap financial rewards from refocusing domestic oilseed production on a product that will be consumed in America. While farmers will always generate some amount of capital through exports, most would gladly trade the export market roller coaster for a crop market in which prices are consistently higher than they were the year before. That market is the fuel market. And one fuel that will help stabilize the U.S. agricultural sector and curb the extinction of the American farm is biodiesel.

Six American Fuel Crops

For thousands of years humans have used vegetable oils for cooking and as ingredients in food. Today vegetable oils are also used in many industrial applications, as emulsifiers, lubricants, plastics, solvents, inks, resins, and fuels. Vegetable oils are biodegradable, have low or no eco-toxicity, and have low or no toxicity to humans. As *feedstocks*, vegetable oils form the basis for the creation of biodiesel fuel.

There are over 350 species of oleaginous, or oil-producing,

plants, and thousands of subspecies. These plants produce beans or seeds that contain natural vegetable oil that can be extracted from the seed by using a press. While there is an oil-producing crop for just about each region of the planet, there are six vegetable-oil crops that are common to the North American continent and have good potential as biodiesel feedstocks.[24]

Soybean

The soybean, or soya, plant is a protein-rich, hardy plant that has been cultivated in East Asia for the past 5,000 years. Today there are more than 2,500 known species of soybeans cultivated around the world. With roughly 70 million acres planted each year, soybeans are America's most commonly grown crop. When crushed, soybeans yield approximately 20% oil and 80% meal by weight.

2000 World Soybean Production

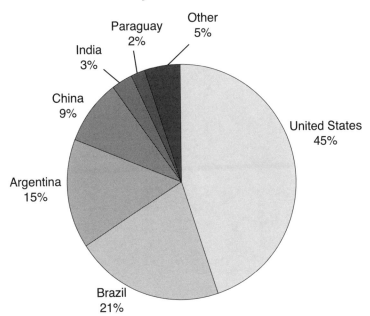

Source: U.S. Department of Agriculture

Each year the United States produces about 2.4 billion gallons of soy oil and 40 million short tons of soy meal. The majority of soy oil–about 1.7 billion gallons–is used as salad oil, cooking oil, and in baking and frying oils. The remainder is used in margarines, paints, plastics, and biodiesel.

The United States produces 45% of the world's soybeans. Brazil produces about 21% and Argentina 15%. In 2004 China was the largest consumer of unprocessed American soybeans, importing just over 36% of the yearly crop. By comparison, the EU imports 14% of the U.S. soybean crop and Mexico imports 12%. The United States is losing footing in the world soybean market, however. Since 1975, Brazil's soybean production has increased 600%, from about 300 million bushels per year to just under 2 billion bushels in 2003. Argentina has likewise increased soybean production, from around 100 million bushels in the 1970s to close to 1.2 billion bushels in 2003.

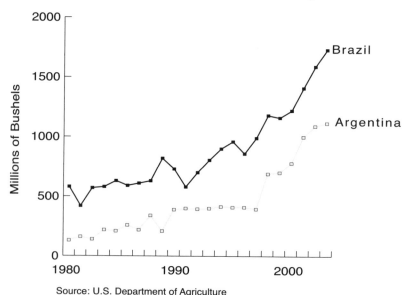

Soybean Production in Brazil & Argentina

Source: U.S. Department of Agriculture

Soybeans: Domestic Use and Exports

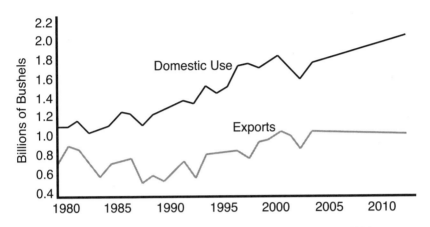

Source: USDA Agricultural Baseline Projections to 2013, February 2004.
Economic Research Service, USDA

Most of the biodiesel made in the United States is made from either virgin soybean oil or used cooking oil that was originally made from soybeans. According to the National Biodiesel Board, only 500,000 gallons of soybean oil were used to make biodiesel in 1999. By 2004, over 25 million gallons of soybean oil were processed into biodiesel in the United States. Due to recent oil price hikes and biodiesel tax relief legislation, the United States Department of Energy estimates this trend will continue, giving farmers a much-needed domestic market for soybean oil.[25]

Rapeseed & Canola

There exists some confusion on the nomenclature of these yellow-flowering crops. Both plants are members of the Brassica family and are related to broccoli, cabbage, and cauliflower. Rapeseed ("raps" as it is known in Germany) is a highly oleaginous crop, yielding small seeds and an oil high in erucic acid. The crop is well suited to colder regions and is grown throughout Europe, especially in Germany and France, where right before harvest season one can see vast fields of iridescent yellow stretching toward the mountains. Although inedible to humans, the meal from the rape plant is an acceptable animal feed. Most of the biodiesel in Europe is made from rapeseed oil. Yields of oil of rapeseed range from 100-200 gallons per acre and are among the highest of any conventional oil crop.

Canola, while physically indistinguishable from its cousin, is actually a hybrid created to remove the unwanted traits found in rapeseed. (The name "canola" is a hybrid/acronym of the words "CANada Oil Low Acid.") Consequently, canola has a low saturated fat content of 7%, very low erucic acid content, and is widely used as a cooking oil and a margarine base. Most of the canola produced in the United States comes from North Dakota, which produces about 1.35 billion pounds of the total 1.5 billion pounds. As the market for high-yield oilseed feedstocks for biodiesel grows, farmers in northern states such as Montana, Idaho, and as far south as Colorado are showing an increasing interest in canola and rapeseed.[27]

Mustard

The mustard seed contains between 25% and 40% oil by weight, and yields of around 2 tons per acre have been achieved, yielding up to 150 gallons of mustard oil for one acre of land. At about 80 million pounds of annual production, the United States produces very little mustard seed. But that could change, thanks to a study conducted by the U.S. Department of Energy, which selected mustard seed for a three-year breeding program to test its viability as a biodiesel feedstock.

A report issued by the U.S. DOE outlines fourteen important criteria for a new crop that could be slowly introduced into the American market as a source for biodiesel feedstock. The criteria outlined in the report are:

1. Ability to supply 6-12 billion gallons of feedstock oil
2. Raw crushed oil can be produced for 10 cents a pound or less
3. Oil must contain more than 90% monosaturates
4. Oil must be inedible for humans and livestock and possess no high value for industrial use
5. Non-oil portion of the crop must possess high market value, in excess of 12 cents per pound
6. Non-oil portion of the crop must face expanding market demand
7. Market demand for non-oil portion of the crop must be large enough to absorb billions of pounds of material
8. Crop must be suitable for large-scale production in the U.S. (not limited to small regions)
9. Crop should be low input and offer significant rotation or other environmental benefits
10. Crop should not be in basic research stage of development, but preferably in an early commercial production stage
11. Suitable production and crushing technology should be available
12. Crop yields per acre are comparable to commercial crops and offer the potential to expand
13. Oil yield is at least 25% to 40% of the crop product
14. Crop is profitable to farmers and crushers[28]

According to NREL, mustard meets all of these criteria. As a result of the study, Colorado-based biodiesel company Blue Sun Biodiesel has established a farmer cooperative that plans to grow mustard seed for biodiesel. While it may be some time before mustard makes a substantial dent in the U.S. oilseed market, mustard seed could one day be a strong contender among biodiesel feedstocks.[29]

Peanut

Native to South America, peanuts grow well in warm climates and sandy soil. In the U.S., where most peanuts are grown for the production of peanut butter, about 1.3 million acres are planted with peanuts, yielding around 4 billion pounds of peanuts annually. The peanut plant has a slightly lower oil yield per acre than rapeseed or canola and a slightly higher average yield than soybeans. While the diesel engine shown at the 1900 World Exhibition in Paris was powered by peanut oil, Georgia is the only U.S. state to express interest in using peanut oil as a feedstock for biodiesel. The University of Georgia has put both a peanut-oil-powered tractor and two peanut-oil-powered buses to work on its campus.[30]

Sunflower

Once upon a time, fields of sunflowers covered thousands of acres of what are today the western plains of the United States. A native North American plant, its cultivation dates back to 3000 B.C., when sunflower seeds were used as a high-protein, highly nutritious food. The large flowering plants grow to between 15 inches and 8 feet tall, and prefer warm temperatures and rich soil. Sunflower crops yield about 100 gallons of oil per acre, slightly less than rapeseed/canola crops. Sunflowers are high in iron and contain numerous other essential vitamins and minerals. Sunflower oil is the second most plentiful edible oil in the world and is used for cooking, margarine, salad dressings, lubricants, soaps, and lighting.[31] In Russia, sunflowers have been grown on irradiated land as an experimental feedstock for biodiesel fuel.

Corn (Maize)

With a market value of roughly $21 billion dollars and with around 80 million acres planted in the United States annually, corn is America's most common grain. A native plant of the Americas, corn has been cultivated for more than 5,000 years at altitudes from sea level to over 9,000 feet. Corn is used for 75% of the world's starch and is the third most common grain in the world after wheat and rice. Corn crops typically reach 6 to 9 feet in height, are resistant to depredation by birds, and produce the largest amount of grain per hour of labor. Since less than 8% of the corn kernel is oil, corn oil is a bonus by-product of the starch. Oil yields for U.S. corn commonly run about 18 gallons of oil per acre. In the United States, corn oil is used extensively as a frying oil for fast foods.[32] Among its many other uses, corn starch is used as a base for the production of the alcohol fuel ethanol. Thus, one corn crop can produce both ethanol and biodiesel fuels.[33]

Fat Food Nation

America is the only country in the world where 96% of school-children can identify Ronald McDonald; the average person eats three hamburgers and four orders of french fries every week; and its citizens spend more than $110 billion a year on fast food. As a result, Americans use more vegetable oil for frying than the people of any other nation.[34] While the bulk of biodiesel production in the U.S. may one day come primarily from *virgin* soybean oil (oil that has not been used for cooking), much of the 1.7 billion gallons of soybean oil and the more than 1 billion gallons of other vegetable oils used for cooking and frying may soon find a new home as a feedstock for biodiesel. A substantial quantity of America's frying oil ends up in grease containers located behind fast food restaurants. Often what can be found in a grease container is a mix of soybean oil, animal fat, trap grease, and other cooking oils. The result is a greasy cocktail with an unmistakably pungent odor.

The rendering industry classifies used cooking oil and fats into different categories. *Yellow grease* is used cooking oil, primarily from fast food restaurants. *Tallow* is beef fat created by slaughter-houses. (Lard is hog fat and chicken fat refers to poultry.) *Brown grease* includes greases from restaurant grease traps, sewage plants, and "black grease" (sludge.) Brown grease is gelatinous at room temperature and has low overall oil content. Both yellow grease and tallow can be made into biodiesel. Brown grease can also be processed into biodiesel, but the costs of processing are higher and the per-gallon biodiesel yield is lower.

According to the USDA, the United States produces just over 11 billion pounds (1.4 billion gallons) of used cooking oil and animal fat each year.[35] Considering the production of such large quantities of this substance, the obvious question is: where does this stuff go? The answer: mostly into feeding the animals we eat. In fact, approximately 74% of the inedible tallow and grease produced in the United States each year goes into animal feed. The remainder is used to make soaps, lubricants, and other products such as biodiesel.[36]

While the thought of eating animals whose diets are based on grease may be unappealing, the European Commission (EC) has deemed it simply unhealthy. Prompted by the recent mad cow disease scare, the Animal By-Products Regulation (ABPR) was enacted to safeguard the health of animals by ensuring that animal by-products in Europe are not used as animal feed. In an EU-wide ruling, the Animal By-Products Regulation went into effect in late 2004. The ABPR says that used cooking oil will be taken away by the normal collectors, but the collectors will have to either supply it to a biodiesel manufacturer, an electricity company for use as generator fuel, or to the oils and chemicals industry. According to the regulation: "The Government strongly supports the recovery of waste cooking oil for such purposes as it underpins its strategies in both reducing dependency upon landfill sites as a means of waste disposal and reducing the use of fossil fuels for energy generation."[37]

The unilateral move by the EC sent biodiesel producers in Germany, England, and France scrambling to incorporate technology to process used cooking oils into their existing biodiesel facilities, but the larger effect of the ruling has been a substantial increase in the quantity of feedstock available to the European biodiesel industry. The result is increased EU biodiesel production and overall growth of the EU biodiesel industry.

In the United States, where renderers make up a large and growing portion of the biodiesel industry, the government has made a number of attempts to encourage the production of biodiesel from rendered feedstocks. Even before the EC ruling on rendered oils, the USDA offered $50 million in loan guarantees for pilot projects to transform waste livestock products to biofuel.[38] Additional recent biodiesel legislation under the 2004 American Jobs Creation Act offers fuel blenders up to 50 cents back from the federal government for each gallon of biodiesel made from the used cooking oil they blend.

But according to some renderers, federal support for biodiesel from rendered feedstocks needs to be stronger if the biodiesel market is going to absorb the rendered oils currently bought by the animal feed market. "We want to turn all of the used oils we can into biodiesel," says Fred Wellons, who operates a facility in southern California that makes biodiesel from used cooking oil. "But to make biodiesel from rendered oils cost-feasible, we need more government support." While U.S. government efforts to help the rendering industry move toward biodiesel may not be as strong as those of the EU, they portend a growing desire from Washington to support the U.S. rendering industry in its intent to transition into a viable biodiesel feedstock and fuel supplier for America.

Algae as a Feedstock

From 1978 to 1996 the Office of Fuels Development, a division of the Department of Energy, funded a $25 million dollar program under the National Renewable Energy Laboratory (NREL) called the "Aquatic Species Program: Biodiesel from Algae." The program investigated, developed, and tested highly oleaginous strains of algae that could be grown for biodiesel production. The project began when NREL researchers working with algae as a means to sequester carbon dioxide emissions from coal power plants discovered that some of algae studied produced unusually high quantities of natural oil. The fast growth rates and high oil content of these algae warranted further investigation, and the researchers began to focus on algae as a possible future feedstock for biodiesel production.

Algae reproduce more rapidly and consume more carbon dioxide than any other form of plant life. Algae reproduce by cellular division, dividing until they either fill their living space or exhaust their nutrient base. The primary ingredients for algal life are carbon dioxide, sunlight, and water. After studying algae facilities in Hawaii and the southwestern United States, NREL researchers were given the green light to build a series of shallow, serpentine "raceway" ponds at a facility in Roswell, New Mexico, where they began to experimental with algae production.

The research confirmed that the algae would proliferate in the hot, dry desert climate of the American southwest. Not surprisingly, the two largest producers of algae in the U.S., Earthrise Farms and Amway, both operate nutritional spirulina algae pond farms in the southern California desert, where daytime temperatures reach 120° Fahrenheit. While the NREL study focused on growing algae in conjunction with coal-fired power plants, researchers noted that algae could also be grown in wastewater treatment facilities.

The NREL study concluded that algae could theoretically produce large quantities of natural oil. At the Roswell site, diatom algae productivity reached 50 grams of algae per square meter per day. Each pond was 1,000 square meters in size. There was a possible daily yield of 50 kilograms, or 110 pounds, of algae per pond. The diatom algae studied are approximately 50% oil by weight. Thus, there was a possible daily yield of 55 pounds of oil per 1,000 square meters.

Using this model, annual production for one pond would yield 20,075 pounds of oil. Since oil weighs about 7.6 pounds per gallon, this would equal 2,640 gallons of algal oil yearly. Comparatively, only 50 gallons of oil can be produced with high-yield canola plants in 1,000 square meters of space. Even at 10% efficient oil extraction, one algae pond could yield 254 gallons of oil annually.[39]

It should be noted that, while oil was successfully extracted from the algae in a bench scale process, no biodiesel was ever actually produced from the algae in the OFT/NREL program. Theoretically, algae could be processed into natural oil using technology and techniques similar to those used with soybeans and other oilseeds. Such methods include: 1) physical extraction whereby centrifugal force or some other force is used to extract the oil; 2) chemical extraction using a closed-loop hexane extraction system (currently the most common and efficient form of vegetable oil extraction); or 3) thermochemical liquification to process the algal oil through extreme heat and pressure. Theoretical oil yields for algae range from 30-40%.

A number of roadblocks stand in the way of successful real-world application of the algae research developed by NREL. Limited salt-water resources indicate that only a handful of locations in the southwestern United States would have suitable water supplies. The need for excess carbon dioxide also limits the geographical location of these ponds, since they would be best located next to power plants. Another problem is evaporation and cross-contamination, since the raceway design is based on shallow, open ponds. Efficient and cost effective oil extraction also remains a barrier. Finally, and perhaps most importantly, the cost of establishing even the smallest-scale facilities needed for successful algal oil production could reach into the hundreds of millions of dollars, with no exact timeline for a return on investment.

The promising results of the NREL Aquatic Species Program warrant further testing and real-world applications of the algae research. In the words of the scientists who wrote the closing report for the DOE on their research with algae, "...[this report] should not be seen as an ending, but as a beginning. When the time is right, we fully expect to see renewed interest in algae as a source of fuels and other chemicals."[40] Hopefully for the U.S., that time will come soon.

How Much Fuel Can We Grow?

Assessing the total potential domestic production of biodiesel today is akin to the difficulty of assessing the potential of the personal computer when it was first invented. In 1943 Thomas Watson, the chairman of IBM, said, "I think there is a world market for maybe five computers." Today, there are almost 600 million personal computers in the world and the United States has about 65 computers for every 100 inhabitants.

The biodiesel industry may never reach the same growth as the computer industry. But until a large-scale, efficient, demand-based biodiesel industry evolves, biodiesel production projections remain heavily speculative. As a result, people interested in biodiesel businesses will find widely varying theories on the total domestic market potential.

As new crop varieties are engineered and the potential production of an acre of land increases, what was true about maximum per-acre agricultural production last year will soon be out of date.

World Vegetable Oil Production 2000

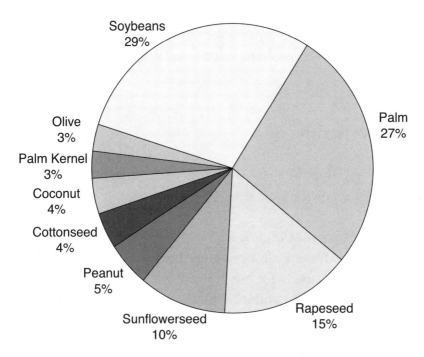

Total World Vegetable Oil Production = 96.1 Million Short Tons
96.1 Million Short Tons = 25.3 billion gallons of veg. oil
[There are 2,000 lbs in a short ton. Vegetable oil weighs 7.6 lbs per gallon.]

Source: U.S. Department of Agriculture

Compounding the difficulty of accurately assessing the potential production of vegetable oils from agriculture is the ever-increasing efficiency of the transport sector. While this doesn't directly affect our ability to predict crop output, it does affect our projected need for fuel production, and thus the way in which we look at potential biodiesel production.

Each year, the United States consumes 125 billion gallons of gasoline and 60 billion gallons of diesel and distillate fuel.[41] Since biodiesel has the potential to replace only diesel fuel, we will concentrate on the 60 billion gallons of diesel fuel consumed annually.

It is important to note here that processing one gallon of vegetable oil will yield one gallon of biodiesel. Thus, for the purposes of our discussion on potential production, the number of gallons of vegetable oil and the potential number of gallons of biodiesel are considered equal.

Three Scenarios

The following three scenarios outline some potential production pathways for biodiesel fuel:

Scenario #1: Current Conditions, Steady Growth

In 2004 the United States produced about 30 million gallons of biodiesel. As markets for biodiesel slowly open and production facilities are built, more of the 1.4 billion gallons of grease and tallow produced by the rendering industry and more of the 1.7 billion gallons of soy oil produced annually will be turned into biodiesel. If the biodiesel industry and the fuels and oils industries continue to cooperate and government support remains strong, domestic biodiesel use will continue to grow. Under these conditions, it would not be unrealistic to expect biodiesel production to increase to ½ - 1 billion gallons annually (a quantity smaller than today's annual ethanol production) by 2010.

Scenario #2: External Economic Conditions, Followed by Heavy Investment

Let's assume momentarily, based on what we know about foreign oil reserves and farm commodity prices, that within the next decade the United States experiences a decrease in the availability of imported oil, combined with a severe deficit in agricultural trade. While nobody can predict future events with certainty, this scenario is within the bounds of reality. Under these conditions, government and private sector support for biodiesel (and other renewables) could increase substantially.

A combination of direct-to-farmer subsidies and private equity investment into infrastructure could significantly increase the production potential of the biodiesel industry. It's feasible that some portion of the 60 million acres of U.S. cropland currently lying fallow (for argument's sake, let's say 40 million acres) would be sown with soybeans and other oil-producing crops, yielding 2 billion additional gallons of vegetable oil. Most of the vegetable oil, grease, and tallow in the U.S. could also be collected and processed into biodiesel. Research and development funds could be allocated to large-scale experiments with higher-oil-yielding crops, including producing algae from aquaculture. In this climate, we might expect to see production of as much as 5 billion gallons of biodiesel (8% of our total diesel fuel usage) by 2010–an extremely optimistic but technologically feasible achievement.

Scenario #3: A Social or Economic Trigger Causes Rapid Public Demand for Domestically Produced Renewable Liquid Fuel
Today the United States is dependent on foreign sources of petroleum for close to 60% of its energy. In the interest of economic and social stability, it's preferable to gradually shift away from foreign sources of energy. However, as America learned from the oil shocks of the 1970s, oil does not always flow from foreign soil without disruption. Due to internal political turmoil, a genuine failure of a giant oilfield, or economic self-interest, it is not unthinkable that one of the major suppliers of U.S. oil, such as Saudi Arabia or Venezuela, could drastically reduce–and potentially even shut down–exports of oil to the United States. While it is difficult to accurately assess the long-term effects of such an event, in the short term, world oil supply disruptions would cause price spikes and supply shortages in the United States. The resulting public pressure for the rapid develop-

ment of alternative fuels could combine with a higher price floor for all liquid fuel to create a national market for increased production of biodiesel.

The reality is that even with a severe oil shortage, the United States could not effectively muster the resources needed to replace 100% of its diesel fuel through conventional biodiesel feedstock production. In the U.S. there are some 2.3 billion acres of land. Of that, 66 million acres is urban land, 450 million acres is used for growing crops (mostly for animal feed), 580 million acres is used for grassland pasture and range, and 60 million acres are arable but fallow. The rest is non arable land. Even with crops such as high-yield mustard, which might produce up to 150 gallons of oil per acre, the United States would theoretically have to plant and harvest 400 million acres of land (an unfeasible number) to produce the 60 billion gallons of biodiesel needed to completely replace its annual diesel fuel usage.[42]

If the social and economic motivators were high enough, the U.S. could feasibly reappropriate the 50 million acres of cropland currently used for growing commodity export crops. If the majority of this acreage was combined with the majority of the 60 million acres of fallow land in the U.S., perhaps 100 million acres of land could be put into the production of biodiesel feedstock crops. Utilizing high-yield oilseed crops, the United States could potentially produce between 10 and 15 billion gallons–about 20-25% of its diesel fuel–from conventional agriculture in this way.[43]

While a $20 to $30 billion dollar a year biodiesel industry would be nothing short of transformative for the American economy, it still would not supply the country with much of its needed diesel fuel in the event of a long-term oil export embargo or disruption. However, Michael Briggs of the University of New Hampshire, who has been working with research originally generated by NREL's Aquatic Species Program, feels there is still much reason to hope that algae may one day be the source of substantial oil production in the U.S.

Briggs says that enough fuel could be grown for the entire fuel needs of the U.S. in 15,000 square miles (roughly 12.5% of the Sonora desert). The 15,000 square miles is equivalent to "9.5 million acres–far less than the 450 million acres currently used for crop farming in the US, and the over 500 million acres used as grazing land for farm animals." Briggs and his team estimate the cost for building the algae oil infrastructure at approximately $308 billion with operating costs at approximately $50 billion annually (half of our annual $100 billion expenditure on foreign oil). [44]

While Briggs's vision is yet to be backed up by real-world examples, it is clear that we can increase the production of biodiesel. To what degree production will increase depends largely on factors far beyond our control or our ability to predict.

Looking Forward

Biodiesel has the potential to heal some of the deep wounds that American agriculture has sustained in recent decades. While we cannot predict exactly how farming in America will change in coming years, we can make some rough assessments based on current trends. First, large-scale farms will continue to battle to sell commodity goods on an ever-more-competitive world market, causing national economic instability and possible national economic disruptions. Second, farming dedicated to the production of feedstocks for biodiesel will become more attractive as large-scale agricultural producers find themselves with fewer foreign markets and less income per bushel sold overseas. Third, the production of biodiesel from domestic feedstocks, particularly soybeans, will substantially increase over the next 5-10 years.

If market factors align themselves for a national leap toward renewable fuels and energies, the growing biodiesel industry could have a net worth of $1 billion by 2010, employing hundreds of thousands of people across the country as farmers, biodiesel plant operators, truck drivers, fuel marketers, and fuel distributors, as well as in the many associated industries that support them. This industry could be accompanied by a host of other renewable technologies and industries, including wind, solar, ethanol, hydrogen, and biomass. Together with biodiesel, the combination of these technologies and energies could free America from the chains of dependence on foreign oil. Forever.

CHAPTER 6

Got Biodiesel?

"Each new Jeep Liberty Diesel coming off our assembly line will be fueled by B5 biodiesel from soy beans... There's great untapped potential for biodiesel..."

Dieter Zetsche, Chrysler Group President and CEO

Biodiesel conferences are the only places where executives from Archer Daniels Midland, BP, and Chrysler find themselves in the buffet line at lunch alongside farmers still covered in field dust and environmentalists wearing tee-shirts with activist messages. When the biodiesel "bug" bites, it bites hard. And it doesn't discriminate by income level, political preference, or appearance. People from all walks of life are drawn to biodiesel for its promise of energy independence. In fact, it's one of the few topics on which Americans from every part of the country can agree.

Although not a perfect fuel, biodiesel offers an immediate solution to curbing our nation's petroleum consumption while reducing our imports of fossil fuels. Its advantages over fuel alternatives such as natural gas and electricity have to do with ease of integration into our existing transportation infrastructure, the simplicity with which it is made, and its efficiency and "renewability."

Collectively, these advantages have driven biodiesel's relatively quick acceptance into the alternative fuels market. Biodiesel is the fastest growing renewable fuel in America today, according to the U.S. Department of Energy. Sales of biodiesel have jumped from 500,000 gallons in 1999 to an estimated 30 million gallons in 2004.[1]

Biodiesel's perceived social value, too, has driven its consumer acceptance and demand. Whether it's a truck driver filling a rig in Texas or a boat captain filling a whale-watching touring boat in Hawaii, biodiesel use is fast becoming a personal statement.

Biodiesel's Backstory

The use of vegetable oil as an alternative fuel dates back to the late 1800s, when Rudolf Diesel began experimenting with peanut oil to power his engines. Vegetable oils were used in diesel engines until shortly after Diesel's death, when alterations were made to the engine that would allow it to run on a cheaper fuel source – what we now know as diesel fuel "number two" (commonly noted as "No. 2"). A by-product of the petroleum refining process, diesel fuel could be cheaply manufactured and distributed, and assured oil magnates continued control of the booming transportation industry.

After the oil shocks of the 1970s sent petroleum prices soaring, researchers were eager to develop a renewable fuel source that could be quickly and inexpensively implemented. Biodiesel was rediscovered as an alternative fuel in early 1980s, when researchers at the Federal Institute for Agricultural Engineering (BLT) in Wieselburg, Austria, began experimenting with vegetable oils as a potential energy source.[2] They decided on rapeseed oil for the experiments because of its wide use in Europe as a rotation crop. Meanwhile, research on vegetable oil as a fuel source also began at the USDA and at several U.S. universities.

Initial experiments using pure vegetable oil or blends of vegetable oil with diesel fuel to power modern diesel engines failed–the oil proved too thick and produced too much carbon when burned. In effect, the vegetable oil molecule (triglyceride) was too large to be burned efficiently in modern diesel engines, which had been modified over the years to burn less viscous petroleum-based diesel fuel. Researchers at BLT began combining the pure oil with alcohol to break down the oil molecules into chains of smaller molecules (mono alkyl esters) through a chemical process called *transesterification*, and in 1982 began a series of pilot tests using the resulting "bio fuel" in diesel farm tractors. By 1988, researchers at Austria's University of Graz had further refined the biodiesel manufacturing process, paving the way for the opening of Austria's first commercial biodiesel processing plant in 1990.[3]

The Birth of American Biodiesel

The initial post-oil-crisis flurry of interest in biodiesel came to a screeching halt as crude oil prices plummeted in the mid-1980s. In 1990 Dr. Don Van Dyne and Dr. Ken Schneeberger, professors from the University of Missouri, accompanied Earle Gavett, then USDA director of the Office of Policy Development, and Gerry Underwood formerly with John Deere, on an educational trip to Europe. The group was fascinated by Europe's widespread use of rapeseed oil for biodiesel production. When Van Dyne and Schneeberger returned, they wrote a paper describing the potential benefits of a U.S.-based rapeseed oil biodiesel industry. The paper was circulated to Kenlon

Johannes, who was the executive director of the Missouri Soybean Merchandising Council. Captivated with the idea of a domestic biodiesel industry, Johannes contacted the University of Missouri and convinced them to investigate the possibility of using soybean oil to produce biodiesel.

Leon Schumacher, an engineering professor at UM, was soon charged with the task of studying biodiesel. To get the first batch of biodiesel, Johannes was again called to the scene. He contacted a company in Kansas City called Interchem, Inc. and spoke with Bill Ayres, who agreed to make the first batches of biodiesel. Ayres's production technique involved mixing the ingredients in a 55-gallon drum using a recalculating pump. The crude production system functioned well enough for testing, and the university soon began publicizing their work with biodiesel.

Not long thereafter Johannes received a call from Bryan Peterson, an adventurer and naturalist. Peterson proposed circumnavigating the globe in a Zodiac Hurricane, a 24-foot-long, semi-inflatable boat powered by a diesel engine running on biodiesel made from soy oil. While Peterson's idea came somewhat from left field, the Missouri Soybean Board decided to partially sponsor the project. From 1992 to 1994 Peterson's biodiesel-powered "Sunrider" project traveled 52,000 miles to 100 cities in 50 countries, sparking the imagination of millions and generating a groundswell of media attention for biodiesel.

But Peterson was not alone in his biodiesel education crusade. Concurrent with his waterborne sojourn in 1992, Missouri Soybean farmers bought a 1992 Ford F250 and began running it on biodiesel. "Old Brownie," as the truck was affectionately named, was a perfect educational tool for the farming community. When Old Brownie debuted at the Norborne, Missouri, Soybean Festival, the vehicle generated more attention than anything else at the event. After the attention generated by Old Brownie in Missouri, Johannes and Ayres decided to take the vehicle on a road trip to Washington, D.C.

They parked the pickup on the front lawn of the White House and spurred a flurry of press attention. Among those who came to see the truck was South Dakota Senator Tom Daschle, who had his photo taken with the Ford. Daschle would become a strong supporter of biodiesel, convincing many people on Capitol Hill of biodiesel benefits. For the next ten years, Tom Verry, a Missouri Soybean Merchandising Council employee, drove Old Brownie 300,000 miles around Missouri on biodiesel. In 2003 Verry, who had by then begun working for the National Biodiesel Board, was accompanied by the NBB's Director of Communications, Jenna Higgins, on a tenth-anniversary trip to Washington, D.C. in Old Brownie, where they were met with enthusiastic press. To this day, Old Brownie continues its faithful service in Missouri as a biodiesel educational vehicle.

Biodiesel Takes Its First Steps

In the United States, soybean farmers banded together in a grassroots effort to develop biodiesel. Encouraged by the USDA, soybean farmers in the early 1990s were attempting to create a "checkoff program," whereby a small percentage of the profits of each bushel of soybeans sold in the United States could be pooled and put to use in soybean research and development. According to John Campbell, who worked at the USDA and was intimately involved in the development of the checkoff program, the program had been an uphill battle until soybean farmers found out about biodiesel.

Campbell states:

Biodiesel captured farmers' imagination. In the early '90s we had just come out of the first Gulf War, and farmers saw biodiesel as a way to contribute to our problem of imported oil. They saw biodiesel as their way to do something good for energy and the environment with their crops. Biodiesel was the issue that pushed the passage of the national soybean checkoff over the top. And in turn, investment of farmer dollars by the national checkoff into the National Biodiesel Board laid the groundwork for biodiesel.[4]

Campbell is now Vice President of Ag. Processing Inc. (AGP), a farmer-owned cooperative, which produces, among other things, biodiesel.

Encouraged by the work of Johannes and others, in 1992 the Missouri Soybean Merchandising Council (MSMC) helped establish the National SoyDiesel Development Board to coordinate biodiesel research efforts at universities nationwide. Research took off across the Midwest and around the country, and the independent entity became known as the National Biodiesel Board (NBB) in 1994.

The NBB's mission quickly became to increase demand for commercially produced biodiesel, giving an economic boost to the soybean industry specifically and to American agriculture in general. But promoting the demand for biodiesel would require ongoing research, development, and testing to substantiate biodiesel's safety and efficiency as an alternative fuel suitable for commercial use. In addition, significant effort would be required to raise public and political awareness of the need for biofuels.

Over the next decade the NBB allocated millions of dollars to help fund biodiesel research and development efforts, and launch biodiesel education campaigns. Under the guidance of the NBB, biodiesel and biodiesel blends were tested in virtually every diesel engine type and every diesel engine application imaginable. All told, more than 50 million successful road miles and countless off-road miles and marine hours were logged with biodiesel.

The NBB soon became known as the national coordinating entity for biodiesel industry efforts and now serves as a clearinghouse for biodiesel information. Today, the NBB also works with engine Original Equipment Manufacturers (OEMs), petroleum companies, and government and private sector user groups to broaden industry acceptance.

One of NBB's most notable accomplishments was its work in establishing industry-wide fuel specifications for commercially producing and using biodiesel. In June of 1994, the NBB helped drive the formation of a biodiesel task force under the American Society for Testing and Materials (ASTM), an internationally recognized standards body that defines fuel specifications in the United States. ASTM fuel standards set minimum requirements for various fuel properties, allowing manufacturers to design their engines according to consumer satisfaction and protection dictates.[5]

After five years of testing, in 1999 the ASTM–comprised of fuel producers, engine equipment manufacturers, and third-party government and corporate parties–released the first provisional fuel specifications for B20, a 20% blend of biodiesel with petroleum diesel. The standard was officially approved in December 2001 and it allowed for higher blends of biodiesel, including B100, "pure" 100% biodiesel, as long as the user consults with their equipment manufacturer prior to using the fuel. Known as ASTM D 6751, the new standard heralded rapid growth for the emerging biodiesel industry. The NBB helped to further integrate the adoption of ASTM D 6751 into the biodiesel marketplace by establishing the National Biodiesel Accreditation Commission (NBAC) to independently audit fuel producers and marketers, and to certify biodiesel marketers that adhere to the ASTM standard.[6]

Dedicated biodiesel refineries began to emerge in the U.S. in 1996. Among the first were the plants run by Ag. Processing Inc. (AGP) in Sergeant Bluff, Iowa; Pacific Biodiesel in Maui, Hawaii; NOPEC in Lakeland, Florida; and West Central in Ralston, Iowa.

A Fit for Transportation

Everything from the food at the grocery store to the book you are currently reading is transported on diesel trucks. Diesel trucks, trains, and boats bring computers, stereos, food, fuel, televisions, and cars from factories to stores. Most farming equipment is powered by diesel engines. Diesel mining equipment extracts the metals that are used to make electronics. From planting seeds to mining copper, diesel engines are used to make and transport the myriad goods we depend on daily.

Biodiesel is an ideal fuel for the transportation industry because it can be used in any diesel engine with few or no modifications. And unlike other alternative fuels, biodiesel doesn't require new fuel distribution systems. It can be stored anywhere that petroleum diesel fuel is stored and dispensed from any fuel station dispensing petroleum diesel. (Biodiesel is already sold at more than 450 retail pumps nationwide.)[7] What's more, biodiesel can be made anywhere oilseed crops are grown or anywhere used cooking oil is produced.

Makin' Biodiesel

Dr. Thomas Reed, an engineering professor in Golden, Colorado, at the Colorado School of Mines, is credited with making some of the earliest biodiesel in the United States.[8] Curious to find out whether animal fats could indeed be used to make fuel, Dr. Reed used paint-stirring machines and recirculating water pumps to mix the ingredients together to make experimental batches of biodiesel in the summer of 1989.

Despite its humble beginnings, the process of making biodiesel has evolved into an exacting science. Today biodiesel is made in at least 35 processing plants across the country.[9] Because the chemical reaction for biodiesel production is similar to that used for soap-making, biodiesel can also be made on a small scale. This makes biodiesel an ideal fuel for use in developing nations.

While there are a few types of chemical reactions used to make biodiesel, the most common reaction utilizes three basic ingredients: vegetable oil or animal fats, an alcohol, and a catalyst. The alcohol used in the biodiesel reaction is typically methanol (also known as "wood alcohol") but ethanol (also known as "grain alcohol") can also be used. The catalyst is often sodium hydroxide (NaOH), commonly known as lye or "caustic soda." To make biodiesel, the large vegetable oil molecules (which have three fatty acids connected to a glycerin molecule) must be "broken down" and combined with methanol to form three new smaller chains called *methyl esters*. Since this method of making biodiesel involves transforming one type of ester into another, the process is called *transesterification*.

The Transesterification Reaction

$$
\begin{array}{ccc}
\text{H} & & \text{H} \\
| & & | \\
\text{H}-\text{C}-\text{COR} & & \text{H}-\text{C}-\text{OH} \quad \text{ROOCH}_3 \\
| & & | \\
\text{H}-\text{C}-\text{COR} \; + \; 3\text{CH}_2\text{OH} \longrightarrow & \text{H}-\text{C}-\text{OH} + \text{ROOCH}_3 \\
| & & | \\
\text{H}-\text{C}-\text{COR} & & \text{H}-\text{C}-\text{OH} \quad \text{ROOCH}_3 \\
| & & | \\
\text{H} & & \text{H}
\end{array}
$$

Vegetable Oil + Methyl Alcohol $\longrightarrow$ Glycerol + Methyl Ester

Glycerin, a sugar, is the syrupy by-product of the transesterification reaction. Glycerin is used in a vast number of household products, including soaps, artificial sweeteners, solvents, cosmetics, inks, plastics, lubricants, and antifreeze.

The U.S. Department of Energy describes a typical recipe for making biodiesel as: "...100 pounds of oils or fats reacted with 10 pounds of a short chain alcohol (usually methanol) in the presence of a catalyst (usually sodium or potassium hydroxide) to form 100 pounds of biodiesel and 10 pounds of glycerin."[10] In simple terms, reacting a gallon of vegetable oil yields about a gallon of finished biodiesel.

Biodiesel Blends

Biodiesel can be blended in any ratio with petroleum diesel. The letter "B" followed by a percentage designates the amount of biodiesel in the blend. For example, a blend of 5% biodiesel and 95% diesel is called B5, a blend of 20% biodiesel with 80% diesel is called B20, and so on. B20 qualifies as a compliance option under EPAct, the DOE's alternative fuels act, as well as under Executive Order 13149 (both discussed in more detail in Chapter 8) and is now widely used to power U.S. vehicle fleets, including those operated by the military, National Parks Service, Postal Service, NASA, and more than 130 schools districts and universities.[11] B20 is also appealing for fleet use because it considerably reduces emissions, is reasonably priced, and requires few if any engine modifications.

A Lubricity Additive

Lubricity describes how a fuel lubricates the fuel system and engine—necessary for prolonging the life of critical engine components. Fuel with poor lubricity will wear and scar engine parts that come in direct contact with fuel, such as injection pumps. Because it is a natural lubricant, biodiesel is an extremely useful and environmentally safe additive for petroleum diesel. Used in this way, biodiesel can prolong the life of critical engine components.[12]

According to BP, diesel fuel relies primarily on sulfur to provide its lubricity. However, the EPA began introducing legislation in 1993 to reduce sulfur levels present in diesel fuel, since sulfur, when burned, produces sulfur dioxide (SO_2)–the primary component of acid rain. A corrosive compound, sulfur also destroys advanced emissions reduction systems, such as those used to reduce nitrogen oxide (NO_x) emissions. By June 2006, the EPA will require oil refiners to nearly eliminate sulfur from their fuel products, reducing sulfur levels from 500 parts per million (ppm) to 15 ppm. Adding just 1% biodiesel (which contains almost no sulfur) to petroleum diesel can restore fuel's lubricity and protect engine parts against premature wear or breakdown.[13]

Biodegradability and Toxicity

Biodiesel is biodegradable and nontoxic. In fact B100 is as biodegradable as dextrose (sugar) and less toxic than table salt. Several studies have shown biodiesel to biodegrade up to four times faster in water than petroleum diesel fuel, with up to 98% biodegrading in three weeks.[14] The reduced emissions, pleasant odor (biodiesel exhaust smells faintly like French fries or donuts), biodegradability, and safety of biodiesel make it well suited for use in marine environments and sensitive ecosystems, such as our national parks and forests.

By contrast, petroleum oil–a known toxic contaminant–poses a serious threat to fresh water and marine environments. An average of 600,000 barrels of petroleum oil a year is accidentally spilled from tankers transporting the fuel, according to the Alaska Oceans Program. Death and disease caused by polluted coastal waters costs our global economy $12.8 billion a year.[15]

Transportation and Storage Safety

Biodiesel will not spontaneously explode or ignite under normal circumstances because it has a high *flashpoint*. In fact, biodiesel has the highest flashpoint of any conventional fuel. ASTM D-6751 specifies a minimum flashpiont of 266° F (130° C) before biodiesel will ignite.[16] Comparatively, petroleum diesel fuel has a flashpoint of 125° F (52° C). Since biodiesel is not explosive under normal circumstances, it can be transported via shipping services such as Yellow Freight and UPS. A Materials Safety and Data Sheet (MSDS) must accompany biodiesel when transported.

Energy Content, Fuel Consumption, Power, and Torque

While biodiesel contains approximately 10% less energy per gallon than diesel fuel, the operation of most vehicles running on biodiesel is not noticeably affected. Biodiesel exhibits the same, and in some cases better, performance than conventional diesel, because biodiesel actually reduces engine friction.

Biodiesel contains approximately 117,000 British Thermal Units (BTUs) per gallon, depending on the feedstock used, whereas diesel fuel No. 2 contains approximately 131,000 BTUs per gallon. However, the difference in useable energy is partially offset by an approximate 7% increase in the combustion efficiency of biodiesel. On average, biodiesel use results in a negligible 2-3% decrease in torque, power, and fuel efficiency.[17]

Energy Balance Ratio

Because biodiesel is made from a renewable source, it has a favorable *energy balance ratio*. An energy balance ratio compares the energy required to grow or extract, process, and distribute a fuel to the energy stored in a fuel. The energy balance ratio of biodiesel is 3.2, according to the USDA. That means for every unit of fossil-fuel-derived energy required to grow (think fertilizers, feedstock, and pesticides), process (think harvest and extract) and transport (from field to refinery to fuel station) biodiesel, there are at least 3.2 units of energy contained in the fuel. By contrast, corn ethanol has an energy balance ratio of 1.34 and petroleum diesel has a negative energy balance ratio of 0.84.[18]

So where does biodiesel get its added energy? Answer: the sun. The primary energy in biodiesel comes from the hydrocarbon bonds that make up vegetable oil. Crops that transform solar energy into chemical bonds create the vegetable oil itself. Since living plants create the chemical blueprint for biodiesel, biodiesel is essentially solar energy stored in liquid form or "liquid solar fuel."

Fuel Net Energy Balance

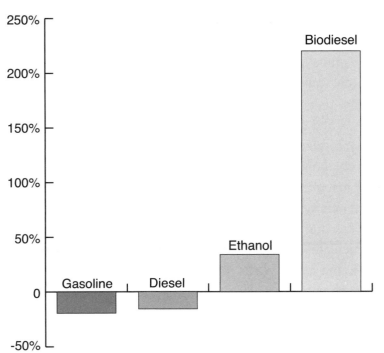

Life cycle yield in liquid fuel BTUs for each BTU of fossil fuel energy consumed.

According to the USDA, the energy balance ratio of biodiesel is nearly three times that of petroleum diesel.

Biodiesel Emissions

Biodiesel tailpipe emissions are substantially cleaner and safer than emissions generated by diesel-powered vehicles and gasoline-powered vehicles. Burning biodiesel emits no sulfur dioxide, 78% less life cycle carbon dioxide, and as much as 50% fewer smog-producing compounds than conventional diesel and gasoline, according to Harvard University's Alternative Fuel Vehicle Program.[20] Both the California Air Resources Board (CARB) and the EPA have classified diesel exhaust as a Toxic Air Contaminant–an air pollutant that may cause or contribute to an increase in mortality or in serious illness, or may pose a hazard to human health.

Biodiesel use eliminates or reduces the levels of harmful compounds contained in diesel exhaust. Consequently, biodiesel use can eliminate or reduce illness associated with short- and long-term exposure to diesel fumes, such as nausea, headaches, respiratory problems, asthma, and even cancer. Research commissioned by the National Renewable Energy Laboratory (NREL) has shown that B100 reduces risk of cancer linked to diesel vehicle emissions by as much as 94% and that the use of B20 reduces cancer risk by 27%.[21] Specifically, biodiesel use dramatically limits exposure to carcinogenic hydrocarbons (phenanthren, benzofloroanthen, benzapyren); respiratory irritants such as particulate matter; and poisonous gases such as carbon monoxide.

The EPA's study of biodiesel emissions confirmed a 47% reduction in particulates and a 48% reduction in carbon monoxide when compared to diesel emissions. Biodiesel is also the only alternative fuel to have completed the Environmental Protection Agency's Tier I and Tier II Health Effects Testing Requirements under its Clean Air Act.[22]

The Tier I and Tier II Health Effects Tests are a series of tests performed on laboratory rats to determine the long-term effects of exposure to inhaling fuel exhaust fumes and of coming into direct contact with the fuel itself. The National Biodiesel Board funded the Tier I Health Effects Tests for biodiesel in 1998 and the Tier II Health Effects Tests for biodiesel in 2000. After 90 days of testing, biodiesel was shown to be benign and nontoxic.[23]

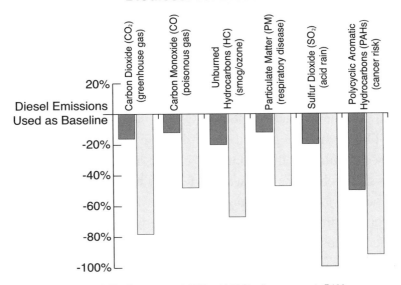

Biodiesel vs. Diesel Emissions

Key: Dark Shading represents B20 · Light Shading represents B100
using petroleum diesel emissions as baseline

Sources: EPA, National Renewable Energy Laboratory, a division of the U.S. Dept. of Energy

While biodiesel offers reduced emissions compared even to gasoline, it is when contrasted with petroleum diesel that biodiesel really shines. Biodiesel (B100) has the following emissions characteristics when compared to those of diesel:

- Reduction of net carbon dioxide (CO_2) emissions by 78%
- Reduction of carbon monoxide (CO) emissions by 48%
- Reduction of hydrocarbon (HC) emissions by 67%
- Reduction of particulate matter (PM) emissions by 47%
- Reduction of sulfur dioxide (SO_2) emissions by nearly 100%

• Reduction of all polycyclic aromatic hydrocarbons (PAHs) and specifically the following carcinogenic PAHs (also found in cigarette smoke):
Reduction of phenanthren by 97%
Reduction of benzofloroanthen by 56%
Reduction of benzapyren by 71%

Carbon Dioxide Emissions

When a fossil fuel is burned in an internal combustion engine, carbon dioxide emissions flow into the atmosphere. This results in a net increase in the balance of global CO_2. On the other hand, when a biofuel like biodiesel is burned, the carbon dioxide that is released is roughly equivalent to the quantity of carbon dioxide absorbed by the plants from which the fuel was made. This is because fuels like biodiesel are part of the natural *carbon cycle*, the biogeochemical cycle through which carbon is exchanged between the biosphere, hydrosphere, geosphere, and atmosphere. Thus, using biodiesel does not significantly increase the global balance of carbon dioxide and does not significantly disturb the natural carbon cycle.

In the *life cycle* of biodiesel, every aspect of manufacturing biodiesel is studied, from planting the crop seeds to transporting the fuel to a service station. Life cycle analyses of biodiesel typically show either a decrease in net carbon dioxide emissions or a very slight increase in net carbon dioxide emissions. For example, in one European life cycle study conducted with biodiesel made from rapeseed, researchers found that "for each kilogram of biodiesel fuel burned in a diesel engine, up to three kilograms of carbon dioxide is consumed, not produced, during the life cycle of biodiesel fuel."[25]

In the U.S., biodiesel produced from soybean oil reduces life cycle carbon dioxide emissions by as much as 78% when compared with petroleum diesel. The reduction in life cycle carbon dioxide is proportional to the amount of biodiesel used. For example, a B20 blend results in a 16% reduction in life cycle carbon dioxide whereas the use of "pure" biodiesel, B100, results in a 78% reduction in life cycle carbon dioxide.

Nitrogen Oxide (NOx) Emissions

One hurdle to biodiesel's widespread adoption has been the assumption that the use of biodiesel increases *nitrogen oxide* (NO_x) emissions. However, new data indicates that biodiesel has a negligible effect (if any) on nitrogen oxide emissions. In addition, new vehicle technologies are available to reduce diesel vehicle NO_x emissions to levels equivalent to those of low emissions vehicles. NO_x emissions are created when nitrogen is burned, or oxidized. Since the earth's atmosphere is approximately 80% nitrogen, any internal combustion engine running on any fuel produces some NO_x emissions. Regardless of the fuel used, the amount of nitrogen oxide emissions an engine produces is directly related to the temperatures reached inside the combustion chamber and is highly dependent on the age and design of the engine.

While some studies show an slight increase in levels of NO_x in biodiesel exhaust when compared to diesel exhaust, other studies show a reduction in NO_x emissions in biodiesel exhaust. According to Dr. Robert McCormick of NREL, the specific engine or vehicle technology being tested, as well as the specific test methods employed can influence results of biodiesel-related NO_x emissions tests. Due to the variability in the results of these tests, there is only sufficient data to say that biodiesel can marginally increase or decrease NO_x emissions, depending on the type of engine tested, the specific technologies installed in the vehicle being tested, and the actual tests used. It is proven, however that burning biodiesel lowers levels of other smog-inducing, health-threatening substances, resulting in a 10%-50% overall reduction in diesel-generated environmental pollutants.[26]

The issue of whether biodiesel slightly increases or decreases NO_x emissions is further mitigated by the fact that most new diesel engines feature built-in NO_x-reduction technologies. These technologies have yet to be incorporated into vehicles sold for the U.S. market, due to the historically high levels of sulfur in U.S. diesel fuel. (Sulfur dioxide emissions harm NO_x reduction devices.) As sulfur levels decrease in response to the coming ULSD fuel mandates, NO_x-reduction technologies can be added to new diesel vehicles sold in the U.S. market, bringing diesel vehicle NO_x emissions down by over 90%.

While an old, poorly tuned diesel engine can produce as much as 12 grams of NO_x per unit of power, newer diesel engines produce as little as 0.2 grams of NO_x per unit of power—fewer NO_x emissions than most natural gas engines by a factor of three to four.[27] In Europe, where low sulfur diesel fuel is the norm and approximately one out of every two new cars sold is powered by a diesel engine, car manufacturers such as Ford Motor Company have successfully implemented NO_x emissions controls to meet Europe's comparatively stringent Stage IV smog requirements.[28]

The Smog Factor

Smog is created when nitrogen oxides react with volatile organic compounds (VOC) and sunlight to form a colorless, odorless gas called ozone. The ozone combines with fine particulate matter called PM 10 (particles less than 10 microns in diameter), or PM 2.5 (particles of less than 2.5 microns in diameter), and unburned hydrocarbons to give smog its brown or gray color before it "sinks" to the ground. According to one UCLA School of Medicine study, repeated exposure to smog and other air pollutants can cause as much damage to the lungs over time as smoking a pack of cigarettes a day.[29] The World Health Organization attributes millions of annual deaths worldwide to suspended particulate matter, much of which comes from diesel exhaust.[30]

Until recently the California Air Resources Board (CARB) maintained that the exhaust from one petroleum-fueled diesel bus had the smog-producing potential of 65 gasoline-powered automobiles. CARB has made the reduction of diesel vehicle exhaust a top priority over the past decade. Unfortunately for CARB and the California public, new data suggests the science on which they have based their now ten-year-long anti-diesel campaign is faulty.

A number of publicly and privately funded studies in California and elsewhere now clearly show an unusual trend: smog levels are substantially higher on the weekends than during weekdays. The so-called "weekend effect" is actually attributable to a reduction in the industrial output of NO_x caused by smokestacks and diesel engines which are not in operation on the weekends. It turns out that smog formation depends not simply on the presence of VOC and NO_x, but also on their ratio. Specifically, if the ratio of VOC to NO_x is higher than ten to one, then smog formation is limited by the availability of NO_x. In this case, limiting NO_x emissions will limit smog formation. But if the ratio of VOC to NO_x is less than ten to one, as it is most of the time in most urban areas such as Los Angeles, smog formation is limited by VOC emissions. In this case, reducing NO_x emissions actually has the adverse effect of *increasing* smog.[31]

Ultimately new technologies will drastically reduce both VOC and NO_x emissions of diesel vehicles. But according to Joel Schwarz, who was the executive officer of the California agency charged with evaluating the state's emissions inspection program and making policy recommendations to the governor and the state legislature, "a more sensible strategy for both the short- and long-term would be for EPA to seek more rapid reductions in VOCs, and, where possible, delay blanket national NO_x reductions for several years."[32] This strategy is a hand-in-glove fit with biodiesel, since biodiesel significantly reduces levels of particulate matter, carbon monoxide, and total VOC. As a result, biodiesel's "smog factor" is nearly 50% less than that of diesel – making it an ideal fuel for Los Angeles, San

Francisco, New York, Chicago, Denver, Houston, Philadelphia, and other major metropolitan areas that suffer from smog.

Challenges for Biodiesel

Despite biodiesel's proven strengths it faces a number of challenges to widespread adoption. Biodiesel's expense relative to conventional diesel often presents a sticking point for consumers. Other adoption hurdles include biodiesel's performance in cold weather and its deteriorating effect on rubber hoses found in older diesel engines. Finally, biodiesel's success will depend largely on the industry's ability to reinforce consumer and corporate confidence through a biodiesel quality testing program and a recognized quality "stamp."

Cost

The higher cost of biodiesel remains the single biggest hurdle to biodiesel's widespread use. The production cost of biodiesel depends mostly on the market price for biodiesel feedstocks-vegetable oil and animal fats, according to the National Biodiesel Board. As of early 2005, the cost of B20 was up to 20 cents more per gallon than conventional diesel. Given biodiesel's advantages, however, using an emissions management system with biodiesel is a least-cost alternative for many fleets. A study by Booz-Allen & Hamilton, Inc. found fleets using B20 reported lower annual vehicle costs than fleets using other alternative fuels.[33] A similar study conducted by the University of Georgia indicates that biodiesel-powered buses are cost-competitive with other alternatively fueled buses, even with B100 biodiesel prices as high as $3 per gallon.[34] Recent tax incentives for biodiesel blenders under the 2004 American Jobs Creation Act and the increasing cost of crude oil could also soon narrow the price gap between biodiesel and petroleum diesel fuel.

Biodiesel in the Cold

Diesel fuels tend to "cloud" and "gel" in cold weather, usually at or below freezing temperatures. Once fuel begins to gel it can clog the fuel system and affect vehicle performance. Biodiesel is not as resistant to cold, and as a result, biodiesel has a higher *cloud point* than conventional diesel. According to the U.S. Department of Energy, pure biodiesel (B100) has a cloud point of between 25°F and 35°F (depending on variables such as feedstock and climate region), while B20 has a cloud point of between 5°F and 25°F. By comparison, petroleum diesel has a cloud point between -10°F and 10°F.[35] In most cases, blends of biodiesel at the B20 or lower level are used in cold climates with no modifications or additives.

Like conventional diesel, biodiesel can be blended with kerosene (diesel No. 1) to lower the fuel's cloud point and ensure reliable operation in colder climates. Contrary to popular belief, however, biodiesel *cannot* be used with conventional "cold flow" additives or winterizing agents typically used for diesel fuel. These additives rely on *polymers* (also known as ethyl vinyl acetate) specifically designed to reduce the cloud point for conventional diesel, but which are chemically incompatible with biodiesel. While some makers of these fuel additives claim their products can be used successfully with biodiesel, no cold flow additives to date have earned broad industry acceptance or endorsement. According to Paul Nazarro, president of fuel consultancy Advanced Fuel Solutions: "We're working very hard to dismiss the controversial marketing claims used by many additive companies that their products are a cold flow panacea for biodiesel users."[36]

Because diesel vehicles have long been operated in cold weather, there are numerous heating devices designed specifically to address cold flow issues in diesel engines. These devices are used to heat fuel tanks, fuel lines, fuel filters, and engine blocks. Properly installed and used, these devices allow biodiesel-powered vehicles to operate at temperatures well below freezing. Such is the case at Yellowstone National Park, where diesel vehicles powered by B20 routinely operate at temperatures as low as -20°F.[37]

Rubber and Biodiesel

Because biodiesel has mild solvent properties, its use can help extend engine life by keeping fuel systems and interior engine components clean. However, these same solvent properties mean that biodiesel also has a tendency to deteriorate certain rubber fuel system parts.

If an engine will be using biodiesel blends of B20 or higher, it is recommended that the user contact their engine manufacturer to determine their recommendation. In some cases, expecially in older engines, rubber fuel hoses and seals may need to be replaced with Viton® or another brand of synthetic *fluroelastomer* hoses and seals. Deterioration of rubber fuel hoses can occur in any vehicle using biodiesel blends above B20, but is more common in older vehicles and at higher blends.

The following rubber parts may need to be replaced with synthetic equivalents: the rubber filler hose that goes from the filler opening to the fuel tank; the rubber fuel lines that run from the fuel tank to the fuel filter; and the fuel line that runs from the fuel filter to the injection pump. In some diesel engines, it may be necessary to use a fuel filter that does not have rubber seals. In rare cases, engines may also contain rubber parts in the fuel injectors and injection pump, making these parts susceptible to deterioration.

Engine Warranties and Biodiesel

Many European diesel engines come with warranties that specifically cover the use of biodiesel because most diesel vehicles sold in Europe (where biodiesel is widely used) come equipped with synthetic hoses, seals, and gaskets in the fuel system. But

American engine manufacturers are only now beginning to address biodiesel and biodiesel blends in their warranty statements. The use of ASTM-grade biodiesel in existing diesel engines does not void parts and materials workmanship warranties of any major U.S. engine manufacturer.[38] Viton® brand or similar synthetic hoses and fuel system parts are also now standard on most diesel vehicles sold in the United States.

The use of "experimental," "homemade," or "off spec" biodiesel, however, confuses engine warranty issues. If a part malfunctions while an engine is operating on homemade fuel, the burden of proof that the fuel was made to industry-standard specifications falls on the operator. Unless the experimental fuel was tested in a laboratory, there is no way to prove that the fuel met specifications set forth by the engine manufacturer. Non-fuel-related warranty issues are not affected by the use of homemade biodiesel.

Straight Vegetable Oil (SVO)

Our previous book on biodiesel included instructions on how to use straight vegetable oil (SVO) as a diesel fuel substitute. At the time, little was known about the long-term effects of using "non-esterified" vegetable oil as fuel. Since then several small companies have sprung up that sell kits to "convert" vehicles to run on straight vegetable oil. These kits typically include elements to heat the oil, in effect temporarily reducing its viscosity. While no official test data on these kits is available, some users have reported experiencing engine failure and other problems. As more data has come to light on the use of SVO as a fuel source, it has become clear that used as a fuel, straight vegetable oil can have severe–and even catastrophic—drawbacks.

Using straight vegetable oil as a fuel voids manufacturers' warranties. For example, according to John Deere, "Raw pressed vegetable oils are NOT acceptable for use for fuel in any concen-

Comparison of Fuel Viscosity Levels

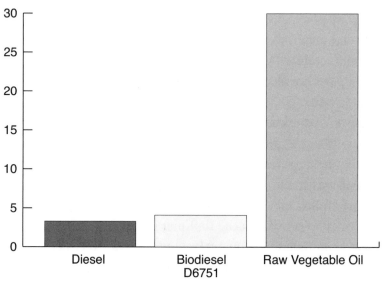

Source: National Biodiesel Board

tration. In John Deere engines, these oils do not burn completely, and will cause engine failure by leaving deposits on injectors and in the combustion chamber."[39] Other engine manufacturers have both officially and unofficially offered similar statements.

The use of straight vegetable oil as a fuel voids engine warranties because the high viscosity of unprocessed vegetable oil–(even in small amounts, such as 5% blends)–can over time cause engines to wear prematurely, even when the straight vegetable oil is heated before being injected into the engine. Because the glycerin is still bonded to the vegetable oil molecule, burning straight vegetable oil inside the engine can lead to "coking," or increased carbon build-up inside the engine. According to the National Biodiesel Board:

The higher viscosity, lower cetane and volatility of unmodified oils or fats have been shown to cause injector coking, piston ring deposits, and other deposits on fuel system parts which will lead to significant decreases in engine performance, horse power, and fuel economy as well as increased exhaust emissions. Use of unmodified oils or fats will also cause excessive fuel dilution of the engine oil, which will eventually lead to buildup of sludge in the engine oil and catastrophic engine failure.[40]

Moreover, using straight vegetable oil kits in diesel vehicles in the United States can, in some cases, be illegal. Steve Howell, whose company, Marc IV Consulting, was instrumental in gaining acceptance for the ASTM specification for biodiesel as well as numerous biodiesel testing and warranty acceptance programs with automakers, explains that Environmental Protection Agency laws specify that users cannot modify fuel delivery systems in diesel vehicles–especially when the modification of those systems can affect emissions. Engine manufacturers themselves are not willing to support the use of straight vegetable oil as a fuel.

For a new fuel, or even a fuel blend, to be approved by an engine manufacturer, the engine manufacturer usually requires tests costing up to $3 to $5 million per engine, says Howell. Thus, approving a vehicle series to run on B5, for example, can cost tens of millions of dollars. If any small modifications must be made to those engines (even the addition of a new type of seal, for example), the tests must be performed again. Engine manufacturers are only willing to do these tests if there is a substantial market of customers who will buy engines based on compatibility with a fuel type such as biodiesel. Because the market for users of straight vegetable oil as a fuel is miniscule, there is no substantial economic incentive for the EPA and the engine manufacturers to pursue straight vegetable oil as a fuel.[41]

Finally, using unmodified vegetable oil as a fuel also creates confusion about biodiesel in the press and other public arenas. Because of the potential damage to engines and the loss of warranty coverage, it is strongly recommended that readers avoid using straight vegetable oil as a fuel for diesel engines.

Fuel Quality Standards

Fuel quality is perhaps the single most important issue faced by any biodiesel distributor or producer. Because fuel is transported through numerous channels before it reaches the consumer, there are many points along the distribution chain where the fuel can become contaminated–and that is assuming the initial fuel is a quality product to begin with. For this reason, the National Biodiesel Board designated an independent commission called the National Biodiesel Accreditation Commission (NBAC). The NBAC created a fuel-quality certification program designed to give fuel producers and distributors a nationally recognized "seal of approval." Known as BQ-9000, the program is a unique combination of adherence to the ASTM standard for biodiesel, ASTM D 6751, as well as adherence to quality standards for storage, sampling, testing, blending, shipping, distribution, and fuel management practices.

According to Steve Howell, the new BQ-9000 standard is being adopted by fuel marketers, distributors, and producers so consumers know they are getting high quality biodiesel fuel. The BQ-9000 standard, explains Howell, is similar but less burdensome than the "ISO-9000" set of quality standards used in manufacturing. Companies or individuals who handle biodiesel and who adhere to the BQ-9000 standard must follow a strict set of procedures to maintain the quality of the fuel and to ensure that it does not become contaminated. Howell explains the new standards are very high. "There's not even a quality system like this for the petroleum industry," he says.[42]

BQ-9000 is supported by the NBB as well as by the Biodiesel Association of Canada. The BQ-9000 accreditation process includes a detailed review of an applicant's fuel practices, followed by a formal audit of the applicant's compliance with the BQ-9000 standards. BQ-9000 accreditation lasts for two years, after which time an applicant must undergo another complete compliance check.

A certification logo is available to any biodiesel marketer or distributor who meets the quality assurance requirements outlined in BQ-9000. Consumers will be encouraged to "look for the BQ-9000 label" when purchasing biodiesel and biodiesel blends.

West Central's 12-million-gallon-per-year soy-based biodiesel plant in Ralston, Iowa, is using the BQ-9000 to ensure that every batch of biodiesel that leaves their facility is high quality biodiesel. Not only does West Central certify their quality biodiesel with a state-of-the-art, on-site laboratory, but the company also ensures its quality biodiesel goes as far as possible before changing hands by shipping fuel via their own rail cars, which are cleaned and regularly checked for contamination. West Central's vigilant pursuit of quality has resulted in a strong customer base that spans America. "Quality is the cornerstone of the biodiesel industry," says Nile Ramsbottom, executive vice president of West Central's Soy and Nutrition Departments, "and BQ-9000 assures that we provide high quality biodiesel fuel to the customer."[43]

Biodiesel's Future

Biodiesel has a bright future as an alternative fuel, both as a fuel blend (B20) and on its own (B100). As biodiesel manufacturing and diesel engine technology improve, we're likely to see biodiesel become more resistant to cold weather and generate even fewer emissions. New government requirements mandating the use of low-sulfur diesel fuels stand to further increase demand for biodiesel as a fuel component, blend, or fuel alternative. While biodiesel does have drawbacks, its similarities to conventional diesel in terms of performance, low cost, and compatibility with our existing fuel infrastructure make it an ideal solution for meeting emerging federal emissions requirements and improving air quality *now*.

CHAPTER 7

Biodiesel Goes to Washington

"For the sake of energy security, for the sake of economic security, we need more ethanol and biodiesel...I envision a day when somebody walks in and says, 'Well Mr. President, the corn crop is up and we're growing more soybeans in America and we're less dependent on foreign sources of oil as a result of it."

President George W. Bush

Rising oil prices, instability in the Middle East, mounting environmental concerns, and a fragile U.S. economy have prompted some lawmakers to get serious about energy policies that promote the use of alternative fuels–including biodiesel. While passing federal legislation supportive of biodiesel has been an uphill battle, there are undeniable signs of progress. Under the American Jobs Creation Act of 2004, biodiesel blenders receive federal tax incentives designed to lower costs and increase demand for biodiesel fuel. As a result, the USDA expects demand for biodiesel to increase substantially from the 25 million gallons sold in the United States in 2004.[1]

Demand for biodiesel is likely to be driven even higher by federally mandated changes to diesel fuel. Under the EPA's new emissions controls for both on- and off-road diesel vehicles, ultra-low sulfur diesel fuel (ULSD) will start to replace conventional diesel fuel in 2006; the new fuel will require the addition of a "lubricity agent" such as biodiesel.

Biodiesel's potential to bring jobs and millions in revenues to states with agriculture-based economies and states that have urban areas with available yellow grease has also prompted legislative support at the state level. Arkansas, Kentucky, Indiana, Maine, Missouri, North Carolina, Montana, Texas, South Dakota, Hawaii, Oregon, and Illinois have already implemented tax incentives intended to lower the price of biodiesel and increase production. Other states, like Minnesota, are mandating the use of biodiesel statewide.

Yet much work remains to be done to successfully legislate adoption of alternative fuels such as biodiesel and limit America's dependence on foreign oil. The U.S. government has a long history of legislating incentives for the mature fossil fuels industry. Consequently oil and gas companies continue to reap substantial financial rewards from U.S. energy policy, even as domestic fossil fuel supplies dwindle. Meanwhile, a number of legislators on both sides of the party divide are working to enact legislation that levels the liquid fuels playing field by encouraging growth of the budding biodiesel industry.

Biodiesel Gets Into EPAct

In 1992, prompted by groundwork laid largely by Illinois Representative John Shimkus (R) and Missouri Representative Karen McCarthy (D), the U.S. Congress passed a law called the Energy Policy Act (EPAct) with the goal of improving air quality and reducing our dependence on foreign oil–and in particular, our government's dependence on foreign oil.[2] Approved by Congress in the wake of the first Gulf War, EPAct (administered by the U.S. Department of Energy) sought to displace 10% of petroleum-based transportation fuels by 2000 and 30% by 2010–a goal that seems as far off today as it did when the landmark legislation was first signed into law.

EPAct called for federal and state agencies and alternative fuel providers to "lead by example" by regularly purchasing alternative fuel vehicles (AFVs). The law–which stressed the need for energy efficiency as well as the need for renewable energy technologies and alternative fuels–also called for federal and state agencies to reduce energy consumption in government office buildings by 35% by 2010.[3]

EPAct mandates that certain federal and state agencies and alternative fuel providers acquire vehicles capable of using alternative fuels when acquiring new vehicles for fleet use. Specifically, EPAct applies to agencies that operate, lease, or control 50 or more *light-duty* vehicles (any vehicle weighing less than 8,500 pounds) within the United States. Of those 50 vehicles, at least 20 must be operated within a single metropolitan area. In fleets covered by EPAct, at least 75% of new vehicles acquired each year must be capable of using alternative fuels such as hydrogen, compressed natural gas, ethanol, and biodiesel, among others. Law enforcement, military, and emergency response vehicles are exempt from EPAct, as are off-road vehicles and those operated by local government agencies.[4]

One hundred percent biodiesel (B100) was added to the U.S. Department of Energy's list of qualifying alternative fuels in 1996. Two years later, in 1998, EPAct was amended through the Energy Conservation Reauthorization Act (ECRA) to allow agencies and alternative fuel providers required to purchase AFVs to meet those requirements in part through the use of a blend of 20% biodiesel (B20).[5]

Lawmakers issued the "Biodiesel Rule" in conjunction with

ECRA to make it easier (and more cost effective) for agencies and alternative fuel providers to comply with EPAct. Under the Biodiesel Rule, agencies and alternative fuel providers can meet up to 50% of their EPAct AFV requirements by running fleet vehicles on biodiesel blends of at least 20%. To earn one AFV credit (the same as one AFV acquisition), agencies and alternative fuel providers must use the equivalent of 450 gallons of B100, or 2,250 gallons of B20.[6]

Compliance Complaints

The original EPAct legislation contained a gaping loophole, however. While EPAct mandated the purchase of vehicles *capable* of using alternative fuels, it didn't mandate the use of those fuels. President Clinton signed Executive Order 13149 in 2000 to close the compliance loophole and add the requirement that federal agencies also *use* alternative fuels in their AFV fleets.[7] Entitled "Greening the Government Through Federal Fleet and Transportation Efficiency," the Presidential Executive Order also set requirements for federal agencies to reduce their petroleum fuel use by 20% compared to 1999 fuel consumption levels by the end of 2005 and improve overall fuel efficiency in non alternative fuel vehicle fleets by 3 mpg.[8]

But even after the Executive Order was issued, few government agencies appeared to comply with the law, and in January 2002 environmental groups filed suit against the federal government for its noncompliance. A ruling issued by Federal District Court Judge William Alsup later that year found that nearly every cabinet-level agency in the government–including the EPA itself–had violated EPAct by failing to buy or lease the required AFVs for their respective fleets.[9]

While Judge Alsup's July 2002 ruling found 18 government agencies–including the Departments of Transportation, Justice, and Defense–in violation of EPAct regulations, it also found that granting *injunctive relief,* a mandatory order to carry out a particular action, to the plaintiffs in the case would detract from, rather than serve, the Act's purposes.[10] To their credit, almost all of the agencies had complied with the rule, but had failed to properly report their alternative fuel usage. Despite this, the publicity brought by the case spurred even more federal agencies into action. EPAct compliance for federal fleets jumped to 96% by the end of 2004, according to the DOE–well beyond the required minimum compliance levels.[11]

Today, some agencies are responding creatively to the challenge of meeting EPAct requirements. NASA, which used alternative fuels to power almost 30% of the light-duty vehicles in its fleet in 2004, has plans to expand its AFV "fueling infrastructure" to further encourage the use of alternative fuels in its vehicle fleet. Specially coded credit cards will be issued to drivers to "disallow" the purchase of petroleum in locations with access to alternative fuel stations.[12]

NASA Alternative Fuel Use 2004

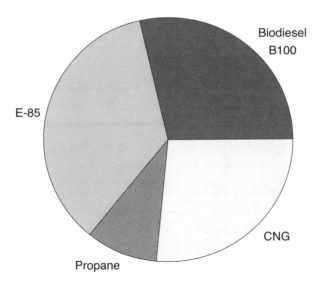

Source: NASA, Fleet Alternative Fuel Vehicle Program Report for FY04

The Pennsylvania Turnpike Commission, a state agency, satisfies half of its AFV acquisition requirements through the purchase of biodiesel, fueling 200 of its heavy-duty trucks with B20 at six of its maintenance facilities.[13] Likewise, the U.S. Postal Service buys an estimated 223,000 gallons of B100 annually to help meet its acquisition requirements.[14] Perhaps the most notable Federal Agency participating in EPAct is the U.S. Navy, which is committed to using B20 in all of its nontactical diesel-powered equipment–the equivalent of over one million gallons of B100 annually.[15] In 2003 state agencies and alternative fuel providers alone purchased more than 2.2 million gallons of biodiesel, acquired more than 8,100 AFVs and traded more than 1,200 AFV credits.[16] Overall, EPAct has put more than 90,000 AFVs on the road since its inception.

Cleaner Cities, Cleaner Air

EPAct has been criticized because it only applies to federal and state vehicle fleets. When EPAct was first signed into law, the U.S. Department of Energy was asked to consider extending EPAct rules to include local government agencies and private sector fleet operators. In response to Judge Alsup's 2002 recommendation that a decision finally be made, the DOE elected not to extend EPAct to include local government and private sector fleets. Instead, the DOE decided it would continue to encourage private and local government fleets to voluntarily use alternative fuels and vehicles through its Clean Cities and Clean School Bus USA Programs.[18]

Established in 1993, the Clean Cities Program awards grant money to support the deployment of alternative fuels and AFVs. Clean Cities carries out its mission through a volunteer network of more than 80 community groups, which work with public and private fleet operators to; promote the use of alternative fuels and alternative fuel blends such as B20; encourage the use of fuel economy practices; increase the acquisition of hybrid vehicles and AFVs; and discourage unnecessary idling in buses and heavy-duty vehicles.

The program's goal is to displace at least 8 billion gallons of petroleum by 2020. To date Clean Cities community groups have added at least 200,000 alternative fuel vehicles to fleets across America, displacing approximately 173 million gallons of petroleum–far short of its goal, but on a par with EPAct results.[19]

The EPA's Clean School Bus USA program, also established in 2003, aims to reduce children's exposure to harmful diesel exhaust by eliminating unnecessary school bus idling, installing effective emission control systems on newer buses, and replacing the oldest buses in the fleet with newer ones. School buses, which drive more than 4 billion miles each year, are notorious polluters. Children run a greater risk of developing health problems associated with air pollution than do adults because their lungs are still developing.[20] Regular exposure to diesel fumes has been linked with respiratory problems, cancer, and asthma–a condition from which 6.3 million U.S. children now suffer.[21] According to the American Lung Association, asthma is the leading cause of absenteeism in schools today.

Through Clean School Bus USA, the EPA has been working to clean up the nation's approximately 440,000 school buses, awarding millions in grants to schools to adopt cleaner burning fuels such as biodiesel and replace older buses with newer, lower-emission buses as well as buses that run on natural gas.[22] More than 100 U.S. school districts have already switched to using biodiesel, according to the National Biodiesel Board, although only a handful received biodiesel-specific funding through the EPA's grant program. (Most of the money distributed by the program has gone to retrofit older school buses with new emissions control devices.) Grants given to school districts by the Clean School Bus USA program to pay for incremental biodiesel costs have ranged from $4,550 to $21,400.[23]

Cleaner Fuel

Tighter emissions controls are also prompting transportation fleet managers and equipment operators to adopt biodiesel as an alternative fuel or fuel component–at least until existing engines and fleets can be replaced with cleaner-burning models. The EPA's Clean Diesel Trucks and Buses program promises to reduce toxic sulfur levels in highway exhaust by 97% when it goes into effect in 2006. It will require on-road heavy-duty vehicles to either replace existing vehicle fleets with more modern, cleaner-burning models or adopt cleaner-burning fuels such as ultra-low sulfur diesel (ULSD) and biodiesel by model year 2007.[24] Similarly, the EPA's newly issued Clean Air Non-Road Diesel Rule will require vehicles used in construction, agriculture, locomotive, and marine transportation to decrease sulfur emissions by 99 percent beginning in 2008. The EPA estimates that its efforts to drastically limit harmful emissions will prevent approximately 12,000 premature deaths, 8,900 hospitalizations, and one million lost workdays by 2030.[25]

Driving the Omnibus Energy Bill

Since 2003 Congress has tried to pass a comprehensive energy bill that would, in theory, further reduce America's dependence on foreign oil. The Energy Policy Act of 2003 (H.R. 6), referred to as the "Omnibus Energy Bill," failed to gain approval in two consecutive Congressional sessions because of its enormous price tag, the inclusion of a liability waiver for companies producing MTBE (a toxic gasoline additive), and its support for mature energy industries. The bill, which contained $28 billion in tax breaks and subsidies for fossil fuels and nuclear energy companies, passed the House of Representatives but failed to pass the Senate by two votes.

A "lite" version of the Energy Policy Act of 2003 was penned to reduce the tax breaks and subsidies to $14 billion ($10.6 billion of which benefit nuclear and fossil fuels companies), but still met with fierce opposition.[26] Rather than continue to subsidize the already mature oil and gas industries, opponents argued that more tax dollars should be spent to promote the use of renewable energy sources such as solar and wind, and fuels such as ethanol and biodiesel.[27]

In January 2005 Senate Majority Leader Bill Frist (R, Tennessee) added the Omnibus Energy Bill to his "top 10" priority list for the 109th Congressional session, and by April, President Bush had held a nationally televised news conference in which he encouraged the Senate to pass a new version of the Omnibus legislation.[28]

H.R.6 was soon revitalized by Representative Joe Barton (R-TX), Richard Pombo (R-CA) and Bill Thomas (R-CA). The bill was eventually amended with 266 amendments, which stipulated among other things: the removal of approval for drilling in the Arctic Wildlife Refuge (ANWR), the removal of the liability waiver for producers of MTBE, provisions for a host of grants and incentives for biodiesel, ethanol, biomass, and renewable energy, and provisions to raise fuel economy standards from 25 miles per gallon, to 33 miles per gallon and to include 10% ethanol into all gasoline by 2015.

The final bill also included a number of provisions important to biodiesel. The bill extended the biodiesel tax credit to December 31, 2008, created a Renewable Fuel Standard (RFS), provided a credit for installations of fueling infrastructure that dispenses blends of B20 or above, provided a $.10/gallon tax credit for agriculturally-based biodiesel producers who have under 60 million gallons of annual production, and provided $5 million/year in funding to test biodiesel in advanced diesel engines.[29]

On August 8th, 2005, after it passed the Senate by an overwhelming majority of 66 to 29, President George W. Bush signed the long-belabored H.R.6 into law at the Sandia National Labs in New Mexico. Despite the successful inclusion of many pro-renewable-energy amendments to the bill, the core of the bill remained unchanged from the previous year. Thus, the majority of monetary benefit from what became the "Energy Act of 2005" will go to the oil, natural gas, coal and nuclear industries.

Viewing the prioritization of renewable fuels as low on the national energy totem pole, some biodiesel and ethanol supporters have moved away from the Omnibus strategy. Instead, they are taking a tactical approach by supporting smaller pieces of legislation with extremely focused objectives.

For example, in January of 2005, Marcy Kaptur (D-Ohio) introduced the "Biofuels Energy Independence Act of 2005" (H.R. 388). The Energy Independence Act grants the Secretary of Agriculture the right to make and grant loans for the production, development, and storage of biofuels, including biodiesel and ethanol. The bill also calls for a national renewable fuels standard that would require 10% ethanol and 5% biodiesel be blended into the nation's fuel supply by 2010.

According to Kaptur, "We need to set ambitious goals so we are not held hostage to our dependence on foreign oil." [30] Indeed, Representative Kaptur may have a point: focus legislation on accomplishing focused goals, namely measurable increases in the use of biodiesel and other forms of renewable energy.

Bush Backs Biodiesel

As President George W. Bush stumped for reelection in 2004, he spoke repeatedly about the critical role renewable fuels can play in reducing America's dependence on foreign oil, and specifically mentioned biodiesel as an important component of the beleaguered Omnibus Energy bill. On the campaign trail through rural America and during the nationally televised presidential debates, Bush frequently endorsed biodiesel as a means to strengthen the U.S. farm economy, create jobs, and put Americans on the road to energy independence. (It should be noted that, while not as vociferous a supporter of biodiesel during the 2004 campaign, Senator John Kerry's bus was running on a 20% [B20] biodiesel blend.) President Bush further showed his support on May 16, 2005, when he became the first active president to visit a biodiesel plant. His speech at the Virginia Biodiesel Refinery in West Point, Virginia, highlighted the importance of biodiesel and encouraged the passage of an omnibus energy bill. Yet some argue that Bush's support for biodiesel could be much stronger.

Proponents of the Bush Administration-backed Omnibus bill say that financial breaks to the fossil fuel industry will increase domestic fuel production. But fossil fuels companies have long explored ways to increase domestic production, and have seen profits steadily increase over the years–despite the added business costs. In fact, the U.S. government has a long history of subsidizing oil, gas, and coal companies, beginning in 1916. Between 1948 and 1998, the DOE spent $26 billion on fossil fuels research and development. A 2000 General Accounting Office study done for Congress showed that in the previous 32 years, the three largest special tax breaks alone for the petroleum industry cost $132 billion, more than 10 times the tax incentives for ethanol and alcohol fuels.[31]

Growing Jobs

Biodiesel supporters reached a major milestone in 2004 with the Congressional passage of the American Jobs Creation Act. Designed to stimulate the U.S. economy by encouraging domestic manufacturing, the Jobs Creation Act delivers $137 billion in tax incentives to American employers over the next ten years. Among those incentives is the biodiesel tax incentive, which promises to increase profits for biodiesel manufacturers and distributors and to lower biodiesel prices at the pump.

The American Jobs Creation Act essentially gives biodiesel "blenders" one penny per percentage point of virgin-oil-based or animal-fat-based biodiesel blended with petroleum diesel. For example, a blender who makes 1,000 gallons of B20 by blending 200 gallons of virgin-oil-based biodiesel with 800 gallons of diesel would accrue $200 worth of tax credits. Blenders using biodiesel made from recycled oil are eligible for one half a penny per percentage point of recycled oil-based biodiesel blended. For example, a blender who makes 1,000 gallons of B20 by blending 200 gallons of recycled-oil-based biodiesel with 800 gallons of diesel would accrue $100 worth of tax credits. The difference in refunds is meant to offset the difference in cost for virgin and recycled oils.[32]

By making biodiesel more cost competitive with diesel fuel, the incentive is expected to exponentially increase biodiesel demand. The increase could mean $1 billion for U.S. farmers over the next five years, and $7 billion in exports, according to a USDA feasibility study. (The United States supplied 44% of the world's soybeans in 2002.)[33] The increased demand could also mean as many as 50,000 new jobs related to biodiesel production.[34]

Bolstered by an extension in the Omnibus Energy Bill, the incentive is scheduled to expire in 2008. To extend the program further, another act of Congress will be necessary. According to Mark Palmer of the American Soybean Association, such an extension will likely have to be bundled into a new Omnibus Bill, thus underscoring the need for a federal energy bill with long-term protection and incentives for biodiesel and other forms of renewable energy.[35]

Bipartisan Biodiesel Support

Backing biodiesel in Washington is a bipartisan, multiregional effort. As northern states increase soybean yields and southern states transition away from cotton and tobacco toward soybeans, senators from both sides of the Mason-Dixon Line are combining forces to protect and promote the use of biodiesel. Nowhere is this unique collaboration more apparent than with Senators Chuck Grassley (R-Iowa) and Blanche Lincoln (D-Arkansas) who work together across party and geographical lines to ensure that biodiesel gets traction in the nation's capitol. Specifically, Grassley and Lincoln were responsible for rallying the political support required to make sure that the same biodiesel tax provisions originally intended for inclusion in the controversial Omnibus Energy package were included in the Jobs Creation Act, emphasizing biodiesel's "Made in the USA" label and its value as an export commodity.

Both senators are particularly active in backing legislation that supports agriculture and reflects the values of their rural American constituents. A lifelong Midwesterner and the only working farmer in the U.S. Senate, Chuck Grassley has used his political clout as chairman of the Senate Finance Committee to secure federal tax incentives for ethanol as well as biodiesel. The youngest woman ever elected to the Senate and a mother of two, Blanche Lincoln has earned a reputation in Congress for reaching across the political aisle to gather bipartisan support for programs designed to spur economic development for rural communities.

Grassley's working-class roots give him credibility with Republicans and Democrats alike–a vital asset in advocating renewable energy development in Congress. Prior to his election to the Senate in 1980, Grassley worked as a farmer, sheet metal shearer, and assembly line worker. Grassley's son is also a farmer; the senator flies home to his hometown of New Harford, Iowa, almost every weekend to spend time with his family. He is on record with his belief that advancing renewable fuels is good public policy that will create jobs and spur economic growth in rural America, increase U.S. energy independence, help clean up the environment, and enhance national security. "Biodiesel is an environmentally sound way to fill the gap between energy supply and demand," Grassley told attendees at the NBB's summer 2004 conference in Washington D.C.[36]

Lincoln's collaborative approach to the legislative process has likewise served to strengthen support for biodiesel-friendly legislation. A member of the Senate New Democrat Coalition and a founding member of the Senate Centrist Coalition, Lincoln is an outspoken advocate of the Renewable Fuels Standard included in the Omnibus Energy package. "I've long supported biodiesel because of its potential for reducing our dependence on foreign oil while providing a much needed boost to agricultural producers and domestic energy producers," Lincoln told attendees.[37] Both Lincoln and Grassley received the National Energy Leadership Award at the 2004 NBB conference for their efforts to promote biodiesel use.

Biodiesel Gains Footing on the State Level

A growing emphasis on domestically produced renewable fuels has prompted at least 26 states to pass new laws encouraging biodiesel use. The laws–almost none of which existed prior to 1998–run the gamut from officially recognizing biodiesel as an alternative fuel, to providing tax breaks for biodiesel producers and consumers, to mandating the use of biodiesel statewide.

Several states, including Hawaii and Washington, have passed legislation defining biodiesel as an alternative fuel or declaring that it meets the definition of biomass. Such legislation allows biodiesel to take advantage of state programs that provide tax breaks and incentives for both alternative fuel businesses and consumers. Hawaii, for example, cut its state taxes on alternative fuels in half in 2004, which effectively lowered tax rates on biodiesel from 15 cents per gallon to 7.5 cents per gallon.

Montana, Texas, North Dakota, Illinois, Missouri, Rhode Island, Pennsylvania, Arkansas, and Indiana are among other states that recently passed legislation giving tax cuts or exemptions for biodiesel use. Illinois, for example, has reduced the state sales tax on blends up to B10, and completely exempted the sales tax for blends B11 and higher. This legislation has had a dramatic, positive impact on the volume of biodiesel sales in Illinois. In the state of Washington, four bills were recently made into law to encourage in-state biodiesel production, the development of retail fuel stations, the use of the alternative fuel in state fleets and school buses, and exemptions for biodiesel production.[38]

Since many of the largest users of diesel fuel are fleets that refuel at central locations, some states are focusing efforts on fleets as an easy way to increase biodiesel use. For example, Missouri and Pennsylvania introduced legislation reimbursing schools for incremental costs of B20 or higher biodiesel blends for school buses. Pennsylvania's legislation also provides grant money to state agencies, nonprofits, and LLCs to cover the incremental cost of purchasing B20. And in Kansas, policy requires that state vehicle operators use a B2 blend.

Minnesota: Great Lakes, Great Legislation

In 2005 Minnesota became the first state in the nation to implement legislation mandating the use of biodiesel. The Minnesota Biodiesel Mandate requires that all diesel fuel sold for transportation use in Minnesota contain at least 2% biodiesel.[39] The mandate could raise the price of diesel fuel by 1-2 cents per gallon, but complaints are few. In fact, the most enthusiastic supporters of the new law are farmers, who consume one-third to one-half of all the diesel fuel covered by the mandate.[40]

Their enthusiasm is understandable: Minnesota is among the top five soybean-producing states in the U.S., producing in excess of 229 million bushels of soybeans each year.[41] The state currently exports about 60% of its soybeans to other states for processing, but that is now changing. The first plant in the state to make biodiesel began operation in the fall of 2004. Called the Farmers Union Marketing and Processing Association (FUMPA), the plant expects to process 2.8 million gallons per year of biodiesel at its Redwood Falls refinery. Two 30-million-gallon-per-year biodiesel facilities are expected to open in 2005, bringing even more jobs and income to the state.

Minnesota's 2% biodiesel mandate mimics the start of another farm-based fuel requirement, ethanol. Since 1997 all gasoline sold in Minnesota must contain at least 10% ethanol, a biofuel derived mainly from corn. The law brought a quick increase in the number of ethanol plants in the state, and it also boosted the price of corn. Minnesota currently operates 14 ethanol plants, producing more than 400 million gallons of the grain-based fuel every year. Twelve of its 14 ethanol plants are farmer cooperatives, which means that local farmers own and operate the plants. Minnesota's renewable fuels policies now inject $500 million into the state's rural economy annually.[42]

The same is expected to happen with biodiesel. Current estimates identify approximately 800 million gallons of diesel fuel used per year in Minnesota, with approximately 550 million gallons used on roads and 250 million used off-road. Meeting 2% of this demand will require at least 16 million gallons of B100 to mix with petroleum diesel.[43]

Illinois, Michigan, and Oregon: Joining the Biodiesel Bandwagon

Other states may soon follow Minnesota's lead. Illinois has similar legislation pending which, if signed into law, would mandate the use of biodiesel in all vehicles owned and operated by the state. The proposed legislation would require schools and state universities, for example, to use fuel blends containing at least 2% biodiesel. To help offset the higher fuel costs, the legislation plans to reimburse schools and other government entities one penny per gallon of fuel consumed by raising taxes on petroleum fuels by 1/10 of a penny.[44]

Illinois, which produces some 450 million bushels of soybeans annually, stands to significantly benefit from the increased demand for biodiesel–and thus the increased demand for soybeans. According to the Illinois Soybean Association, an increase of 5 cents per bushel in soybean prices would bring the state an additional $22.5 million in revenues. The legislation also promises to clean up hazardous diesel emissions, particularly among the state's more than 18,000 school buses.[45] An independent study conducted by LECG, a company specializing in international economic analysis, concluded that the Illinois legislation would result in the creation of as many as 7,547 new jobs by 2012, an increase in the gross output of the Illinois economy of more than $6.6 billion, and an increase of income for Illinois consumers of approximately $1.3 billion.[46]

Another soy-producing state attempting to mandate biodiesel use is Michigan. If passed into law, Michigan's proposed biodiesel legislation will mirror Minnesota's biodiesel legislation requiring 2% biodiesel be blended into the state's diesel fuel. Oregon, too, has legislation pending that calls for the state to require on- and off-road diesel vehicles to use biodiesel blends of 2% or higher, as well as reduce the fuel tax on biodiesel purchased for use in passenger vehicles by $.0024 per percent of biodiesel blended with diesel fuel.[47]

A Groundswell of Voices

The considerable legwork that was needed to ensure successful passage of the recent biodiesel tax incentive continues as biodiesel-related issues are discussed by the Senate Environment and Public Works Committee, the Senate Agriculture Committee, the Senate Finance Committee, and the House Appropriations Committee. Filled with representatives from both parties, these committees help decide the future of a fuel that is largely grown by America's 24,000 soybean farmers. While the battle for a renewable fuels standard and for permanent government tax breaks for biodiesel is not over, there are many voices supporting biodiesel in both the House and the Senate.

Senators Kit Bond (R-Missouri), Jim Talent (R-Missouri), and Tim Johnson (D-South Dakota) regularly back biodiesel in the Senate–particularly to encourage higher minimums for biodiesel use in meeting EPAct requirements for government alternative fuel use, and to preserve funding for renewable fuels education programs. In 2003 Senators Norm Coleman (R-Minnesota) and Tom Harkin (D-Iowa) banded together with Senators Lincoln and Talent to form the Senate Biofuels Caucus, a committee created to promote the use and development of renewable fuels. Harkin chaired the Agriculture Committee, which placed the first energy title in a farm bill in 2002, providing grants and other needed support for farmers who grow crops for energy.

In the House, Representatives John Shimkus (R-Illinois), Kenny Hulshof (R-Missouri), and Marcy Kaptur (D-Ohio) have been equally active. A member of the House Appropriations Committee, Kaptur was instrumental in lobbying DaimlerChrysler to fill every new 2005 Jeep Liberty Diesel vehicle with B5 as it leaves the factory in Kaptur's home state of Ohio. In January 2005, Congresswoman Kaptur–also a member of the Subcommittee on Agricultural Appropriations–introduced legislation that aims to provide greater federal assistance for the manufacturing and marketing of biofuels, including ethanol and biodiesel.

Biodiesel continues to turn heads on both sides of the party divide. Democrats and Republicans are working together, both at the state and federal level, to pass legislation supportive of biodiesel. Despite the short-term setbacks faced by some recent energy legislation, biodiesel is supported through a powerful grassroots network of soybean farmers, environmentalists, and members of the fuels and oils industry. And as the support for biodiesel grows, stronger legislation is likely to pave the way for increased biodiesel use throughout America.

CHAPTER 8

Biodiesel's Speedy Growth

"Biodiesel offers us a way to grow our way out of the situation we find ourselves in."

Willie Nelson, Singer/songwriter

W hen rock legend Neil Young took to the open road last year for his "Greendale" tour, he took biodiesel with him. From Vancouver, British Columbia, to Amherst, Massachusetts, Young and his band Crazy Horse fueled their trucks and tour buses with B20 bought from Iowa-based fuel cooperative West Central Soy, and rallied their fans with enthusiasm for the farmer-grown fuel.

But biodiesel isn't just big in the music industry. From Corporate America to the U.S. military to schools and cities around the nation, biodiesel is being used to cleanly power everything from cars, trucks, and buses to earthmovers and snowplows to ships, trains, and even planes. Biodiesel is also seeing rapid adoption as a home heating fuel.

The Stars of Biodiesel

Young isn't the only celebrity musician backing biodiesel. Singer-songwriter Willie Nelson recently formed a company to market his own brand of B20 called "BioWillie" to truckers at truck stops across America.[1] Nelson's company, Willie Nelson's Biodiesel, is currently negotiating with several major truck stops to carry the fuel at locations nationwide.

Oscar-nominated actor Woody Harrelson of *Cheers* and *The People vs. Larry Flynt* fame completed a 2001 tour of the west coast in a former Chicago transit bus fueled with B100. "The Mothership," as Harrelson's bus is called, served as the support vehicle for Harrelson's Simple Organic Living (SOL) Tour, a ten-person cycling tour from Burbank, California, to Seattle, Washington. During the SOL Tour, Harrelson and his crew stopped at sustainable living fairs, colleges, and town halls, where they were the focus of an educational and media campaign promoting renewable energy and environmentally conscious living.[2] The SOL Tour inspired both a documentary film about the adventure, *Go Further*, which premiered at the Toronto International Film Festival, and a new book, *How to Go Further: A Guide to Simple Organic Living*.

Famous for her roles in *Bladerunner* and *Splash*, actress Daryl Hannah is a strong supporter of biodiesel. While GM actually gave Hannah a large, sparkly new diesel pickup truck after hearing her speak about biodiesel on Fox News Channel's *The O'Reilly Factor,* Hannah prefers to drive a simpler, more "low key" 1981 Chevrolet El Camino outfitted with a stock diesel engine and powered by B100. Hannah uses biodiesel on both her Colorado and California solar powered ranches. "As I got older, my concerns grew about air, water, and natural-resource protection," says Hannah. "I began to see humanitarian and environmental concerns as one and the same."[3]

Environmental activist Julia "Butterfly" Hill is among the other celebrities using their star power to promote biodiesel. Julia Butterfly Hill–who lived in the branches of a redwood tree for two years to protest the logging of ancient redwood trees – insisted that biodiesel be used to power her tour bus, an annual music festival she hosts, and the generators used in the making of a feature-length film chronicling her experiences.[4] Other celebrities who have used the fuel on tour or in their personal vehicles include singer/song-writers Bonnie Raitt, the Indigo Girls, Concrete Blonde, and Perry Farrell of the band Jane's Addiction, who steered the music festival Lollapalooza to use biodiesel to power its generators on its 2003 tour.[5] Also in 2003, actor Dennis Weaver, famous for his role as a cowboy deputy in *Gunsmoke*, led a different kind of trailblazing cadre in a cross-country convoy called the "Drive to Survive." The purpose of his road trip was to raise awareness for alternative fuels like biodiesel.

Presidential Seal of Approval

President George W. Bush's "I believe in biodiesel" statement to more than 10,000 Iowan farmers at the Farm Progress Show in August 2004 confirmed his position to promote adoption of domes-tically produced renewable fuels.[6]

While Bush is the first president to publicly utter the "B" word, Presidents Carter, Clinton, and Bush Sr. have also expressed similar support. In August 2003, some 25 years after first advocating alter-native fuels, President Jimmy Carter met with legislators in his home state of Georgia to promote biodiesel production as a way to bring millions in revenue to the agriculturally driven state. Georgians burn one million gallons of petroleum diesel every day, but the state also grows 7.2 billion pounds of chickens every year – a potential source for making biodiesel.[7]

President Clinton set the wheels in motion for the government to begin using biodiesel when he signed his "Greening the Government" Executive Order in 1998, giving purchasing preference to bio-based products for federal use and clearing biodiesel for use in complying with the Energy Policy Act of 1992 (EPAct).[8]

Former presidential candidate and Massachusetts Senator John Kerry also emphasized biodiesel's importance as an alternative fuel by using it in his campaign bus, as well as speaking about biodiesel on his appearance on *The Daily Show* in the fall of 2004. Noted Kerry on the talk show: "There is no possible way for us to drill our way out of this crisis, we have to invent our way out of it–by moving to alternatives, renewables, fuel efficient vehicles, biomass, biodiesel."[9]

Corporate Use

The best and brightest in Corporate America are also playing a part in publicly endorsing biodiesel as a clean-burning, renewable alternative fuel. In October 2004 Google–arguably the world's most successful Internet company–began shuttling its San Francisco-based employees to work on a luxury coach fueled by biodiesel. Carrying some 155 passengers the 75-mile roundtrip to Google's Mountain View headquarters and back displaces some 2,325 gallons of petroleum fuel each week, according to the $3.2 billion Internet search wonder. The added expense for the B20 is negligible; the shuttle service is considered a company perk, and also a perk for residents of the surrounding, often traffic-clogged neighborhoods.[10]

Boeing, Clif Bar, and Quiksilver are among several major retailers looking to gain customer kudos through their corporate use of biodiesel. Energy-bar maker Clif Bar and surf-chic retailer Quiksilver have both taken biodiesel-fueled vehicles on publicity tours to promote their company's environmentally friendly practices. Clif Bar's mobile marketing tour featured a bus running B100 that traveled from Tampa, Florida, to Boston in the summer of 2004, educating customers about the benefits of biodiesel fuel and the role vehicles play in global warming by burning fossil fuels. The $110 million privately held company–known for virtually reinventing the sports and nutrition snacks market–attributes much of its success to building a "green" brand that attracts a loyal following of customers. Likewise, Quiksilver employees took to the high seas, sailing a biodiesel-powered yacht around the world and stopping along the eastern coast of the United States to educate surf enthusiasts about marine conservation.[11]

Fort Bragg, California-based Thanksgiving Coffee fuels its delivery trucks with B100 to demonstrate its commitment to reducing its ecological footprint. The environmentally friendly company, which plants trees in Ethiopia to offset the emissions created by its daily operations, financed the switch to B100 through a county Air Quality Management District grant. Headquartered in Freeport, Maine, clothing retailer L. L. Bean uses biodiesel blends to fuel its warehouse distribution heavy-duty truck fleet.[12] Added to the list of "earth friendly" companies that use biodiesel are New Belgium Brewery in Ft. Collins, Colorado, and Fetzer Vineyards in Hopland, California. Both companies pride themselves on producing clean spirits from organic crops.

Uncle Sam Goes Green

By far biodiesel's biggest consumer is the U.S. government. NASA, the U.S. Postal Service, and the National Parks Service are among the many government agencies routinely using biodiesel in their vehicle fleets. Beginning with a pilot project at Yellowstone National Park in 1995, biodiesel use in the national parks was expanded through the Green Energy Parks Program. Presently 23 parks are using biodiesel or biodiesel blends to fuel some 675 vehicles and diesel-powered equipment.[13]

Government agencies using biodiesel currently include the Iowa Department of Transportation at all their 19 locations, the U.S. Postal Service at numerous locations in Florida, and the National Oceanographic and Atmospheric Administration (NOAA) on research vessels in the Florida Keys National Marine Sanctuary.

All branches of the U.S. military use biodiesel at various bases, including Camp Lejune Marine Corps Base in North Carolina, the Air Force Space Command in Colorado, the Army's Ft. Leonard Wood in Missouri, and Everett Naval Station in Washington State. Most of the military installations using biodiesel obtain it through the Defense Energy Support Center (DESC), which coordinates the federal government's fuel purchases.[14] DESC is the largest single purchaser of biodiesel in this country, and has been procuring B20 for its administrative vehicles since 2001. For the contract period 2003 to 2004, DESC bought 5.2 million gallons of B20 for use at military and civilian locations throughout the country.[15]

The U.S. Navy is the world's largest consumer of diesel fuel and largest single user of biodiesel in America. A new directive specifies that most our their non tactical Naval and marine vehicles will use B20.[16] The U.S. Navy is even testing a mobile processing unit in California that turns used cooking oil into biodiesel. If the test is successful, similar units could soon accompany all branches of the military on overseas deployments. The idea is to use biodiesel to ensure "energy security." If petroleum sources are cut off in the event of a crisis, the military will be able to produce its own fuel.[17]

Who Uses Biodiesel?

A sampling of users:

National Park Service (at 23 parks, including Yellowstone)
Northstar at Tahoe
U.S. Postal Service
U.S. Dept. of Agriculture
NASA
All four branches of the military, including:
　　Peterson Air Force Base
　　Camp Pendleton Marine Corps Base
　　Ft. Leonard Wood
　　Naval Base Ventura County
Omaha Public Power District
Alabama Power
Georgia Power
Pacific Gas & Electric
San Diego Gas & Electric
Florida Power & Light
Madison Gas & Electric
Duke Energy
New Jersey Transit
South West Ohio Transit
Bloomington Transit
Missouri Department of Transportation
North Carolina Department of Traffic
St. Louis Lambert International Airport
The State of Delaware
The State of Alabama
Pacific Waste
The State of Connecticut
San Luis Obispo Police Department

University of Colorado
Harvard University
University of Idaho
Purdue University
University of Kansas
Medford Township School District, New Jersey
City of Las Vegas, Nevada
City of Dallas, Texas
City of Seattle, Washington
City of Aspen, Colorado
Clark County School District
Chicago School District
Denver Public Schools

Biodiesel Goes Back to School

Arguably one of the most important uses of biodiesel is fueling America's school buses. On a typical school day, some 450,000 yellow school buses–390,000 of which are powered by heavy-duty diesel engines–transport more than 24 million children to and from schools and school-related activities.[18] According to recent studies conducted by Yale University, the University of Southern California, and UCLA, children riding inside diesel-fueled buses are exposed to high levels of harmful diesel exhaust.

Yale's 2002 study (conducted with Environment and Human Health, Inc. a nonprofit research organization) found exposure levels to harmful particulates inside Connecticut school buses to be five to ten times higher than levels outside the buses.[19] A similar study conducted by UCLA, UC Riverside, and the California Air Resources Board (CARB) concluded that children who ride diesel buses for thirteen school years have a 4% higher risk of developing cancer and a 6% higher risk of developing other respiratory problems such as asthma.[20]

While CARB's assessment of children's increased risk of cancer and respiratory illness due to diesel exhaust exposure in school buses seems relatively small, doctors, toxicologists, and the EPA itself have suggested a more direct link between the inhalation of diesel exhaust and illness. Mark Cullen, M.D., Professor of Medicine and Public Health at the Yale School of Medicine and director of Yale's Occupational and Environmental Medicine Program, says that "components of diesel exhaust can adversely affect lung function in children with underlying respiratory illnesses such as asthma, bronchitis, and infections." Robert LaCamera, M.D., Clinical Professor of Pediatrics at the Yale School of Medicine, says that "there is no known safe level of exposure to diesel exhaust for children, especially those with respiratory illness." LaCamera adds that many of the 4.8 million children who suffer from asthma in the United States ride diesel school buses.[21]

The American Lung Association includes in the triggers for asthma: irritating gases, particles in the air, and cigarette smoke–which contains some of the same compounds as diesel fuel exhaust. According to the ALA, asthma is the third leading cause of hospitalization among children under the age of 15, the leading cause of chronic illness among children, and the leading cause of absenteeism. All told, asthma accounted for 14.6 million lost school days in 2002.[22]

The Environmental Protection Agency has also been clear in its assessment of the negative health effects of diesel exhaust and has developed an aggressive set of mandates to begin to combat the problem. After implementing a ruling that will enforce the reduction of sulfur in diesel fuel as well as mandate the use of cleaner-burning diesel engines by 2010, the EPA stated that the rule will have the following effect:

An estimated 8,300 premature deaths, 5,500 cases of chronic bronchitis and 17,600 cases of acute bronchitis in children will also be prevented annually. It is also estimated to help avoid more than 360,000 asthma attacks and 386,000 cases of respiratory symptoms in asthmatic children every year. In addition, 1.5 million lost workdays, 7,100 hospital visits and 2,400 emergency room visits for asthma will be prevented.[23]

The EPA clearly sees diesel exhaust as a serious health threat.

In response to specific concerns over the negative effects of diesel school bus emissions, the EPA implemented its Clean School Bus USA program in 2003. The program has three distinct goals: to eliminate unnecessary school bus idling, to retrofit buses with better emissions technologies, and to replace the oldest buses with cleaner-burning buses. The program also calls for using cleaner fuels, like biodiesel–which can reduce particulates and aromatics, the main airborne toxic emissions associated with diesel fuel. While much of the $17.5 million in grants awarded by the program were for the purchase of emissions control devices and newer school buses, a portion of the funds has also been used to offset the incremental cost of biodiesel.[24] School districts in five states, including those in Missoula County, Montana; Ann Arbor, Michigan; Warwick, Rhode Island; Littleton, Colorado; and districts throughout Iowa, have received between $4,550 and $21,400 from the Clean School Bus USA program to pay for the increase in fuel costs associated with biodiesel.[25]

"We're ecstatic about being able to use biodiesel again," said Jeff Knasiak, director of transportation for Manchester, Michigan, Public Schools, one of the EPA grant recipients using biodiesel. "We had a great experience when we used biodiesel in the past and noticed an amazing decrease in the amount of exhaust and fumes. There were never any start-up problems, even during cold Michigan winters."[26]

In addition to the schools operating under grants from the Clean School Bus USA program, almost 100 school districts nationwide have made the switch to biodiesel–many of them without federal or state funding assistance. Even though biodiesel is more expensive for some of these school districts, the nontoxic fuel remains one of the cheapest, most practical methods to reduce dangerous emissions. "I felt we should try biodiesel for the simple reason that it puts fewer pollutants into the air," says Edward Harkins, transportation supervisor for Mahopac Central School District in Mahopac Falls, New York. The district, which serves 52 schools, has been using B20 in its fleet of 100 diesel buses since 2001. While B20 costs the district roughly $0.15 to $0.30 per gallon more than petroleum diesel, Harkins was able to squeeze the added expense into Mahopac's transportation budget without having to apply for special funding.[27]

Going the Distance

While several cities nationwide, including Cleveland, Cincinnati, St. Louis, and Cedar Rapids, Iowa, have adopted biodiesel to fuel municipal buses and utilities fleets, Berkeley, California, is the first city of its size in the United States to use 100% biodiesel in all of its vehicles. Berkeley began using B100 to fuel its city fleets–including Departments of Public Works, Parks, Fire, Police, and Health and Human Services–in January 2002. The northern California city had already experimented with other alternative fuels, including electric, electric-gas hybrids, compressed natural gas (CNG), and B20. But Berkeley decided to go with B100 to fuel its fleet of 192 garbage trucks, fire engines, school buses, and municipal vehicles despite the fuel's higher cost. "We figured it worked out to an extra scone and a latte per resident each year," said Dave Williamson, who ran the city's recycling program at the Berkeley Ecology Center.[28]

Auto Companies Take a Test Drive

DaimlerChrysler is another company publicly endorsing biodiesel. The automaker began fueling each new diesel Jeep Liberty with a B5 biodiesel blend at its Jeep factory in January 2005.[29] In a similar show of endorsement, farm equipment manufacturer John Deere began pre-filling all of its diesel-powered machines with a B2 biodiesel blend at its factories in 2005.[30] General Motors is following suit, announcing increased support for biodiesel last fall by updating warranties for all GM vehicles with diesel engines to reflect the allowed use of B20.[31]

In Europe, DaimlerChrysler, Volkswagen, Citroen, Peugeot, Renault, Ford, and others have all released light-duty consumer vehicles with warranties that fully cover the use of biodiesel. The share of diesels in the new passenger car market in Europe has reached an all-time high, according to market data published by Robert Bosch, GmbH. In October 2004, 51.9% of all newly registered passenger cars in Europe came equipped with a diesel engine.[32] Automakers hope that sales of diesel vehicles stateside follow the same upward trend as those overseas. In 2004 DaimlerChrysler released its first diesel vehicle for the U.S. market in six years, the Mercedes-Benz E320 CDI sedan. The company sold out its initial supply of 3,000 vehicles and is ramping up production for another 1,000 vehicles.[33]

The Oil Industry Plants a Stake

Petroleum companies like BP (along with Gulf Oil, a major shareholder in biodiesel producer World Energy) are jumping into the biodiesel business, a sharp shift in an industry that once considered biodiesel a fringe fuel. The change has already started to occur. BP, for example, has changed its name to Beyond Petroleum in an effort to ready consumers for its transition to offering alternative fuels. Likewise, Royal Dutch/Shell pledged to spend $1 billion per year on alternative energy research and development by the end of the decade.[34]

Biodiesel may prove itself useful to oil companies as a renewable lubricity additive as the U.S. transitions to using EPA-mandated Ultra Low Sulfur Diesel (ULSD) fuels in 2006.[35] Testing at labs such as Southwest Research Institute and Standyne Automotive and Engineering Testing Services have demonstrated that biodiesel significantly improves diesel fuel lubricity, even at blends as low as 1% (B1).[36] Oil companies would not have to add a synthetic lubricity replacement to diesel fuel if biodiesel was used as a lubricity enhancer, thereby easing the transition to making ULSD fuel available nationwide.

Heating Things Up

Biodiesel is gaining ground as a fuel for heating homes as well as a transportation fuel. In the northeastern United States, where three out of four homeowners use No. 2 diesel as heating oil, biodiesel offers a cleaner burning alternative. Commercially sold biodiesel heating oil–usually blended with No. 2 diesel heating oil–must meet strict federal guidelines for ensuring quality: the diesel heating oil must meet its ASTM specification, ASTM D 396, and the biodiesel must meet its ASTM specification, ASTM D 6751, before they are blended together.[37]

Biodiesel as a heating oil first attracted industry attention in 2000, when heating oil prices climbed from $1.21 to $1.99 per gallon. The price hike didn't last, but adopters of the biodiesel blends found that, in addition to providing price stability, biodiesel blends could produce fewer harmful emissions and actually reduced maintenance costs for furnaces and boilers. As rising fuel prices and achieving energy independence again become a concern, biodiesel has increasingly become the subject of research studies, pilot projects, and commercial rollouts. A study of biodiesel use in boilers in the Warwick Rhode Island School District sponsored by the National Renewable Energy Lab, for example, concluded a cleaner burning B20 blend improves the efficiency of filters, strainers, nozzles, and all fuel-affected parts whose premature failure means high repair and replacement costs.[38]

The move to adopt cleaner-burning biodiesel may even give a much-needed boost to diesel home heating oil companies. Businesses selling No. 2 diesel heating oil are losing market share to natural gas, due to the ability of natural gas to be used as a clean-burning heating fuel. Only 4% of new homes in the U.S. come equipped with oil furnaces, down from 20% of new homes built in the 1970s.[39]

Residential consumption of No. 2 heating oil in 2001 was 6.6 billion gallons nationwide, according to the Energy Information Agency. If every residential furnace switched to B20, approximately 1.3 billion gallons of biodiesel would be needed—40 times as much biodiesel as was sold in the U.S. in 2004. Officials at the USDA Agricultural Research Center in Beltsville, Maryland, estimate that if everyone in the Northeast used a B5 blend in their oil furnaces, 50 million gallons of regular heating oil a year could be displaced. The Center has been heating its many buildings successfully with biodiesel since 2000.[40]

In Augusta, Maine, government buildings such as the State Building and Department of Motor Vehicles are heated using B10 and B20 heating oil. Last winter the state government purchased 360,000 gallons of B10, an increase over the previous year's purchase of 27,000 gallons of B20. Similarly, the Warwick, Rhode Island, school district has been using biodiesel on a trial basis since 2001.

In Newburgh, New York, fuel oil dealer Abbot & Mills is conducting a biodiesel field trial involving 100 homes. Fred M.

Schildwachter & Sons, a New York supplier, now offers a B20 blend to its residential customers. In Massachusetts, Mass Biofuel began offering a similar blend to customers at the beginning of November; Worley & Obetz of Manheim, Pennsylvania also recently began selling biodiesel heating fuel to its customers.

All Aboard the Biodiesel Express

Modern diesel locomotives are essentially giant generators. They use electricity generated by their diesel engines to power industrial-strength electrical motors that move trains along railroad tracks. For this reason, California is investigating the use of stationary biodiesel fueled locomotives to produce electricity for its power grid.[41]

In Brazil, América Latina Logística (ALL), a large rail company with 580 trains and 15,000 miles of track, is testing B20 to power its trains using locally grown fuel. The company estimates it will use 9.3 million gallons of B20 to power its trains.[42] In India, the Railway Board has similarly directed all zonal railways to test biodiesel as an alternative to diesel for locomotives and vehicles.

Biodiesel Ahoy

Protecting the environment is a particularly good reason to use biodiesel in ships, a class of vehicle whose emissions often occur in areas especially vulnerable to pollution. Diesel fuel spills in harbors and waterways regularly make the evening news, while the more insidious everyday petroleum diesel pollution caused by shipboard motors does not. An estimated 21 million barrels of oil run into the oceans each year from street run-off, effluent from factories, and from ships flushing their tanks, according to the Alaska Oceans Program.[43]

Government and the private sector are beginning to look to biodiesel as an environmentally friendly fuel whose use will remove much of the pollution risks to fish, wildlife, and marine habitats. The Channel Islands National Park Service is running its fleet of ferries and ships on biodiesel.[44] The U.S. Coast Guard is similarly testing biodiesel for marine use, running at least one of its utility boats on B20.[45]

On the private sector side, Ventura Harbor in southern California now makes biodiesel available to all its boating clientele; farther north, San Francisco-based Splash Tours runs its sea tours on biodiesel. In Hawaii, the Pacific Whale Foundation and Maui Scuba Tours have also switched to using biodiesel.

But biodiesel isn't only used in coastal locations. The Marina at the Lake of the Ozarks Lodge of the Four Seasons also offers B20 at the pump. Some of the largest yachts on the lake use the biodiesel blend, including the "Bud Boat," the famous luxury yacht owned by Anheuser-Busch–a nice tie-in, considering that Adolphus Busch, creator of the company, first brought diesel engines to America almost 100 years ago.

Biodiesel Takes Flight

Aircraft are not only major consumers of diesel fuel in the U.S., they pollute sensitive layers of the atmosphere. For the past 18 years, Baylor University's Renewable Aviation Fuels Development Center (RAFDC) has been researching less toxic ways to power airplanes. The center is now test-flying aircraft using B10 and B20 biodiesel blends. The idea is to seek FAA certification for biodiesel fuels and institute a nationwide education program through the Baylor University/International Center for Aviation and the Environment's Clean Airports Program.[46] If successful, the program could lead to biodiesel blends being used in smaller aircraft, such as those used as crop dusters. Such aircraft can be outfitted with a number of newly designed aircraft diesel engines.[47]

In the near term, however, biodiesel is more likely to be found on airport tarmacs than in airplane fuel tanks. At Miami International Airport, for example, researchers are examining the use of the biodiesel to power baggage handling and group support equipment. The U.S. Department of Energy and the Florida Energy Office, together with Gold Coast Clean Cities Coalition and the Miami Dade Aviation Department, will assess the feasibility of replacing diesel with biodiesel fuel in baggage transport equipment and fuel trucks. The $54,000 project will also assess the market potential for biodiesel, explore its compatibility with current systems, and test fuel quality, performance, and storage requirements.[48] Similarly, Salt Lake City International Airport has used biodiesel blends to fuel its ground transport diesel vehicles since 2001. In 2002, the airport purchased approximately 37,000 gallons of B100.[49]

Biodiesel Goes Global

Taking note of the worsening international politics of petroleum, the shift toward biodiesel in a number of countries has been swift; many are enacting tax laws and incentives to benefit biodiesel. Biodiesel plays an increasingly important economic role in the European Union (EU). After many years of the existence of various country-specific biodiesel standards, a Europe-wide standard for biodiesel was adopted in 2004 to ensure fuel quality and require public filling stations to declare fuel blends and quality standards on the fuel pump.

In Germany, which produces roughly half of all biodiesel made in the EU, biodiesel (B100) is sold at more than 1,700 service stations.[50] The success of biodiesel in Germany is due largely to the German government's favorable biodiesel tax legislation. Since fuels in Germany are taxed according to carbon emissions, and biodiesel has very low carbon emissions, the fuel receives a healthy tax break, making it slightly cheaper than diesel fuel.

Biodiesel has been produced on an industrial scale in the European Union since 1992. Today some 50 biodiesel processing plants in Western Europe produce more than 410 million gallons annually.[51] Most of diesel fuel in France is mixed with biodiesel today. Specific legislation to promote and regulate the use of biodiesel is in force in many countries including Austria, France, Germany, Italy, and Sweden.

Africa and Asia will likely see numerous small-scale biodiesel plants that work within villages and cooperative models. Some investigation has been done into creating micro-loans through the World Bank or directly through governments such as India to build such small scale "bio-refineries." Exploding population growth in India, China, and surrounding countries could further lead to biodiesel's adoption as a primary fuel source and economic stimulus. Biodiesel processing plants are also popping up in major cities in Central and South America.

CHAPTER 9

Turning Biodiesel Into Bucks

"No one can possibly achieve any real and lasting success or get rich in business by being a conformist."

J. Paul Getty, Oil Tycoon (b.1892 - d.1976)

Underneath you, under the ground you walk on, under the buildings, streets, highways, and state borders, lies a network of pipelines. Like arteries carrying blood from an enormous heart, these pipelines transport the fluid needed to sustain our society. Just as we are completely unaware of our body's circulatory functions, so too are we oblivious to the web of conduits that bring oil from the refineries at our coastal ports.

The oil pipelines begin at the massive refinery complexes that stretch from the mouth of the Mississippi river in Louisiana all the way to the Texas Gulf. The pipes travel north, northeast, and northwest, connecting cities and towns to the lifeline of oil. Still more pipelines reach eastward from California, intersecting and crisscrossing inland in what, on paper, looks like an "Internet" of oil.

At the historic port city of New Orleans, at the port of Corpus Christi, Texas, in Long Beach and Port Richmond, California, and in Seattle, Washington, and Portland, Oregon, massive tanker ships unload their precious cargo. From these points of entry, petroleum begins its stateside journey. Oil and gas are stored and processed close to the port cities. The refineries transform the crude or semi-crude petroleum into usable fuels. From there, the finished fuel products move along a nationwide system of distribution channels that include pipelines, rail cars, and transport trucks. Fuel distributors are the conductors directing each stage in fossil fuel's long journey to reach fuel stations across America.

Like any network of retailers, these distributors take the product from upstream and package it into continuously smaller quantities, relabeling and rebranding the fuel along the way. Finally, an eighteen-wheeler tanker truck arrives at a service station and delivers the fuel. Motorists, unaware of the many connections or the trillions of dollars'-worth of infrastructure that ensures their continuous mobility, enjoy the freedom of stopping at any one of hundreds of thousands of service stations to fill their tanks.

Despite the distances fuel travels and the various transport mechanisms used to move it, the consumer can always rely on a high standard of fuel quality, no matter when or where he or she "fills up." By contrast, in the developing world fuel of often-questionable quality is hoarded. In these countries one never knows when fuel will be available or if the fuel will be of good quality when it arrives. Western nations prioritize the ability of their fuel infrastructure to deliver consistently high quality fuel to their populations. This consistent fuel ensures our mobility, and is the cornerstone of our commerce and social services and food distribution. Thus, a great deal of money changes hands to keep America moving.

The Business of Biodiesel

Biodiesel cannot function without the backbone of the petroleum industry. A single petroleum refinery represents billions of dollars of investment and can process between 200,000 and 500,000 barrels of petroleum per day. While a few biodiesel suppliers will operate in conjunction with refineries, or may be part of a larger conglomerate that operates refineries, most biodiesel companies tend to partner with petroleum companies further down the pipeline, at the level of a *fuel distributor*. Fuel distributors typically operate under franchise from a large petroleum company. These distributors fill their fuel transport trucks from the pipelines at *terminals*. Some distributors then take fuel to *satellite terminals* or *bulk plants,* where fuels are separated and stored according to the grade. For example, diesel fuel that is stored in a diesel fuel tank at a terminal will eventually be distributed to diesel fuel pumps at fleet stations or at service stations.

Biodiesel is usually delivered to the terminal as B100, a "neat" concentration with no additives or other fuels mixed into it. At the terminal it may be stored as neat biodiesel, or it may be blended with diesel and stored as B5, B20, or as some other blend. Today the biodiesel industry is moving biodiesel at such a rapid pace that the fuel spends little time at the terminal. By the time biodiesel arrives, it is usually mixed directly into the rail tanker or truck, which will transport it to a fuel *rack*, or a sub terminal where eighteen-wheeler tankers and other rail car tankers can be filled. The biodiesel is carefully *blended*, meaning it is mixed in a specific proportion with diesel fuel.

A fuel *jobber* is responsible for delivering fuel to the service stations. In the case of biodiesel, this person usually handles specific accounts with truck stops or fleet pumps that use diesel fuel. In order for a biodiesel blend to be sold at a retail location, the fuel jobber and the petroleum company (and also the distributor, if involved) must all approve the biodiesel being used in the equipment under their supervision.

Because biodiesel has cleansing properties, the storage, handling, and blending of biodiesel must be done with care. Distributors and jobbers who work with biodiesel have the added responsibilities of ensuring that all of their transport and storage tanks are clean and dry prior to contact with biodiesel. They must use a high quality diesel fuel to make and certify the various blends of biodiesel. They will also attempt to minimize the time that biodiesel is stored between transport and final use.

Shaking Hands, Kissing Babies

Because no amount of infrastructure will guarantee that people will buy a product, the market for biodiesel must be developed before building a plant, buying fuel sales equipment, or starting a biodiesel business. Invested wisely, marketing dollars can return valuable customers. But even before marketing efforts begin, most biodiesel fuel distributors and producers face a critical challenge–public relations. Before a specific group of people can even be considered part of a potential biodiesel market, they have to first learn about biodiesel and why they should use it.

Historically, the National Biodiesel Board has been responsible for public relations for the biodiesel industry, a task rife with challenges–the least of which is a limited budget. From 2001 to 2005, the NBB's annual communications budget averaged $150,000– about the same cost as a thirty-second commercial on a major television network. Jenna Higgins, director of communications for the National Biodiesel Board, believes that public education continues to be one of the biggest barriers to widespread biodiesel use. Following a strategy of "earned media," the NBB has worked hard to tie biodiesel's positive aspects to current events and gain main-stream media coverage. The NBB has also concentrated its outreach efforts largely on fleets, since less than 2% of individuals in America currently drive diesel vehicles.

State soybean organizations and the Clean Cities Program have also been instrumental in mounting biodiesel outreach efforts. For example, when Tom Verry drove the biodiesel-powered Ford pickup truck, "Old Brownie," throughout Missouri for ten years to educate the public about biodiesel, his work was a form of outreach adminis-tered by the Missouri Soybean Merchandising Council. Along with the help and endorsement from celebrities like Willie Nelson and Neil Young, the media's coverage of biodiesel has increased by 30% each year since 2001, says Higgins.

The task of educating the public remains a top priority, since, as Higgins explains, there are still many people who think that biodiesel is pure soy oil or oil mixed with diesel fuel. Incorrect assumptions about cold weather use and warranty acceptance further confuse the public. "Our consumer research shows that one in four Americans knows what biodiesel is," Higgins says. "We want to get that up to 90% – the same level of awareness the public has about ethanol."[1]

The National Biodiesel Board is not alone on its educational quest. Many of the more than 500 fleets that use biodiesel have taken steps to educate their constituents about the fuel. Indeed, for many such fleet operators, using biodiesel has the added bonus of increased public exposure for their companies.

Many distributors who want to sell biodiesel have joined indus-try efforts to educate their potential markets about biodiesel. Joel Glatz and Brad Taylor are co-owners of Frontier Energy, a fuel oils distribution company in China, Maine. They focus on the industrial and home heating market, and during the last several years have been the state's largest retailer for biodiesel sold for heating. Glatz and Taylor say that public education appropriate to their target market has been critical to Frontier's success selling biodiesel. The partners began showcasing biodiesel at what they call "alternative lifestyle events" such as Maine's Common Ground Community Fair, which is organized around organic farming and social action. About 30,000 people attend the event each year. The first year Frontier showcased biodiesel for heating, nobody knew what it was. "We had to educate every single person we spoke with," says Glatz. "It was excruciating."

The work paid off, however, and the next year the partners found only three people at the fair who didn't know about biodiesel. Their public relations efforts fostered positive word of mouth, and suddenly an entire community was aware of their product. Soon, companies like American clothing manufacturer L. L. Bean began ordering their fuel. Frontier now distributes about 1,500 gallons of blended B20 to the clothing company for use as a heating fuel each month. The company also recently secured a seed grant from Maine's Technology Institute to help them do market research and begin serious marketing. "We're a small company," says Glatz, "but we feel we have the tiger by the tail."[2]

Small companies aren't the only ones that have been heavily involved in biodiesel public relations. Griffin Industries is one of the largest grease renderers in the United States. With 1,200 employees in 14 states, Griffin was well positioned to enter the biodiesel market. In 1998 Griffin built a "multifeedstock" biodiesel plant in Cold Spring, Kentucky, and has seen growing sales of biodiesel ever since.

Hart Moore, who runs the biodiesel division of Griffin, says a key factor to getting new customers is exposure. Moore says that one of Griffin's biggest successes with biodiesel was working with the National Biodiesel Board to organize biodiesel use at Earth Day 2000 on the Mall in Washington, D.C. Griffin provided biodiesel fuel for the large generators powering the Earth Day event, including the 60-foot-tall megatron screens on which the concert was broadcast live. "It was one of the first times the word 'biodiesel' was even pronounced at an Earth Day," Moore explains. Despite the fact that much of the possible national media coverage Griffin had hoped to receive from that particular event was displaced on the morning of the event by a small boy from Cuba named Elian Gonzalez, Moore used the event to springboard Griffin into supplying biodiesel fuel for large concert and event generators–a market that, at the time, was totally untapped.[3]

The NBB's Higgins says the collective efforts of the right kind of PR done by certified fuel distributors are having positive effects. "It's getting better all the time," she says. "I am always struck by how impressed people are with biodiesel. I've rarely met anyone who doesn't think that it's a great idea."[4] Fuel distributors are learning that biodiesel's media cachet and public appeal drastically shorten the road from public relations to a customer purchases. For this reason, biodiesel offers small and medium-sized companies involved in fuel distribution an attractive avenue for market growth and added income.

The Psychology of Buying Biodiesel

The majority of biodiesel sales fall into three categories: government fleet, private fleet, or personal or small business use. Biodiesel sales typically follow diesel sales. Since there are few personal diesel vehicles in the United States at this time, most of the 60 billion gallons of diesel fuel sold goes to heavy-duty vehicles used in transport, agriculture, and other industries requiring large machinery. Thus, when addressing where best to market biodiesel, companies often look toward users of large quantities of diesel fuel. Such users include government-run bodies such as the Department of Transportation, the military, and the National Parks and Recreation Service.

Hence, for now, the biodiesel market is made up more of companies and institutions than individuals. The layers of bureaucracy inherent in most companies and almost all government entities can either help biodiesel sales (as in the case of government agencies that must comply with EPAct) or hinder sales (as in the case of fleets that are managed by bureaucratic institutions not interested in the hassle or cost of adopting a new fuel). Even in large institutions, one "hero"–somebody who believes his or her company should buy biodiesel–can make the difference in an entire institution's making the switch to biodiesel.

The use of diesel fuel is an obvious prerequisite for potential biodiesel markets, but it is not the only factor that pushes biodiesel fuel sales. Opinion and attitude often have as much to do with why a potential customer switches to biodiesel. Gene Gebolys is CEO of World Energy, a company that has cornered a large portion of the U.S. biodiesel market. The 42-person company supplies biodiesel to the military, utility fleets, and branches of the U.S. Postal Service. Until recently the company focused strictly on sales and marketing–moving the biodiesel made by the biodiesel plants located primarily in the Midwest out to customers along the coasts and in the south.

Gebolys says that biodiesel is rarely bought on the merits of its fuel quality alone. Instead, Gebolys says, people generally buy biodiesel because of the social implications of their purchase. He explains that people may buy biodiesel because of an interest in clean air, domestic energy, or public health. "Buying biodiesel," he says, "gives people a way to address those social concerns."[5] Gebolys addresses something critical to understanding the biodiesel business: when customers buy biodiesel, they are purchasing something with a substantial amount of perceived value; value from which they do not actually receive tangible benefit. In other words, customers are buying the ideals of independence from foreign oil, cleaner air, lower emissions, and an American-grown fuel, all wrapped up in a package called biodiesel. Said another way, customers are "voting" with their dollars.

As a supplier of substantial quantities of biodiesel in the United States, Gebolys's observations carry a lot of weight. But he's not alone. Russ Teall is CEO of Biodiesel Industries, a company that constructs biodiesel plants and then partners in their operation. His five plants are spread around the world in places like India and Australia. Teall's plants are on the smaller side and average about 4 million gallons per year in capacity. According to Teall, perceived value is a critical element in selling biodiesel.

Teall cites the example of the Las Vegas school district, which began using biodiesel several years ago, even though it was not mandated to do so. When the national media began to pick up on stories about diesel school buses causing cancer, concerned parents began contacting the school district. "They called up ready to jump all over the school district," explains Teall. "The district said, 'Hey–we started using biodiesel a year ago, and it's non toxic.' So even though they didn't do it for the purpose of PR, the PR was great for them."[6]

Kelly and Bob King run a company called Pacific Biodiesel, which, in addition to providing biodiesel plant construction services, operates biodiesel plants on the islands of Maui and Oahu, Hawaii. Kelly King's experience mirrors that of Gebolys's and Teall's. "Some people buy biodiesel because they are totally dedicated to the environment. Some of them have political motivations; they feel like they are furthering conflict in the Middle East by buying petroleum, and they don't want to do that," says King. Biodiesel acceptance in Hawaii has been so strong that much of the fuel tax on biodiesel has been lifted–making it competitive in price with diesel fuel.[7]

Whatever the psychological trigger, biodiesel has an appeal that allows buyers to look beyond its price tag. Despite the fact that biodiesel usually comes at a premium when compared to diesel fuel, *biodiesel sales are growing by 50% per year.* The psychological importance of biodiesel in the market should not be underestimated. Because it carries such strong emotional ties, many people in the biodiesel business speak about biodiesel with an uncanny reverence. Just as there is a perceived added value for biodiesel customers, there is also a perceived value for the distributors in bringing this important fuel to their friends, neighbors, and countrymen.

To Market, To Market

Be it ExxonMobil, BP, or Shell, the process of putting "a tiger in your tank" or filling your fuel tank with conventional gasoline or diesel fuel is essentially the same no matter what the brand. A similar situation is emerging with biodiesel, which is now sold under many different labels including: SoyPower, SoyGold, Bio G-3000, and Biotane. These various biodiesel brands must all conform to the most recent ASTM fuel standard.[8] At this time in the evolution of the biodiesel industry, the only major difference between the brands concerns their cold-flow characteristics. Biodiesel made from used cooking oil or from animal fat is less resistant to cold weather than biodiesel made from virgin soybean oil or most other virgin oils. As additives are developed specifically for the biodiesel industry, even this distinction could soon disappear. As long as it meets ASTM specifications, carries the BQ-9000 quality seal, and comes from a reputable distributor, biodiesel is as predictable in its characteristics as diesel fuel or gasoline.

Fuel quality is perhaps the single most important issue faced by any biodiesel distributor or producer. Because fuel is transported through many channels before it reaches the consumer, there are many points along the distribution chain where the fuel could become contaminated–assuming the fuel has met quality standards initially. For this reason, every batch of biodiesel that leaves West Central's 12 million gallon per year biodiesel plant in Ralston, Iowa, is strictly tested.

Because biodiesel sales are still off the radar of most petroleum distributors, the potential market for biodiesel is considerable. How biodiesel distributors attract and keep their markets is as critical to their success as is high fuel quality. According to Pacific Biodiesel's Kelly King, one of the most important aspects of the success of securing a biodiesel market is her company's close relationship with a local petroleum distributor. King says that the Chevron distributor on the island of Maui moves more B20 than any of their other distributors. It has a lot to do with the recognition and respect for the brand, says King. Pacific sells about a million gallons of biodiesel annually to a number of fleets around Hawaii, including the counties of Honolulu and Maui. Their market has also expanded to include tour buses, pleasure boats, and personal automobiles.[9]

While relationships are critical to succeeding in the fuels industry, convenience is also a key factor in securing markets. Gene Gebolys of World Energy says that making biodiesel easy for customers to obtain is crucial to maintaining a strong market presence. In assessing the needs of his market, Gebolys begins with the customer and works backwards. "When the average customer buys our product," says Gebolys, "he has no idea how much work has gone into to making that process simple for him."[10]

According to Jeff Irvin, president of the Petroleum Marketers Association of America (PMAA), which represents 8,000 petroleum marketers across the nation, biodiesel offers a means for fuel companies to grow sales. Irvin is also CEO of ITL, his family's fuel distribution company in Southern California, which sells between eight and ten million gallons of fuel a month. Irvin says that his company began selling biodiesel after learning that using biodiesel leads to a reduction in particulate emissions. While ITL could be selling much more biodiesel if it were more competitively priced compared with diesel fuel and if California would lift some of its restrictions on biodiesel sales, Irvin is confident his company, and the petroleum industry as a whole, is poised for a rapid growth in biodiesel sales. "It's a great opportunity for us," says Irvin. "I'd like to see us selling 500,000 gallons of biodiesel per month in the near future."[11]

As in any business, biodiesel marketing is a process of addressing the needs and desires of the potential market. And as in any business, in addition to affordability, biodiesel customers want what customers always want: to have confidence, convenience, and safety. Confidence often comes in the form of the stamp of approval from an oil company or the BQ-9000 stamp; convenience comes from the fuel distributor; and the understanding that biodiesel meets all safety requirements comes from the public relations work done by biodiesel experts like the National Biodiesel Board, the National Renewable Energy Laboratory (NREL), the Department of Energy (DOE), and the United States Department of Agriculture (USDA). Understanding and effectively utilizing this formula is critical to the success of biodiesel businesses and critical to the success of the biodiesel industry as a whole.

Biodiesel Plants

A biodiesel *plant* is a facility in which biodiesel is processed (not to be confused with the plants grown as biodiesel *feedstocks*). Biodiesel plants range in size, design, and effective output. Some plants process biodiesel one batch at a time and are thus called *batch process* plants. Other plants require a continuous flow of inputs and produce a continuous flow of outputs. Not surprisingly, these are called *continuous flow plants*. And just as no set of rules is complete without exceptions, there are also biodiesel plants known as "continous flow/batch process," in which biodiesel is processed in batches but continuously flows out of the plant.

Biodiesel plants are made to process different feedstocks. Some plants are designed specifically for soybean oil or used cooking oil, whereas other plants combine different process technologies to deal with different inputs and are thus called *multifeedstock* plants. Biodiesel plants that process virgin soy oil, for example, are generally located near a *crushing* facility where soybeans are crushed and separated into soybean meal and soy oil. The most efficient design for such a plant is a *biorefinery,* where the raw agricultural products come in straight from the field and leave as different value-added products ready for market. West Central Soy in Ralston, Iowa operates such a biorefinery.

At the Ralston plant, soybeans are trucked in from nearby farming fields, weighed, and then stored in massive grain silos (also called *grain bins*). From the silos, the soybeans move in a continuous line along a conveyor belt that takes the beans to a separate building where they are crushed. Inside the crushing facility, the beans are first smashed into flakes. The flakes move into a series of *expeller presses*, devices that squeeze the soybean pieces by way of large *augers*, or screws. The meal falls into the press and travels along the threads of the screw, getting squeezed. In the process, the press produces soybean oil and soybean meal. The meal follows a separate production path, via which it becomes a powdered livestock feed.[12] The raw soy oil is *degummed*, meaning all of the leftover plant matter is removed. It is further purified and sent through a large pipe, which takes it to the biodiesel plant.

Standing among the stainless steel pipes, tanks, and valves of a biodiesel plant feels a little like standing inside a high-tech video game. The biodiesel plant combines the vegetable oil with an alcohol and a catalyst such as lye. Modern biodiesel plants are so efficient that they use relatively little alcohol (less than 10% of the total reaction mixture) and little catalyst (less than 0.1% of the reaction mix). The biodiesel plant produces both biodiesel and glycerin. The glycerin can be purified in a sub process for the pharmaceuticals market, or it can be sold "as-is" to companies that purify it for market. The biodiesel typically moves directly out of the plant and into awaiting rail cars. At the Ralston plant, rail cars and eighteen-wheeler tanker trucks arrive around the clock to carry the biodiesel fuel across the continent.

While the process of making vegetable oil from agricultural stocks necessitates extra facilities to process those stocks, it also yields multiple products. West Central Soy produces biodiesel fuel, glycerin, soybean meal, and a number of sub products for food, pharmaceutical, and animal-feed markets. Biodiesel plants that process used cooking oil or tallow and fat require additional processes to purify their feedstock before the biodiesel process can begin. Consequently, these plants cost more and have less valuable by-products.

The cost for building a biodiesel plant was once approximately equal to one dollar per installed gallon of annual capacity. Thus, a 20-million-gallon-per-year plant cost approximately $20 million to purchase and install. However, the cost of installing biodiesel plants is dropping. Some biodiesel plant manufacturers are now claiming costs as low as $0.65 per installed gallon of capacity. The cost also declines as plant size increases. Thus, the cost difference between a 10-million-gallon-per-year plant and a 20-million-gallon-per-year plant is greater than the cost difference between a 20-million-gallon-per-year plant and a 30-million-gallon-pe-year plant. Due to advances in technology, innovation, and competition, the cost of biodiesel plants will likely decline even further over time. As with any technology-driven product, next year's model will be cheaper, smaller, faster, quieter, and more efficient.

How Big Should a Biodiesel Plant Be?

As it relates to biodiesel plants, size is everything. Lest the word "size" be confused with "big," a cursory look at the biodiesel business brings to light one of the most important truths – the size and shape of the market of people who buy biodiesel in a given region defines the parameters of the biodiesel plant. By looking first at the market, planners can get a very clear idea of the type, size, and location of the biodiesel plant that the available market can sustain.

Views on the appropriate size for a biodiesel plant vary, but only within the context of the target market. Gebolys says that small-scale biodiesel facilities and overly large facilities don't make economic sense. He explains that it is challenging for small-scale facilities to generate enough capital to ensure that each batch of fuel is quality tested. Enormous plants, he says, have a completely different problem. Since large plants have to operate at full capacity all the time, they often create a situation where supply pushes demand instead of the other way around. The result is higher operating costs. Gebolys says he believes the appropriate size for biodiesel plants today should range between 12 and 25 million gallons per year. Gebolys's opinion is close to that of a number of businesspeople and market analysts, many of whom see the "magic number" for a biodiesel plant as between 10 and 30 million gallons per year.[13]

Gebolys and his company work on a large playing field relative to a number of smaller biodiesel producers, who each sell between one and five million gallons. Such a producer is Kelly King, who, along with her husband Bob King, has gained a unique perspective on biodiesel plant size after operating a biodiesel plant on an island for almost a decade.

King believes that small plants can play an important role in the biodiesel marketplace. According to her, small-scale biodiesel plants of between one and three million gallons per year make sense in regional markets because most people who build biodiesel plants aren't in the fuels business. Learning how to operate a five-million-gallon facility or more requires intimate knowledge of your feedstock and fuel market. Small plants, on the other hand, can be operated by one person without a lot of infrastructure and paperwork. "You can take your community's resources, process those resources into energy for your community, and put the energy and the money back into the community," says King. "Your whole energy economy is right there."[14]

On the other side of the plant size spectrum from Gebolys is former Silicon Valley chip executive Rudi Wiedemann. The inventor of proprietary hardware for companies such as Silicon Graphics, Wiedemann now runs Biodiesel Solutions, a company that manufactures small-scale biodiesel-making equipment. Wiedemann feels the future of the biodiesel plant may be in something that looks more like an industrial refrigerator. While he recognizes the limitations for such a device in a 60-billion-gallon-per-year diesel fuel marketplace, Wiedemann sees the ½-to 1-million-gallon-per-year unit as viable for communities with access to large quantities of vegetable oil. For instance, says Wiedemann, "If you have a cooperative-owned seed crushing facility or a small rendering facility, why not have a unit that makes ASTM specification-grade biodiesel as an accessory to your operation?" The key, says Wiedemann, is not the technology but rather the availability of feedstock. Wiedemann also sees such a unit as being perfect for overseas markets where labor and feedstocks are inexpensive but large-scale technology is difficult to install.[15]

Since the basic formula for manufacturing biodiesel is relatively simple, biodiesel can be made on a small scale. But Steve Howell and Alan Weber of Marc IV Consulting, who ran the numbers on small-scale operations, concluded that in most circumstances, smaller biodiesel operations are not competitive with larger operations. "Think of it like beer brewing," says Howell. "A lot of people make beer in their basements. It's a hobby and it's fun for enthusiasts, but don't expect to save a lot of money, especially if you value your time."[16]

Howell and Weber caution that like beer, it's one thing to manufacture biodiesel and another thing to sell it. To sell biodiesel in the United States, an operation must undergo all of the proper quality testing, permitting, and quality assurance programs, as well as charge and pay sales tax, regardless of size. This laundry list of requirements adds to the cost of production and increases the competitive disparity between large and small plants. Judging from the biodiesel enthusiasts who congregate on the Internet, Weber is correct: small scale biodiesel "brewing" is a hobby rather than a profitable enterprise. Nevertheless, to handle the needs of small-scale biodiesel producers, the National Biodiesel Board created a small-scale manufacturers membership.

The Future of the "Biz"

When the first biodiesel plants came online in the early 1990s, demand was miniscule. The first nationwide surveys revealed estimates that biodiesel production had reached approximately 500,000 gallons by 1999. According to the National Biodiesel Board, production of biodiesel grew fiftyfold in five years–to 25 million gallons in 2004.[17] Some estimates put biodiesel's potential production at almost one billion gallons by the end of the decade–an astonishing increase. But can the biodiesel business continue to grow at such a rapid rate?

Most of the big players in the biodiesel market agree that low blends of biodiesel such as B2 and B5 show the highest growth potential. These low blends offer several advantages. First, low blends can be seamlessly integrated into the large-scale fuel industry infrastructure. Almost no new technology need be added. In fact, biodiesel is the only alternative fuel that can be seamlessly injected at low blends into fuel pipelines. This is common in Europe, where over a million tons of biodiesel are annually blended into diesel fuel and transported via pipeline. Second, low blends have been widely tested and are now endorsed by engine and vehicle manufacturers such as DaimlerChrysler, John Deere, and Cummins. Third, low blends of biodiesel offer the increased lubricity needed by engine manufacturers and by the fuels industry. Fourth, the physical growth potential of the biodiesel industry matches the market potential for lower blends.

The biodiesel industry is not poised to produce 100% of America's liquid diesel fuel, but it could easily supply 2%-10% in the near future. By supplying low blends of biodiesel, the industry will provide powerful payback to the U.S. economy. According to the economic research firm AUS Consultants, the growth in biodiesel sales will spur the biodiesel industry to:

- Invest approximately $345 million in structures, machinery, and equipment needed to build its facilities;
- Add $7.8 billion to the United States economy;
- Create 52,400 new jobs by 2010;
- Increase real household income (the actual income earned by Americans) by $3.9 billion by 2010.[18]

Senator Chuck Grassley (R, Iowa) points out another hard-to-calculate cost benefit to the social investment into biodiesel: more jobs and lower imports of foreign oil. "The tax credits for biodiesel and other renewable fuels included in the [Jobs Creation Act of 2004] will allow us to begin looking to farmers, rather than the Middle East, to fuel our future," says Grassley.[19]

Biodiesel will soon reach a "tipping point" where public aware-ness of the fuel furthers even greater public awareness, creating an atmosphere of understanding about biodiesel. As public pressure for domestic, renewable sources of energy increases, the fuel industry will comply with increases in training, awareness, demand, and most importantly, sales. Within the next ten years, the biodiesel industry will likely grow tenfold, bringing billions of dollars–dollars that are currently flowing overseas–back to the American economy. Biodiesel will grow into an economic engine that harvests both money and fuel well into the future.

CHAPTER 10

The Road Ahead

"Quod Severis Metes" – *"As ye sew so shall ye reap"*

Galatians 6:7

I
n October 2004, oil hit an all-time record high price of $55 a barrel.[1] That same month was problematic for the oil industry in Iraq. There were ten attacks on Iraqi oil pipelines and one attack on an oil executive. These marked the 129th through 138th attacks since June 2003, when strikes on Iraqi oil infrastructure began to intensify. Among the October attacks was the assassination of the Northern Oil Company oil product department director, Sana Toma Sulaiman, who had been riding in a taxi on his way to work.[2] Despite the success of Operation Iraqi Freedom, the U.S. was (and still is) having difficulty keeping things in the small desert nation under control.

A House of Cards

Things looked bad at the end of 2004 for the oil-producing nation of Iraq, and the number one producer of oil, Saudi Arabia, was not faring much better. While Saudi Arabia has been tightly closed to western media since the early part of this century, the establishment of the Arab-run al-Jazeera television news network in 1996 ushered in a brash new breed of Arab journalism. After it was discovered that fifteen of the September 11th terrorists were from Saudi Arabia, the international media joined in what quickly became a field day, prying open the oil-producing nation's lid of secrecy. What they found was unnerving.

As questions about Saudi Arabia's connections to the al-Qaeda terrorists arose, journalists began to take a fresh look at the Saudi government. The House of Saud, which established itself as the ruling family of what became known as Saudi Arabia in 1932, owns about 25% of the world's oil and has 30,000 members. The family is particularly polygamous. Thus, it is not uncommon for a Saudi prince to father from 40 to 70 children during his lifetime. The result is an exponential growth of the Saud family, a growth that could place its membership at 60,000 people within the next decade. The country as a whole is also expanding at an alarming rate, with 37 births for every 1,000 citizens in 2002. The Royal Saudi baby boom has created a top-heavy ruling class and put downward economic pressure on an increasingly large Saudi society.[3]

The result has been nothing short of economic cannibalization of the middle class by the elite. While princes receive monthly stipends of between $800 and $270,000, the average Saudi citizen's per capita income has plummeted from $28,600 in 1981 to $6,800 in 2001–a trend that continues today. Meanwhile, the country owes approximately $164 billion, right on par with the Saudi GNP.[4] These financial follies have drained the country of the $120 billion cash assets it enjoyed in the 1980s, leaving the Saudi treasury holding only about $20 billion today.[5]

The rapid disintegration of the middle class has also helped drive the popularity of the particularly fundamentalist Islamist, Saudi-based sect called al-Qaeda. A recent report commissioned by the UN Secretary Council indicated that Saudi Arabia has transferred $500 million to al-Qaeda over the past decade.[6]

It appears that Osama bin Laden is not wasting any time putting his Saudi money to use. Starting in 2003 al-Qaeda terrorists began a series of targeted attacks on Saudi government buildings. Included in the attacks was the U.S. consulate compound in the Red Sea city of Jeddah, where five people were killed. Even before the attacks began, the U.S. government had commissioned the Defense Policy Board to provide a briefing and recommendations on dealing with Saudi Arabia.[7] The private group–whose members include former Vice President Dan Quayle, former Secretary of State Henry Kissinger, former Defense Secretaries James Schlesinger and Harold Brown, former House speakers Newt Gingrich and Thomas Foley, and several retired senior military officers–was taken aback by one assessment of the Saudi situation. In an August 2002 briefing to the Defense Policy Board, Rand Coporation's International Analyst Laurent Murawiec stated: "The Saudis are active at every level of the terror chain, from planners to financiers, from cadre to foot-soldier, from ideologist to cheerleader…Saudi Arabia supports our enemies and attacks our allies…"[8]

While the political future of a nation as awash in oil and arms as Saudi Arabia is difficult to predict, CIA veteran, recipient of the Career Intelligence Medal, and author Robert Baer says: "…sometime soon, one way or another, the House of Saud is coming down."[9] With an unemployment rate of up to 25%, internal religious unrest, a king in his seventies, and his nearest successors biting at his heels, Saudi Arabia is looking less like the world's friendly Arab oil merchant and more like a ticking time bomb.[10]

So why should we care about the problems of Saudi Arabia–or even those of Iraq for that matter? In an open letter to the American people, Robert C. McFarlane, former National Security Advisor, and R. James Woolsey, co-chairman on the Committee on Present Danger, state: "...it is dangerous to be buying billions of dollars worth of oil from nations that are sponsors of or allied with radical Islamists who foment hatred against the United States. The petro-dollars we provide such nations contribute materially to the terrorist threats we face."[11] In summary, America is feeding its enemies cash and they are, in turn, feeding us oil.

Iraq and Saudi Arabia combined represent the largest single geographical source of oil on the planet. Every aspect of our daily lives relies on the predictability of the flow of oil from under their sands. Their oil is the key to the world economy. However, the very societies that control the world's oil are disintegrating. The destabi-lization of the Middle East undermines our national security almost as much as our national attitude that the oil inside the Ghawar field and its nearby oil fields is limitless–despite evidence to the contrary. While oil from this region of the world will never completely "run out," at some point in the near future the flow of Saudi and Middle East oil will become unpredictable and will, in turn, affect America in unpredictable ways. That is unless, of course, we begin a rapid national shift toward adopting domestic energy sources.

Support for Change

Although information on the happenings inside Saudi Arabia is still relatively absent from daily U.S. media, post-September 11th public opinion of the desert nation reflects a growing distrust. In a 2004 survey of 800 likely voters, the Hudson Institute and the Luntz

Research Company found the following:

- By an almost 3 to 1 margin, Americans prioritize "reducing
  our reliance on foreign oil" over "cheaper prices for oil
  and gas"
- 91% of Americans agreed (74% strongly agree) that "when
  it comes to energy, we need an America that relies on its
  own ingenuity and innovation – not the Saudi royal
  family"
- 83% of Americans agree that "reducing our dependence on
  foreign oil must be a top priority for the next
  administration"
- 50% of Americans–when told that Saudi Arabia is the #1
  holder of oil reserves among OPEC nations–support
  pursuing new sources of energy right here in America.
  That's more than an 8 to 1 margin over the 6% who would
  favor pursuing a closer relationship with the Saudis.[12]

According to Dr. Mey Wurmser, director of the Center for
Middle East Policy at Hudson Institute: "Americans want American
energy. They refuse to accept our reliance on foreign sources of oil,
especially when that oil is coming primarily from hostile countries
in the Middle East."[13] Public opinion is solidly in favor of reducing
dependence on Middle Eastern sources of oil, and strongly in favor
of developing domestic, American-made energy sources. Americans
are willing to put their money where their mouths are to support
domestic energy and break the shackles of Middle East oil dependence. But are the attitudes in Washington consistent with national
opinion?

A New Look at National Energy Security

The clear and present danger associated with our dependence
on Middle Eastern oil has not gone unnoticed on Capitol Hill. As
President George H.W. Bush's 1991 energy plan explained:

> Popular opinion aside, our vulnerability to price shocks is
> not determined by how much oil we import. Our vulnerabil-
> ity to oil price shocks is more directly linked to: (1) how oil
> dependent our economy is; (2) our capacity for switching to
> alternative fuels; (3) reserve oil stocks around the world; and
> (4) the spare worldwide oil production capacity that can be
> quickly brought on line.[14]

In other words, it is not just our dependence on foreign oil, but
our dependence on oil *itself,* that puts the United States in a vulnerable position. This is due largely to the fact that oil is an international
commodity, and a price shock crosses all borders, regardless of the
source of the oil. Secondly, while our potential for switching to alternative fuels may be vast, our ability to make that switch in a timely
manner is questionable at best. Lastly, looking at reserve capacity
gives us little confidence in our potential to reduce our vulnerability
to oil shocks.

As in the 1970s, it is clear that the political leaders in America
at least recognize the problem. In fact, that recognition has grown
with time. As power has moved from President H.W. Bush to his
son, policy language has reflected an increased awareness of the
vulnerability of the United States in regard to oil and, consequently,
the need for alternative fuels development. And as President George
W. Bush's energy plan stated ten years later:

> We should not...look at energy security in isolation from the

rest of the world. In a global energy marketplace, U.S. energy and economic security are directly linked not only to our domestic and international energy supplies but to those of our trading partners as well. A significant disruption in world oil supplies could adversely affect our economy and our ability to promote key foreign and economic policy objectives, regardless of the level of U.S. dependence on oil imports. The first step toward a sound international energy policy is to use our own capability to produce, process, and transport the energy resources we need in an efficient and environmentally sustainable manner. Market solutions to limit the growth in our oil imports would reduce oil consumption for our economy and increase our economic flexibility in responding to any...disruption....[15]

These words constitute a call to action for the American people. But while the problem of our oil dependence is increasingly obvious, the solution–creating our own fuel in an "efficient and environmentally sustainable manner"–has been left to market economics and limited government intervention. Hence, not even the government has a cohesive strategy for how to get America out of its oily predicament.

America is poised for growth in at least one form of alternative energy called biodiesel. But the challenges that confront biodiesel, or any other form of renewable energy, are characterized by a lack of national action. The technology for such fuels exists; public opinion, at least on paper, supports implementing that technology. It is widely accepted that the safety of our nation, our communities, and our homes all hinge on our national ability to implement renewable energy technology as soon as possible. Despite all of this, America appears to lack the impetus to shift into overdrive and head toward energy independence.

A Plan for the Nation

"Energy independence" has become a political buzz phrase in Washington, D.C. and across the nation. Sales of hybrid vehicles have increased to such a degree that Toyota, Lexus, Ford, and Honda will all soon release their next generation of fuel-conserving hybrids. Despite the excitement around energy independence, America has yet to put into action a complete plan for changing its national petroleum diet to one of homegrown energy.

In his recent book, *Winning the Oil Endgame*, physicist Amory Lovins outlines a plan for the future of American energy. Lovins's 32-year career as an energy expert has taken him from advising BP and other oil companies to consulting with heads of state such as the Australian, German, and Dutch governments to giving expert testimony for the U.S. Congress, Energy, and Defense departments. In his book, Lovins states that no new set of economic principles or technologies need be developed for America to break its oil habit. Instead, the transition to an oil-free society can come through the rigorous application of orthodox market economics. Lovins explains that since the alternatives to oil are generally cheaper when all costs and externalities are factored in, they can be implemented into the marketplace rapidly.

"The services Americans get from oil could be more cheaply provided," says Lovins, "by wringing more work from the oil we use and substituting non-oil sources for the rest."[16] While he states that the transition should be guided more by profit than regulation, Lovins maintains that government intervention will be essential to jump-start the move toward energy efficiency and energy alternatives.

In his book, which he refers to as a "coherent strategy for ending oil dependence," Lovins and his team of experts outline four primary ways to displace oil and revitalize the American economy:

- Using oil more efficiently, through smarter technologies that bring more (and often better) services from less oil;
- Substituting liquids made from biomass or wastes for petroleum fuels;
- Substituting natural gas for oil in situations where they're interchangeable, such as in furnaces and boilers. (Note that gas and oil, though sometimes found and thought of together, are utterly different in geology, economics, industry, and culture);
- Replacing oil with hydrogen made from non-oil resources.[17]

Using these methods, Lovins outlines with stunning clarity a plan to move America completely away from oil in two decades.

While this may sound like a dream, the plan is based primarily on creating economic incentives to motivate both manufacturers of vehicles and consumers to build and buy efficient modes of transportation. For Detroit, these incentives would offset the cost for automakers to retool manufacturing plants to build more efficient cars as well as *multifuel* cars that can run on a variety of fuels.[18] For the consumer, the incentives would come in the form of rebates from the government for the purchase of hybrid cars, multifuel cars, and cars that are substantially more fuel efficient.

In a tax-the-rich scheme, the converse would also be true. Instead of the government providing tax breaks for the purchase of large luxury vehicles like civilian Hummers, which are rarely used for business and have instead become status symbols, "large vehicle taxes" would be levied against both the manufacturer and the purchaser of light-duty vehicles that are inefficient or grossly overweight. (Note the "light-duty" distinction; Lovins is not proposing that tax be levied on heavy-duty vehicles such as trucks or buses.) The tax money gained from such levies could be easily appropriated to rebates and incentives providing a means to completely refocus the automobile industry.

The problem with moving America toward energy independence is not technological or public or even political; rather, it is social. We must create the social infrastructure, or the legislation, needed to refocus both industry and markets toward new, better, faster, more efficient, and in the long run, cheaper technology, so America can rapidly embrace a new energy diet. In fact, we have already proven the ability of bipartisan-led government focused legislation to do this.

In 1975 Congress enacted the Corporate Average Fuel Economy (CAFE) standards. The standards were not controversial; they simply set minimum fuel efficiency and emissions standards for light-duty vehicles in the United States. When the CAFE standards were first enacted, there was no such thing as a commercially manufactured catalytic converter (an emissions reduction device now standard on all gasoline cars), and there were very few small, efficient cars. But in the eight years that followed the passage of the standards, U.S. oil use dropped 7% and oil imports dropped by 23%, while GDP grew by 37%. In short, the standards were a success.[19]

Since 1975 CAFE standards have been relaxed, fuel efficiency has dropped, and our nation has become the world's largest oil importer as opposed to the largest oil exporter we once were. This scenario is unacceptable. There is no reason America cannot move away from all foreign sources of fuel and energy. Fuels like biodiesel are here now, and they work. To ensure that every American is supportive of such fuels costs nothing–public opinion is already in favor of domestic energy. The switch to renewable energy also costs nothing. On the contrary, it will revitalize the agricultural, automotive, and energy industries, putting billions of dollars that are currently flowing overseas back into the pockets of Americans. The technology for energy independence exists today. The real question is, are we prepared to embrace it?

Industrial Evolution

Biodiesel does not herald an evolution in technology, but rather an evolution in thinking. Biodiesel is joined by a host of other fuels, energy carriers, and technologies that portend a renewed technological universe. These fuels include ethanol, hydrogen, and other fuels synthesized from natural, renewable components. The energy technologies that accompany biodiesel into the future will be a mix of solar, wind, super-efficient automobiles, rail systems, airplanes, and ships, and even ultra-efficient light bulbs.

At the turn of the last century, the Industrial Revolution took flight. The power with which it transformed society was possible through the foundation of thinking laid by economists and philosophers. New ideas in centralized social design inspired centralized designs in engineering. The car, the assembly line, and the factory were products of this revolution in thought.

As technology affected the world and nations advanced, the standard of living in the West rose rapidly. A new world, based on new social values, emerged. In no country was this new society more evident than in the United States. Like a butterfly emerging from a cocoon, the United States shed the skin of the old world. America embodied the opposite of the past–the opposite of the oppression of the masses, the opposite of slavery, the opposite of poverty. As a society, it was shiny, powerful, and new. America stormed forth onto the world playing field like a giant teenager, muscles bulging from its huge frame. It fed itself on oil and the resulting growth spurt lasted one hundred and fifty years, producing a society that, in many respects, still leads the world.

Now, like a child who finds itself in an adult body, America is awakening to a new era not without challenge. Its roads and cities are built. Its commerce and agricultural systems are functioning. But lacking the basic necessity of life, it seeks a new form of nourishment. According to a growing body of research and evidence from the media, from those within the energy economy, and from the government itself, that new form of nourishment could be just around the corner.

In the February 2005 *Fortune Small Business* (FSB) cover story, "The New Color of Oil," the dollars-and-sense magazine reviews entrepreneurs who are leaders in the next generation of energy products. FSB looked at technologies ranging from a paper-thin "tape" that gathers solar energy to a biodiesel-like fuel made from leftover turkey parts. Its conclusion? "In every industry, from autos to aeronautics to infotech, breakthroughs come from entrepreneurs. (Think Henry Ford, the Wright brothers, and Steve Jobs.) . . . Advances in nanotechnology and electronic controls are driving down the costs of alternative energy even as prices of fossil fuels climb. . . In Silicon Valley, hydrogen, solar, and wind power are being talked about as if they were the next Internet."[20]

Lovins concurs with other researchers in his assessment of how new technology can affect America. His work is founded in study after study detailing the applied potential of American ingenuity. From tracking composite car plastics to new engines for the trucking industry, Lovins has his finger on the pulse of technological evolution. According to Lovins, we are a mere technological hop, skip, and jump away from a quantum leap in energy efficiency. He envisions the following:

Imagine a revitalized and globally competitive U.S. motor-vehicle industry delivering a new generation of highly efficient, safe, incredibly durable, fun-to-drive vehicles that consumers want. Imagine equally rugged and efficient heavy trucks that boost truckers' gross profits by $7.5 billion per year... Envision a secure national fuels infrastructure based largely or wholly on U.S. energy resources and on

vibrant rural communities farming biofuel, plastics, wind
and carbon. Think of over one million new, high-wage jobs
and the broad wealth creation from infusing the economy
with $133 billion per year of new disposable income from
lower crude-oil costs...Finally, envision one of the largest
and broadest-based tax cuts in U.S. history from eliminating
the implicit tax that oil dependence imposes on our country
by bleeding purchasing power, inflating military and subsidy
costs, and suppressing homegrown energy solutions. Sound
utopian? It is not.[21]

For Lovins, the goal is cost savings, and not just a few million
here and there. His plan would put $90 billion over the next two
decades into retooling the automotive, trucking, and airplane industries and another $90 billion into domestic energy infrastructure.
The return on the public's investment would be $130 billion in new
revenue added to the economy in 2025 and every year thereafter.
The cash return for this investment is incalculably high. The investment would also buy America something too valuable to put a price
tag on: independence.[22]

The real bang for this buck (the total of which equals roughly
two years of U.S. expenditures on foreign oil) would be an "oil-
free" future. A future that nobody, not even the oil companies that
stand to make billions in increased revenues from the sale of domestic energy products, can argue against.

The Silver Bullet

People often ask how much biodiesel can be produced or how
much it will cost to buy a gallon of the fuel. Like putting the cart
before the horse, these questions do not address the fundamental
issue facing America today. The burning question we face as a

nation of individuals comfortable in our lifestyles with relative lack of economic or social crisis is: Are we as Americans prepared for a national effort to steer the bow of our great country away from the iceberg toward which we are currently headed?

This fundamental question is, of course, loaded, but not in the way that most people think. When the words "energy efficiency" or "clean energy" or "alternative fuel" are spoken, they are often associated with the concept of sacrifice. Somewhere deep in the American psyche, solar panels mean living without showers; alternative fuel means cars that are unreliable; and a fuel-saving device is something that costs more, functions poorly, and looks funny. We as a nation have bought into the idea that clean and green isn't cool, and until recently it certainly wasn't something we wanted to park in our driveways or take our kids to school in.

Added to the perception that individual sacrifice must be made to lower our dependence on foreign oil is the concept that the nation as a whole would have to undergo some sort of painful and dubious transition to less-than-reliable sources of energy. Somehow, again, we've bought into the idea that fuel from corn and soybeans means that our cars won't go as fast or as far, that electricity from the sun means we won't have power at night, and that slowing trade with the Middle East will result in global instability. Empirical science, billions of dollars in tests, and real world application show that none of this holds true. Nevertheless, these beliefs undermine our nation's ability to move into position as a global energy leader.

The people within the biodiesel industry like to use a standard disclaimer when excitement is high around biodiesel. The disclaimer is quoted at so many press conferences and conventions that one wonders why it is not printed on the side of every tank of biodiesel sold. They say: "Biodiesel is not the 'silver bullet' solution to our national energy problems. Biodiesel is a good fuel, not a perfect fuel. Just like any other fuel, there are problems with biodiesel. And biodiesel is just one of a whole host of energy solutions that we need to embrace. Ultimately, we have to work together with every other form of energy and energy supplier to dig ourselves out of this mess." Truer and more heartfelt words are rarely spoken. Having spent almost a decade of my life researching alternative energies, I tend to agree: There is no "silver bullet" fuel.

A Wake-Up Call

At the turn of the last century, America had less than 160,000 miles of paved roads and only around 8,000 cars, which were considered for the most part to be rich men's toys. America had never manufactured a commercial plane, never mind a luxury jetliner; such things were not even yet conceptualized. America had not yet engaged in war overseas. America had not attempted brain surgery or heart-transplants. America had never traveled over 100 miles per hour. America had never been to space.

Only 50 years later, Americans had changed the face of their country and in so doing, changed the world. America created a canal to link the Atlantic and Pacific. America won two World Wars. America had even sent men to the moon. America had transmitted the first ever picture of the planet we call home. America had innovated, grown up, and become great.

And America had pulled itself up by its bootstraps. Ravaged by dust storms in the 1930s, American agriculture had suffered greatly. The nation had no time to recover from the Dustbowl as it slammed, face first, into what would become the Great Depression. Shortly thereafter, our nation found itself embroiled in the First and Second World Wars.

As men went off to war and women joined the workforce during the Second World War, America embarked on an era of fundamental social change. Americans plowed their backyards, vacant lots, parks, baseball fields, and schoolyards to plant gardens. All told 20 million

"victory gardens" were established, growing 40% of America's calories. Women turned in their nylons to make parachutes for soldiers
and collected rags to make tents and textiles. Automotive fuel, tires,
alcohol, and cigarettes were rationed. Americans sacrificed and did
without so that their troops could do with more.

What really happened to our parents and grandparents–the generation of people who lived through the times of war–is that they
became empowered. Individuals suddenly had the power to change
the course of a nation. By turning stockings into parachutes and
gardens into a national food supply, those on the home front "did
their part" to clear a path to victory. The work citizens did formed
a tangible connection to solving what, at many points, seemed like
an insurmountable problem. Both at home and abroad, Americans
empowered themselves to save their country and to save the world.

For the most part, the 1980s and 1990s were quiet decades in
America. The Vietnam War was over. The oil shocks were a distant
memory–a "hiccup" in the supply of oil. Detroit was making big,
fast, comfy cars, and we had plenty of oil. It was as if America had
settled down to take a nice cozy nap in a big easy chair. But the nap
didn't last long.

America's wake-up call came on the morning of September 11,
2001, when terrorists from the Middle East violated our nation. We
are still grappling with the implications of what happened that day.
Certainly, the shock and horror of those terrible moments will replay
themselves in our collective social conscience for the rest of our
lives. While America was sleeping, the Middle East was deteriorating. The result has been a catastrophic clash of cultures in which
the United States has realized that no amount of military force can
ensure that terrorists do not constrict the flow of oil. In essence, we
have disempowered ourselves.

Biodiesel, America!

If history is our greatest teacher, then the strength of our American forefathers is one of our greatest lessons. Neither Thomas Jefferson, who drafted the Declaration of Independence, nor Abraham Lincoln, who reunited a nation divided by civil war, would have allowed this nation to abrogate its power to a group of hostile desert states in return for a substance that can be grown on American soil. And for that matter, nor should we.

Our generation has already begun the shift toward lasting energy independence. In schools, in homes, on television, and on the Internet, energy and energy efficiency are becoming topics of discussion. Automotive companies are targeting the *LOHAS* (Lifestyles of Health and Sustainability) sector, a market for cars that are more efficient, more compact, and "greener." Hydrogen, hybrids, and healing the planet are acceptable cocktail party conversation. Liberals and conservatives are discussing energy policy every day. The need for domestic energy is becoming part of the social conscience. And social action is not far behind.

Consumers are voting with their dollars and so are investment firms. Across the nation, solar power facilities and wind turbines are popping up. Biodiesel plants are pumping out millions of gallons of farmed fuel. New biodiesel plants are under construction. Energy-efficient light bulbs are sold next to their less-efficient counterparts. Magazines at newsstands show homeowners how to install solar panels. These efforts may at first glance seem cursory, but they portend a change unlike anything that America has seen since the Industrial Revolution.

Biodiesel will play an important role in this new America, but it will also be accompanied by many other energy carriers and technologies. From silent monorails to cars that get over 100 miles per gallon, our transport infrastructure will take a quantum leap forward.

From solar roof shingles that make electricity meters spin backwards to wind turbines that pump out gigawatts of clean energy, renewable energy carriers like ethanol, hydrogen, solar, and wind will also become mainstream.

This special mix of enabling technologies and renewable energies will free the country from much of its foreign expenditures. As America transitions to renewable energies, scores of skilled labor jobs will be created in high technology research and development, science, agriculture, energy, and in supporting industries. Believe it or not, these jobs and the associated technologies are just around the corner.

America has not lost its ability to innovate. And Americans have not lost their ability to be great. There may be no silver bullet fuel or technology, but I believe there is one single solution to our entire energy crisis, our farming crisis, and the crisis in our confidence in America. That solution is the heart and soul of the American people. A people who, because of a willpower and belief born of a unique diversity, have exceeded their own expectations and risen to every challenge history has brought them.

As a nation, we will make a concerted effort to move forward. As the innovators we have always been, Americans will embrace the challenge ahead. We'll educate ourselves about energy. We'll educate our children. We'll talk about it at coffee shops, in hair salons, on construction sites, and in the office. We'll talk to our spouses, our families, our coworkers, and our policymakers. And we'll demand change from ourselves. We will do these things happily, knowing that, just as we've always done, Americans will rise to the challenge ahead. We'll become energy independent. The alternative is unthinkable.

I've taken you this far. The rest of the journey is up to you.

WHAT YOU CAN DO NOW

A One-Year Program to Increase Your Energy Security, Decrease Your Dependence on Middle East Oil, and Make Money

Most of us have time, each week, to do something that we know will help save us money and increase our energy security. By completing one item from this list each week, you can save hundreds to thousands of dollars a year, decrease your environmental "footprint" including the emissions for which you are responsible, and increase the energy security of your home, community, and country. Many of these items cost little or nothing and take only a few minutes. Your investment of time and money, however, will create measurable returns.

For an updated list as well as links to companies, organizations, and resources, see www.BiodieselAmerica.org. For biodiesel suppliers, research, and information see www.Biodiesel.org.

To Increase the Energy Security and the Use of Renewable Energy in Your City and State:

1) Send copies of this book to your friends, or donate copies to your local libraries or schools.
2) Send copies of this book to your state and federal representatives, as well as your mayor, local school bus fleet manager, and local bus fleet manager.

3) Write a review of this book and send it to your local paper and/or email it to your favorite website or chat group.
4) Speak with your Parent Teachers Association and mayor about getting biodiesel into your local school bus fleets.
5) Get biodiesel, solar, wind, and other renewable energy education into your local school curriculum.
6) Call your favorite TV talk show or radio show and tell them you'd like to see a program dedicated to biodiesel and other renewable energies.
7) Encourage truckers, bus drivers, and anyone who operates a diesel fleet to buy diesel fuel with biodiesel blended into it.
8) Investigate the platforms of people running for public office. Support candidates with strong policies in favor of increasing true renewable energy resources such as solar, wind, biodiesel, and ethanol.
9) Write to your senators and congress people and ask them their position on biodiesel and other alternative fuels.
   a. If they are already supporters of biodiesel, thank them and encourage them to continue.
   b. If they are not yet supporters, explain the benefits and encourage them to support biodiesel.
10) Support local and national bills and initiatives to increase the use of solar, wind, and biofuels, as well as bills that develop public transportation and bills that encourage or mandate energy efficiency in industrial and residential areas.
11) Research the companies in your stock portfolio. Do any of them promote the use of nonrenewable energies like coal and nuclear? Consider transferring your assets into stocks of companies working on renewable energies like solar, wind and biodiesel.

12) Donate to a nonprofit organization that promotes the use of renewable energies, public transportation, and energy efficiency.

13) Host a renewable energy, energy efficiency, and energy security night at your home or community center each month. Bring in books, magazines, and articles from the internet for your community and friends.

To Save Money and Decrease the Fuel Use of Your Car:

14) Ensure your tires are fully inflated. Properly inflated tires increase the miles per gallon of your vehicle and decrease the vehicle's emissions.

15) Remove excess weight and bulk from your car. Items such as snow chains can decrease your car's fuel efficiency.

16) Keep your car properly tuned up. Simple things like making sure your car's air filter is clean can save up to 10% of the fuel you use each year.

17) Avoid letting your car idle. Idling for more than 10 seconds uses more fuel that shutting off the engine and turning it back on.

18) Fill your tank after the sun goes down or before it comes up. Gasoline is more dense (meaning you get more for you buck) and emits less fumes when it is dark and cold outside.

19) When filling up, avoid "topping off," as this causes fuel to spill and evaporate.

20) Avoid buying gasoline with MTBE when possible.

21) Buy gasoline with ethanol blended into it when possible.

22) Buy diesel fuel with biodiesel blended into it when possible.

23) The next time you buy a car, consider buying a turbo diesel car and using biodiesel.
24) Consider trading in your SUV for a more efficient car or a hybrid car. The recent trend in increased SUV sales has increased America's fuel use by 15%.
25) If you only need a car for short trips, consider buying or leasing an electric vehicle (EV).
26) Investigate getting "Transit Checks" from your work. Some companies now offer money back for employees who walk, ride a bike, carpool or use public transport.
27) Take old motor oil to an engine oil recycling facility.
28) Car pool. Look up the Ride Finders Network in your local phone book or on the Internet. This can save you hundreds of dollars in fuel, insurance, tolls, and parking fees each year
29) WALK. BIKE. RUN. ROLLERBLADE. Every day, Americans take 123 million car trips for which they could walk.

To Save Money and Increase the Energy Efficiency and Energy Security of Your Home:

30) Call your local utility company and ask for an "energy audit" for your home to find out which of your appliances are using more electricity than they should, as well as other ways you can save electricity and money.
31) Replace your most used light bulbs with compact fluorescent bulbs. This can save you up to $30 per year.
32) Use motion sensors to activate exterior lights.
33) Buy things online rather than going shopping. eCommerce uses 1/16 of the energy of shopping.
34) Get off bulk mailing lists. Bulk mail increases the weight of mail and the fuel used by the United States Postal Service.

35) Work from home. Telecommuting saves fuel and energy.

36) Buy food made and grown locally, or better yet, plant a vegetable garden. The average American plate of food has traveled 12,000 miles and taken more calories of diesel fuel to produce than it contains.

37) Adjust the doors of your fridge so that a dollar squeaks when you pass it through.

38) Caulk or install weatherstripping around doors and windows to plug air leaks. This measure alone can save you $35 a year.

39) Replace your shower heads with low-flow shower heads. These use less hot water and save energy.

40) Wash your clothes in cold or warm water. Avoid using the hot setting on your washing machine.

41) In the spring, summer, and fall, consider air-drying your clothes. This can save you up to $45 a year and your clothes will smell and feel cleaner.

42) Clean or replace your air conditioner filter as recommended. Cleaning a dirty filter can save 5% of the energy used by an air conditioner.

43) Run your dishwasher only when it is full. Use the energy saving setting (if available) to dry dishes. Avoid using heat to dry dishes.

44) Turn down the thermostat on your water heater. Most water heaters are set 20-30% too high. 120 degrees is usually hot enough.

45) If your water heater is 5 years old or older, wrap it in an insulating jacket. These are available at your local hardware store.

46) When you purchase an appliance, pay close attention to its EnergyStar rating. Purchasing more efficient appliances saves energy and money.

47) Get solar PV panels to make electricity for your home. Investigate state and federal tax incentives for purchasing a grid "intertie" system. You can make your meter spin backwards!

48) Install a solar hot water heating system. Most new solar water heating systems have a 3-5 year payback period, after which you can enjoy hot water for free.

49) Investigate the potential of buying "green" electricity from your electricity company to support the use of renewable energy.

50) Plant trees in your garden or neighborhood. Each tree decreases the carbon dioxide in the atmosphere by 13 pounds per year.

51) Recycle all plastics (they are made from oil) including cell phones, ink cartridges, and plastic bottles.

52) Get up-to-date and educated on issues surrounding renewable energy and energy security. This book contains an extensive bibliography of other books and articles to read. Search your local newspaper for articles on petroleum and energy issues. There are also magazines about renewable energy, as well as thousands of web sites, blogs, and chat groups.

BIBLIOGRAPHY

Ackman, Dan. Oil Hits $55 Alarm; Greenspan Hits Snooze. *Forbes Magazine,* October 18, 2004. http://www.forbes.com/energy/2004/10/18/cx_da1018topnews.html

Ahya, Chetan, and Andy Xie. New Tigers of Asia. Morgan Stanley, July 26, 2004. http://www.ibef.org/attachdisplay.aspx?cat_id=135&art _id=3150

Alternative Fuel Vehicle Program. *Report on Biodiesel.* Cambridge: Harvard University, August 13, 2001. http://www.biofuels.coop/archive/harvard_biodiesel.pdf

American Soybean Association. *Soy Stats: U.S. Biodiesel Consumption.* American Soybean Association, 2004. http://www.soystats.com/2004/Default-frames.htm

——. *Soy Stats 2004.* American Soybean Association, 2004. http://www.soystats.com

Appenzeller, Tim. The End of Cheap Oil. *National Geographic,* June 2004.

Audi Company Press Center. Audi A2 1.2 TDI: The Three-Liter Car from Audi. *Audi World,* November 28, 1999. http://www.audiworld.com/news/99/a2_2/content.shtml

——. EU IV Diesel Range: Less Taxing… More Rewarding. *Audi United Kingdom,* http://www.audi.co.uk/acs/ownershipbenefits/details. jsp?id=11615 (accessed May 11, 2005).

——. A World First: The A2. *Audi United Kingdom,* October 24, 1999. http://www.audi.co.uk/company/pressrelease.jsp?id=552& backPage=presscentre

Baard, Erik. Choo-Choo Trains on Energy Crunch. *Wired News,* July 3, 2002. http://www.wired.com/news/technology/0,1282,53591,00.html

Baer, Robert. The Fall of the House of Saud. *Atlantic Monthly,* May 2003.

BBC News, "Green Light for BP-Arco Merger," April 14, 2000.

http://news.bbc.co.uk/1/hi/business/712962.stm

Beckjord, Eric S., executive director. *The Future of Nuclear Power.*
Cambridge, MA: Massachusetts Institute of Technology, 2003.
http://web.mit.edu/nuclearpower/

Bell, Peter. Will the Oil Companies Resist Biodiesel? *Distribution Drive,*
2002. http://www.distributiondrive.com/Article12.html

Blume, David. *Alcohol Can Be a Gas!* Gabriola Island, British Columbia:
New Society Publishers, 2006.

——. *Alcohol Can Be A Gas!* International Institute for Ecological
Agriculture, 2006. http://www.permaculture.com/alcohol/book/intro.
shtml

BP News, "Solar Energy Helps BP Meet 10% Savings Target," August 1,
2001.
http://www.bp.co.nz/bin/press/item.pl?id=996627341&showarchive=yes

Brandt, Karl. *Whale Oil an Economic Analysis.* Stanford: Food Research
Institute Stanford University, 1940.

Briggs, Michael. Widescale Biodiesel Production from Algae. University
of New Hampshire Biodiesel Group, August 2004.
http://www.unh.edu/p2/biodiesel/article_alge.html

British Petroleum. *BP Sustainability Report 2003.* http://www.bp.com/
liveassets/bp_internet/globalbp/STAGING/global_assets/downloads/B/
BP_Sustainability
_Report_2003.pdf

Bush, George W. *Executive Order no. 13,149 — Greening the Government
through Federal Fleet and Transportation Efficiency.* Presidential
Documents, April 21, 2000.
http://ceq.eh.doe.gov/nepa/regs/eos/eo13149.html

Callanan, Bob. President Bush: 'I Believe in Biodiesel.' National
Biodiesel Board Press Release, September 7, 2004. http://www.biodiesel.
org/resources/pressreleases/gen/20040907_Bush_believe.pdf

Campbell, Colin J. *The Coming Oil Crisis.* Brentwood, England: Multi-
Science Publishing Company & Petroconsultants, 1997.

——. "Peak Oil: A Turning Point for Mankind." Technical University of
Clausthal, Clausthal-Zellerfeld, Germany, December 2000.

http://www.geologie.tu-clausthal.de/Campbell/lecture.html

Campbell, Colin J., and Jean H. Laherrère. The End of Cheap Oil.
Scientific American, March 1998.

Canadian Driver, "Mercedes-Benz Shows Hybrid Diesel Version of S-Class Sedan," January 9, 2005.
http://www.canadiandriver.com/news/05detroit/s-class-h.htm

Caparella, Tina. Washington Gets Biodiesel Friendly. *Render Magazine*,
June 2003. www.rendermagazine.com/June2003/BiodieselBulletin.html

Carter, Jimmy. "The Crisis of Confidence." July 15, 1979.
http://usa.usembassy.de/etexts/speeches/rhetoric/jccrisis.htm

——. "State of the Union Address 1981." Jimmy Carter Library and
Museum. http://www.jimmycarterlibrary.org/documents/speeches/
su81jec.phtml

*Center for Biological Diversity, Bluewater Network, and Sierra Club v.
Spencer Abraham, et al.*, U.S. Dist. Ct. M.D. Cal., 218 F. Supp.2d 1143
(July 26, 2002).

Intelligence Agency. *The World Factbook*. Washington D.C.: Central
Intelligence Agency, 2005.

Chalkley, A.P. *Diesel Engines for Land and Marine Work*. Introduction
by Rudolf Diesel. London: Constable & Company, 1922.

Chambers, Matt. Uranium Prices are Set to Climb. *International Herald
Tribune Online,* January 5, 2005. http://www.iht.com/bin/print_ipub
.php?file=/articles/2005/01/04/bloomberg/sxnuke.html

Champion, Daryl. The Kingdom of Saudi Arabia: Elements of Instability
within Stability. *Middle East Review of International Affairs*, December
1999.
http://meria.idc.ac.il/journal/1999/issue4/jv3n4a4.html

Clinton, William J. *Executive Order 13101—Greening the Government
Through Waste Prevention, Recycling, and Federal Acquisition.*
Presidential Documents, September 16, 1998.
http://www.epa.gov/EPA-WASTE/1998/September/Day-16/f25023.htm

Conrad, Dennis. Measure Could Give Ethanol Preference in Federal

Purchasing Practices. *AP News Wire Report*, November 23, 2001.

Conte, Christopher. *An Outline of the U.S. Economy*. Washington, D.C.: U.S. Department of State, February 2001. http://usinfo.state.gov/products/pubs/oecon/chap8.htm

Cran, William. *The Prize: The Epic Quest for Oil, Money and Power.* VHS. Chicago: Public Media Video, 1993.

Creswell, Julie. Oil Without End. *Fortune Magazine,* February 17, 2003.

Curry, Matt. Willie Nelson's New Gig: Biodiesel. *The Associated Press,* January 14, 2005. http://msnbc.msn.com/id/6826994/

Daimler Chrysler AG. DaimlerChrysler's Mercedes S-Class Most Powerful 'Hybrid' Yet. Daimler Chrysler AG, January 10, 2005. http://www.advancedautobat.com/market.html

——. Diesel Engine Combined with Electric Engine: Mercedes-Benz Sprinter Now Available with Hybrid Drive. Daimler Chrysler AG, July 30, 2004. http://www.daimlerchrysler.com/dccom/0,,0-5-7165-1-428612 -1-0-0-0-0-0-1371-7165-0-0-0-0-0-0-0,00.html

——. MB Unveils New Interpretation of the Vision Grand Sports Tourer. Daimler Chrysler AG, December 18, 2003. http://www.germancarfans .com/news.cfm/newsid/2031218.002/page/1/lang/eng/mercedes/1.html

——. Mercedes-Benz GST: Series Production in Tuscaloosa. Daimler Chrysler AG, August 27, 2002. http://www.germancarfans.com/news .cfm/NewsID/2020827.001/mercedes/1.html

Darley, Julian. *High Noon for Natural Gas*. White River Junction, VT: Chelsea Green, 2004.

Davis, Lance. *In Pursuit of Leviathan: Technology, Institutions, Productivity, and Profits in American Whaling*. Chicago: University of Chicago Press, 1997.

Department of Aviation Sciences, Baylor University. *Development of a Bio-Based Fuel for Turbine Engines*. Waco, Texas: Baylor University, October 1998. http://www.biodiesel.org/resources/reportsdatabase/ reports/gen/19981001_gen-106.pdf

Diesel Technology Forum. *In Wake of High Gas Prices, News Reports*

Indicate Growing Market for Diesel Vehicles. Diesel Technology Forum,
2005. http://www.dieselforum.org/news/mar_30_2005.html
——. *Diesel-Electric Hybrid Vehicles*. Diesel Technology Forum. http://
www.dieselforum.org/whitepaper/downloads/diesel-electric.pdf

Duke, James A. *Handbook of Energy Crops*. Purdue University Center
for New Crops & Plant Products, 2003. http://www.hort.purdue.edu/
newcrop

Dumaine, Brian. The New Color of Oil. *Fortune Small Business*,
February 2005.

Economic Research Service. *Farm Income and Costs*. U.S. Department
of Agriculture, October 28, 2003.
http://www.ers.usda.gov/briefing/farmincome/Glossary/def_debt.htm

Energy Information Administration. *Annual Energy Review 2003*.
Washington D.C.: U.S Department of Energy, September 2003.
http://www.eia.doe.gov/emeu/aer/pdf/pages/sec3_11.pdf

——. *Annual Energy Outlook 2004*. Washington D.C.: U.S. Department of
Energy, January 2004.

——. *Residential Energy Consumption Survey 2001: Consumption and
Expenditure Data Tables*. Washington, D.C.: U.S. Department of Energy,
2001. http://www.eia.doe.gov/emeu/recs/recs2001/ce_pdf/enduse/
ce1-4c_housingunits2001.pdf

——. *1999 Commercial Buildings Energy Consumption Survey:
Consumption and Expenditures Tables*. Washington, D.C.: U.S.
Department of Energy, 1999.
http://www.eia.doe.gov/emeu/cbecs/pdf/allce.pdf

——. *Voluntary Reporting of Greenhouse Gases
Program: Fuels and Energy Source Codes and Emissions Coefficients*.
Washington, D.C.: U.S. Department of Energy, 2003.
http://www.eia.doe.gov/oiaf/1605/coefficients.html

——. *Fuel Oil and Kerosene Sales 2003*. Washington, D.C.: U.S.
Department of Energy, 2003. http://www.eia.doe.gov/pub/oil_gas/
petroleum/data_publications/fuel_oil_and_kerosene_sales/current/pdf/
table13.pdf

Energy Policy Act of 1992, Public Law 102-486, 102nd Cong. 2d sess.

(October 24, 1992). http://www.dnr.state.la.us/sec/execdiv/techasmt/
resources/legislation/Energy_Policy_Act_1992.pdf

Energy Star. Change a Light, Change the World. U.S. Environmental
Protection Agency, 2005.
http://www.energystar.gov/index.cfm?c=lighting.pr_lighting

Environment and Human Health, Inc. *Children's Exposure to Diesel
Exhaust on School Buses.* EHHI Reports& Publications.
http://www.ehhi.org/reports/diesel/summary.htm

Environmental Working Group. *What's the Plan: U.S. Farm Subsidies,
1995 through 2003.* Farm Subsidy Database, 2005.
http://www.ewg.org/farm/findings.php

Erhan, Sevim. *New Uses of Vegetable Oils.* International Starch
Technology Conference, 2003. http://www.ars.usda.gov/research/
publications/publications.htm?SEQ_NO_115=145286

European New Car Assessment Program. Audi A2. European New Car
Assessment Program, 2005. http://www.euroncap.com/content/safety
_ratings/details.php?id1=1&id2=111

Farm Security and Rural Investment Act of 2002, Public Law 107-171d,
107th Cong., 2nd sess. May 13, 2002.
http://www.usda.gov/farmbill/conference_report/title9.pdf

Food and Agricultural Policy Research Institute. *Impacts of Increased
Ethanol and Biodiesel Demand.* Food and Agricultural Policy Research
Institute, October 2001. http://www.fapri.missouri.edu/outreach/
publications/2001/FAPRI_UMC_Report_13_01.pdf

Food Standards Agency. Waste Cooking Oil from Catering Premises.
Food Standards Agency, November 9, 2004.
http://www.food.gov.uk/foodindustry/guidancenotes/foodguid/
wastecookingoil

Ford Motor Company. *Corporate Citizenship Report 2003-2004.*
http://www.ford.com/en/company/about/corporateCitizenship/report/
principlesProductsPerformanceDiesel.htm

Gartner, John. Automakers Give Biodiesel a Boost. *Wired News,*
September 23, 2004.
http://www.wired.com/news/print/0,1294,65054,00.html

Gerth, Jeff. Forecast of Rising Oil Demand Challenges Tired Saudi Fields. *The New York Times*, February, 24, 2004, late edition.

Gold, Thomas. The Deep, Hot Biosphere. July 2002. http://people.cornell.edu/pages/tg21/DHB.html

Goodrum, John W. *Review of Biodiesel Research at the University of Georgia*. University of Georgia, 1996. http://www.biodiesel.org/resources/reportsdatabase/reports/gen/19960601_gen-073.pdf

Green Car Congress. Audi Picks Up 10 Awards at Challenge Bibendum. *Green Car Congress*, October 29, 2004. http://www.greencarcongress.com/2004/10/audi_picks_up_1.html

Greene, David L. and Nataliya I. Tishchishyna. *Cost of Oil Dependence: A 2000 Update*. Oak Ridge, Tennessee: Oak Ridge National Laboratory, May 2000. http://www-cta.ornl.gov/cta/Publications/pdf/ORNL_TM_2000_152.pdf

Grosser, Morton. *Diesel: The Man and the Machine*. Brattleboro, Vermont: Book Press, 1978.

Handwerk, Brian. China's Car Boom Tests Safety, Pollution Practices. *National Geographic News*, June 28, 2004. http://news.nationalgeographic.com/news/2004/06/0628_040628_chinacars.html#main

Harrison, Alisa and Tim McNeilly. USDA Establishes a Pilot Project for Renewable Energy Funding Small Businesses that Generate Energy Production from Cattle Products. U. S. Department of Agriculture, May 17, 2004.

Hayward, Steven F. and Joel Schwartz. Emissions Down, Smog Up. Say What? *American Enterprise Institute Online*, January 20, 2004. http://www.aei.org/publications/pubID.19746/pub_detail.asp

Hofbauer, Peter. *Advanced Diesel Engines for the EU and US Automotive Markets*. FEV Engine Technology, Inc. http://www.usea.org/G8%20proceedings/Hofbauer-Pr%C3%A4sentation1-USE%20THIS.pdf

Hoppe, Robert A., ed. *Structural and Financial Characteristics of U.S. Farms: 2001 Family Farm Report*. Washington, D.C.: U.S. Department of Agriculture, May 2001. http://www.ers.usda.gov/publications/aib768/aib768.pdf

Huber, Peter and Mark Mills. Oil, Oil, Everywhere... *Wall Street Journal*, January 27, 2005, eastern edition.

——. *The Bottomless Well*. New York: Basic Books, 2005.

Hudson Institute. *Voters See Saudi Arabia as Greatest Source of Global Terror*. Hudson Institute, August 20, 2004. http://www.hudson.org/index. cfm?fuseaction=publication_details&id=3444&pubType=HI _NEW@HUDSON

Illinois Environmental Protection Agency. Recent Illinois Clean School Bus Activities. Illinois Clean School Bus Program, 2004. http://www.epa.state.il.us/air/cleanbus/activities.html

Institute for the Analysis of Global Security. *How Much are We Paying for a Gallon of Gas?* Institute for the Analysis of Global Security, 2005. http://www.iags.org/costofoil.html

——. *NDCF Report: The Hidden Cost of Imported Oil*. Institute for the Analysis of Global Security, October 30, 2003. http://www.iags.org/n1030034.htm

——. *Set America Free: A Blueprint for U.S. Energy Security*. Institute for the Analysis of Global Security, 2004. http://www.iags.org/safn.pdf

Interactive European Network for Industrial Crops and their Applications. http://www.ienica.net/cropsdatabase.htm

Jarnefeld, Judy, and John Urbanchuk. *Statewide Feasibility Study for a Potential New York State Biodiesel Industry, Final Report*. Albany, NY: New York State Energy Research and Development Authority, April 2004. http://www.nyserda.org/publications/biodieselreport.pdf

Jeep Co. Jeep Liberty 2.8L CRD. Jeep Co., 2004. http://www.jeep.com/autoshow/news/2004_04_02_05_jeep_liberty_crd _68888.html?context=home&type=promo3_img

John Deere. John Deere to Use B2 Biodiesel Fuel in U. S. Manufacturing Plants. *John Deere 2005 News Releases and Information*, February 1, 2005. http://www.deere.com/en_US/newsroom/2005/releases/farmersand ranchers/050201_biodiesel.html

Kansas Corn Commission. *U.S. Ethanol Production*. Kansas Corn Commission, March 8, 2005. http://www.ksgrains.com/ethanol/useth.html

Kerr, Jim. Bio-diesel—a Renewable Energy Source. *Canadian Driver*, August 25, 2004. http://www.canadiandriver.com/articles/jk/040825.htm

Kilman, Scott. Surging Imports of Food Threaten Wider Trade Gap: U.S. Agriculture Exports, Relied on to Ease Deficit, Feel Heat of Competition. *Wall Street Journal*, November 8, 2004, eastern edition.

Körbitz, Werner. *The Technical, Energy and Environmental Properties of BioDiesel*. Vienna, Austria: Körbitz Consulting, 1993.

Krawzcyk, Tom. Biodiesel Alternative Fuel Makes Inroads But Hurdles Remain. *INFORM* (International News on Fats, Oils, and Related Materials), Vol. 7, no.8, August 1996.

Lavelle, Marianne. Living Without Oil. *U.S. News*, February 17, 2003. http://www.usnewsclassroom.com/issue/030217/usnews/17oil.htm

Lehr, Ron L., and Will Guild. *Listening to Customers: How Deliberative Polling Helped Build 1,000 MW of Renewable Energy Projects in Texas*. Golden, CO: National Renewable Energy Laboratory, June 2003. http://www.gldgrp.com/PDF%20Files/NREL%20Report.pdf

Lindhjem, C., and A. Pollack. *Impact of Biodiesel Fuels on Air Quality and Human Health: Task 1 Report*. National Renewable Energy Laboratory, May 2003. http://www.nrel.gov/docs/fy03osti/33794.pdf

Lovelace Respiratory Research Institute. *Tier 2 Testing of Biodiesel Exhaust Emissions* Albuquerque, New Mexico: Lovelace Respiratory Research Institute, May 22, 2000. http://www.worldenergy.net/pdfs/TierIIReport.pdf

Lovins, Amory B., E. Kyle Datta, Odd-Even Bustnes, Jonathan G. Koomey, and Nathan J. Glasgow. *Winning the Oil End Game*. Colorado: Rocky Mountain Institute, 2004. http://www.oilendgame.org/pdfs/WtOEg_72dpi.pdf

McDonald, Dale. Industry Giants: Part II. *Farm Industry News*, March 1, 2001. http://farmindustrynews.com/mag/farming_industry_giants_part/

Meadows, Donella H., Dennis L. Meadows, and Jorgen Randers. *Beyond the Limits*. White River Junction, Vermont: Chelsea Green, 1992.

Minnesota State Legislature. *The Minnesota Biodiesel Mandate.* Minnesota Session Laws, chapter 239 SF-1495, March 15, 2002. http://www.revisor.leg.state.mn.us/slaws/2002/c244.html

Minor, Elliott. Conference Will Focus on Georgia's Potential for Biodiesel. *The Associated Press*, August 20, 2003. http://www .ledger-enquirer.com/mld/ledgerenquirer/news/politics/6577308.htm Mintz, S. The Politics of Oil. Digital History, May 10, 2005. http://www.digitalhistory.uh.edu/historyonline/oil.cfm

Morgan, David P. *Diesels West!* Milwaukee, Wisconsin: Kalmbach Publishing Co. 1963.

Moteur Developpment International. The Air Car: Lifestyle, Ecology, Economy. Moteur Developpment International, 2002. http://www.theaircar.com/models.html

National Aeronautics and Space Administration. *Fleet Alternative Fuel Vehicle Program Report for Fiscal Year 2004.* National Aeronautics and Space Administration, December 29, 2004. http://www.logistics.hq.nasa.gov/AFV/PDF/NASA_AFV_2004.pdf

National Biodiesel Board. Chicago School Buses Adopt Biodiesel. National Biodiesel Board, April 22, 2005. http://www.biodiesel.org/ resources/pressreleases/sch/20050422_chicagoschoolbusesearthday.pdf

———. Current and Proposed Biodiesel Production Plants. National Biodiesel Board, April 2005. http://www.biodiesel.org/buyingbiodiesel/ producers_marketers/ProducersMap-existingandpotential.pdf

———. EPA Clean School Bus Grants to Fund Biodiesel Programs in Five States," National Biodiesel Board, July 14, 2004. http://www.biodiesel. org/resources/pressreleases/sch/20040715_epa_clean_schoolbus _grants.pdf

———. Lifecycle Summary. National Biodiesel Board. http://www .biodiesel.org/pdf_files/fuelfactsheets/LifeCycle_Summary.PDF

———. Missouri and Iowa Biodiesel Plants Join Growing Number of

Production Facilities. National Biodiesel Board, April 29, 2005. http://www.biodiesel.org/resources/pressreleases/far/20050429_midambiofuels.pdf

———. National Biodiesel Board, Daimler Chrysler Set Energy Security Example. National Biodiesel Board, November 17, 2004. http://www.biodiesel.org/resources/pressreleases/pas/20041117_jeep_liberty_ride_drive.pdf

———. National Biodiesel Day Marked by Unstable Petroleum Prices. National Biodiesel Board, March 17, 2005. http://www.biodiesel.org/resources/pressreleases/gen/20050317_nat_biod_day.pdf

———. Safer, Cleaner Market for Government Fleets. National Biodiesel Board. http://biodiesel.org/markets/fle/default.asp

———. Standards and Warranties. National Biodiesel Board. http://www.biodiesel.org/resources/fuelfactsheets/standards_and_warranties.shtm

———. *Summary Results from NBB/USEPA Tier I Health and Environmental Effects Testing for Biodiesel Under the Requirement for USEPA Registration of Fuels and Fuel Additives.* National Biodiesel Board, March 1998. http://www.biodiesel.org/resources/reportsdatabase/reports/gen/19980301_gen-063.pdf

———. Tax Incentive Fact Sheet. National Biodiesel Board. http://www.biodiesel.org/news/taxincentive/

———. U.S. Navy to Produce Its Own Biodiesel. National Biodiesel Board, October 30, 2003. http://www.biodiesel.org/resources/pressreleases/gen/20031030_navy_to_produce_biodiesel.pdf

National Corn Growers Association. *Corn Production Trends.* National Corn Growers Association, July 17, 2003. http://www.ncga.com/02profits/main/index.html

New Rules Project. Biodiesel Mandate-Minnesota. New Rules Project: Agriculture Sector, March 15, 2002. http://www.newrules.org/agri/biodieselmn.html

Office of Energy Efficiency and Renewable Energy. Clean Cities Program. U.S. Department of Energy, December 15, 2004. http://www.eere.energy.gov/cleancities/index.html

——. Energy Efficiency. U.S. Department of Energy, 2005. http://www
.eia.doe.gov/kids/energyfacts/saving/efficiency/savingenergy.html

——. Environmental Policy Act. U.S. Department of Energy, March 16,
2005. http://www.eere.energy.gov/vehiclesandfuels/epact/

——. *EPAct Fleet Information and Regulations, 2003/2004 Annual Report.*
U.S. Department of Energy, September 2004.
http://www.nrel.gov/docs/fy04osti/36690.pdf

——. Fleet Successes: Salt Lake City International Airport. U.S.
Department of Energy, July 7, 2003. http://www.eere.energy.gov/
cleancities/vbg/fleets/progs/success_ddown.cgi?7

——. Hydrogen Production & Delivery. U.S. Department of Energy,
March 4, 2005.
http://www.eere.energy.gov/hydrogenandfuelcells/production/basics.html

——. Propane Vehicles. U.S. Department of Energy, March 3, 2005.
http://www.eere.energy.gov/afdc/afv/prop_vehicles.html

——. Save Energy with Home Improvements. U.S. Department of Energy,
June 28, 2004.
http://www.eere.energy.gov/consumerinfo/saveenergy/save_nocost.html

——. U.S. Military Uses Biodiesel. U.S. Department on Energy, June 25,
2003.
http://www.eere.energy.gov/afdc/progs/new_success_ddown.cgi?122

Office of the National Park Service. *Channel Islands National Park
Launches Marine Biodiesel Program.* U.S. Department of the Interior,
August 8, 2000. http://www.nps.gov/chis/press8800.htm

——. *Greening the National Park Service: Biodiesel in the National
Parks.* U.S. Department of the Interior, February 28, 2005.
http://www.nps.gov/renew/NPSBiodiesel.xls

Oregon Environmental Council. 2005 Legislative Agenda.
http://www.orcouncil.org/Laws/2005%20agenda.htm (accessed April 21,
2005)

Orr, Carolyn L. *Rural Implications of the American Jobs Creation Act:
HR 4520 Signed into Law October 22, 2004 by President Bush.* Council
of State Governments, New York, 2004.
http://www.csgeast.org/pdfs/agriculture/JOBSanalysis.pdf

Osava, Mario. Biodiesel Trains on the Right Track. *Inter Press Service News Agency*, December 26, 2003. http://ipsnews.net/interna.asp?idnews=21707

Pearl, Gary G. "Biodiesel Production in the U.S." (presentation, Australian Renderers Association, 6th International Symposium, July 25-27, 2001). http://www.rendermagazine.com/August2001/TechTopics.html

Peterson, Charles L., and Dick L. Auld. *Technical Overview of Vegetable Oil as a Transportation Fuel*. Moscow, Idaho: University of Idaho, 1991. http://www.biodiesel.org/resources/reportsdatabase/reports/gen/19910101_gen-292.pdf

Phal, Greg. *Biodiesel: Growing a New Energy Economy*. White River Junction, VT: Chelsea Green, 2005.

Render Magazine, "California Requires Dispenser Labeling; Florida Embraces Biodiesel," June 2004. http://www.rendermagazine.com/June2004/BiodieselBulletin.html

Renewable Fuels Association. Bush Signs Important Pro-Ethanol Tax Measures Into Law. *Ethanol Report*, November 8, 2004. http://www.ethanolrfa.org/ereports/er110804.html

Reuters News Service, "Eco-Activist's Tale Headed to Big Screen," October 6, 2004. http://www.planetark.com/dailynewsstory.cfm/newsid/27532/story.htm

Ricardo Inc. *Annual Diesel Report*. http://www.ricardo.com/pages/dieselreport.asp (accessed 23 Nov. 2004)

Ricks, Thomas E. Briefing Depicts Saudis as Enemies Ultimatum Urged to Pentagon Board. *Washington Post*, August 6, 2002.

Romm, Joseph J. *The Hype About Hydrogen*. Washington: Island Press, 2004.

Saunders, Laura. Blubber Capitalism. *Forbes Magazine*, October 11, 2004. http://www.forbes.com/forbes/2004/1011/096_print.html.

Scheer, Hermann. *The Solar Economy: Renewable Energy for a*

Sustainable Global Future. London: Earth Scan Publications, 2002.

Schefter, Kellen. Jeep Liberty CRD. *Green Car Journal Online*, 2005. http://www.greencar.com/index.cfm?content=topstory3

Schlosser, Eric. *Fast Food Nation: The Dark Side of the All American Meal*. New York: Houghton Mifflin Company, 2001.

Scott, Robert E. *Exported to Death: The Failure of Agricultural Deregulation*. Economic Policy Institute, July 1999. http://www.epinet.org/content.cfm/briefingpapers_exportdeath

Senter Novem. *The Development of Biodiesel*. Senter Novem, October 21, 2004. http://www.senternovem.nl/mmfiles/The%20Development%20 of%20Biodiesel_tcm24-117024.pdf

Shah, Sonia. "Crude: The Story of Oil." Lecture, Global Public Media, October 1, 2004. http://www.globalpublicmedia.com/transcripts/sonia_ shah_on_crude_the_story_of_oil

Shapouri, Hosein, James A. Duffield, and Michael Wang. *The Energy Balance of Corn Ethanol: An Update*. Washington, D.C.: U.S. Department of Agriculture, July 2002. http://web.mit.edu/1.149/www/ Corn.EtOH.pdf

Shapouri, Hosein, James A. Duffield, and Michael S. Graboski. *Estimating the Net Energy Balance of Corn Ethanol*. Washington, D.C.: U. S. Department of Agriculture, July 1995. http://www.ers.usda.gov/ publications/aer721/aer721.pdf

Sheehan, John, Terri Dunahay, John Benemann, and Paul Roessler. *A Look Back at the U.S. Department of Energy's Aquatic Species Program: Biodiesel from Algae*. Golden, Colorado: National Renewable Energy Laboratory, July 1998.

Sheenan, J., V. Camobreco, J. Duffied, M. Graboski, and H. Shapouri. *Life Cycle Inventory of Biodiesel and Petroleum Diesel for Use in an Urban Bus*. U.S. Department of Commerce, Springfield, July 1998.

Siegel, Charles. *The End of Economic Growth*. Berkeley: Preservation Institute Policy Study, 1998. http://www.preservenet.com/endgrowth/ EndGrowth.html

Sierra Club. *Health Effects Associated with Diesel Emissions.* Sierra Club, August 20, 2003. http://www.sierraclub.org/cleanair/factsheets/diesel.asp

Simmons, Matthew R. *The World's Giant Oilfields.* Houston: Simmons & Company International, 2002.

———. "Twilight in the Desert: The Fading of Saudi Arabia's Oil." Presentation, Hudson Institute, Washington, D.C., September 9, 2004.

———. "Senate Budget Committee Testimony." Washington, D.C. January 30, 2001. http://www.senate.gov/~budget/republican/about/hearing2001/simmons.htm

———. "Matt Simmons Speaks with Julian Darley about Natural Gas." Julian Darley, *Global Public Media,* May 19, 2004. http://www.globalpublicmedia.com/transcripts/213

The Soy Daily, "Lollapalooza 2003 Powers Tour with Cleaner Burning Biodiesel," 2003. http://www.thesoydailyclub.com/BiodieselBiobased/lollapalooza07082003.asp

Spivack, Cari. Worth the Drive. Google Blog, September 14, 2004. http://www.google.com/googleblog/2004/09/worth-drive_13.html

Sustainable Agriculture Research and Extension Program. *The New American Farmer.* Washington D.C.: U.S. Department of Agriculture, 2001. http://www.sare.org/publications/naf/naf.pdf

Steil, Mark. Biodiesel Production Begins in Minnesota. *Minnesota Public Radio,* January 7, 2005. http://news.minnesota.publicradio.org/features/2004/01/07_steilm_biodiesel/

Szylioxicz, Joseph S. *Energy Crisis and US Foreign Policy.* London: Praeger Publishers, 1975.

Tally, Steve. Plant Oils Will Replace Petroleum in Coming Years. *Purdue News,* August 2000. http://www.purdue.edu/UNS/html4ever/0007.Tao.biofuels.html

Taxpayers for Common Sense. Oppose the $89 Billion Energy Bill. *TCS Energy Bill Watch.* http://www.taxpayer.net/energy/pdf/EBillOppApr19.pdf (accessed May 2, 2005).

——. Energy Campaign.
http://www.taxpayer.net/energy/index.htm (accessed May 2, 2005).

Tiffany, Douglas G. *Biodiesel: A Policy Choice for Minnesota.*
University of Minnesota Staff Paper Series, May 2001.
http://www.misa.umn.edu/programs/biodiesel.pdf

Thornberry, Mac. Oil Imports Threaten Our Security. *Roll Call,*
http://www.anwr.org/features/thornber.htm (access May 10 2005).

Thornton, Ted. *Sources of the Iranian Revolution.* History of the Middle
East Database. October 2003. http://www.nmhschool.org/tthornton/
mehistorydatabase/sources_of_the_iranian_revolutio.htm

Tyson, K. Shaine. *Biodiesel Handling and Use Guidelines.* U.S.
Department of Energy: Office of Energy Efficiency and Renewable
Energy, September 2004. http://www.nrel.gov/vehiclesandfuels/npbf/
pdfs/tp36182.pdf

Tyson, K. Shaine, Jack Brown, and Matthew Morra. *Industrial Mustard
Crops for Biodiesel and Biopesticides.* Golden, Colorado: National
Renewable Energy Laboratory.
http://www.bioproducts-bioenergy.gov/pdfs/bcota/abstracts/19/z347.pdf

United Soybean Board. *Soybean Almanac.* United Soybean Board, 2002.
http://www.unitedsoybean.org/soystats2002/ussoystats/
soybeancrush.html

Urbanchuk, John M. *The Contribution of the Ethanol Industry to the
American Economy in 2004.* Wayne, PA: LECG, March 12, 2004.
http://www.ncga.com/ethanol/pdfs/EthanolEconomicContributionREV
.pdf

——. *An Economic Analysis of Legislation for a Renewable Fuels
Requirement for Highway Motor Fuels.* AUS Consultants, November 7,
2001. http://www.ncga.com/ethanol/pdfs/Urbanchuk_Final_Report.pdf

U.S. Census Bureau. *Statistical Abstract of the United States: 2004-2005.*
124th ed., Washington: Government Printing Office, 2005.
http://www.census.gov/prod/2004pubs/04statab/pop.pdf

U.S. Coast Guard Academy. Cadets Launch Operation Soy Boat in an
Effort to Turn the Coast Guard 'Green.' *Academy News.*
http://www.cga.edu/newsstoriesread3462.htm

U.S. Department of Commerce. February 2005 U.S. Foreign Trade
Developments. *Monthly Trade Update*, April 12, 2005.
http://www.ita.doc.gov/TD/Industry/OTEA/usftu/current.pdf

U.S. Environmental Protection Agency. *About Asthma*. April 5, 2005.
http://www.epa.gov/asthma/about.html#How%20does%20Asthma
%20Affect%20Children

——. *Asthma and Indoor Environments*. April 5, 2005. http://www.epa.
gov/asthma/about.html#How%20does%20Asthma%20Affect
%20Children

——. *Clean Diesel Trucks and Buses Rule*. March 25, 2005.
http://www.epa.gov/otaq/diesel.htm#hd2007

——. *Clean School Bus USA: Grants and Funding*. April 12, 2005.
http://www.epa.gov/otaq/schoolbus/funding.htm

——. *EPA420-F-03-022: Diesel Exhaust in the United States*. June 2003.
http://www.epa.gov/otaq/retrofit/documents/420f03022.pdf

Vaitheeswaran, Vijay. Big Oil's Biggest Monster. *The Economist*, January
8, 2005.

Wilson, Greg. Feature: VW 1-Litre-Car. *Canadian Driver,* June 5, 2002.
http://www.canadiandriver.com/articles/gw/vw1litre.htm

Yergin, Daniel. *The Prize*. New York: Free Press, 1991.

G L O S S A R Y

Air car—A vehicle powered by compressed air. The pressurized air is fed into a "motor" designed around a pneumatic cylinder.

Air toxics—Airborne pollution that is toxic to humans, animals, or other members of the natural ecology.

Algae—Single or multicelled organisms displaying the characteristics of both plants and animals, which formed the basis for the oil we use today. Algae internally produce oil as a means to store energy and buoy themselves up in water.

B100 – 100% neat biodiesel. Biodiesel can be blended and used in any ratio with diesel fuel. The "B" designator points to the percentage of the total "blend" that is biodiesel. For example, B20 is a blend of 20% biodiesel with 80% diesel. B50 is a blend of 50% biodiesel with 50% diesel and so on. B100 is a popular choice for biodiesel use in sensitive ecosystems such as marine habitats.

Biodiesel—A diesel fuel substitute or additive that is made by converting vegetable oil or animal fat into a mixture of mono alkyl esters and long chain fatty acids. Biodiesel has similar combustion properties to diesel fuel but reduced toxicity, emissions, and health risks.

Biofuels—Fuels derived primarily from biological or agricultural sources, such as biodiesel and ethanol.

Biomass—Organic or agricultural products such as grass, hay, wood chips, oilseeds, mulch, and straw.

Biorefinery—A facility in which a form of biomass (such as soybeans) is converted into multiple value-added products (such as biodiesel, heat, animal feed, protein powder, and electricity).

Black grease—Defined loosely as greases resulting from sewage and/or other unconventional oil sources. Has a low conversion factor to biodiesel due to its high free-fatty-acid content.

"Black Mistress"—Rudolf Diesel's affectionate name for his first engine.

Brown grease—generally defined as a combination of greases and trappings from the slaughter industry.

British Thermal Unit—BTU. A unit of energy equivalent to 1,055 joules. Gasoline contains 115,400 BTU's per gallon.

California Air Resources Board (CARB) - the "clean air agency" for the state of California. It is known for setting stringent air quality standards, which have resulted in the manufacture of special gasoline for the state of California as well as statewide and nationwide changes to automobile and heavy-duty vehicle emissions systems.

Carbon cycle—The biogeochemical cycle through which carbon is exchanged between the biosphere, hydrosphere, geosphere, and atmosphere of the earth. When a fossil fuel is burned in an internal combustion engine, carbon dioxide emissions flow into the atmosphere. This results in a net increase in the balance of global CO_2 and, consequently, a disturbance of the natural carbon cycle. On the other hand, when a biofuel is burned, the carbon dioxide that is released is roughly equivalent to the quantity of carbon dioxide absorbed by the plants from which the fuel was made. This results in almost no net gain in the global balance of carbon dioxide and does not significantly disturb the natural carbon cycle.

Common Rail Direct Injection, (CDI)—The newest, cleanest, and most efficient form of diesel engine technology, in which extremely high fuel pressure is maintained throughout the injection system. The fuel injectors are connected to a common fuel line called a "rail." Unlike conventional diesel engines in which the fuel injector pump pushes fuel to one injector at a time, a CDI engine maintains high fuel pressure throughout the injection system and simply opens the injectors to allow the fuel to be injected into the combustion chamber.

Cellulostic ethanol production—The process of producing ethanol from the breakdown of biomass other than starches. This new process offers a higher yield of ethanol at higher conversion efficiency and opens a range of biomass (including simple crops like switch grass) for ethanol production.

Cetane number (CN)—A measure of a diesel fuel's combustion quality. Cetane is to diesel fuel what "octane" is to gasoline. All diesel fuels are indexed against cetane, a compound that ignites very easily under compression and is therefore given a cetane number of 100. A fuel with a high cetane number will ignite easily under pressure inside a diesel engine, while a fuel with a low cetane number will not ignite as easily and is considered of poorer quality. Diesel fuel number 2 typically has a cetane number of between 40-46, whereas biodiesel's cetane number is generally from 47-60. The ASTM D-6751 standard sets a minimum cetane number of 47 for biodiesel.

Cloud point—As temperature drops, heavier fuels such as diesel and biodiesel begin to crystallize. The crystals appear to "cloud" the fuel. Clouded fuel can clog fuel filters and temporarily disable vehicle operation. Thus the "cloud point" refers to temperature at which a fuel begins to cloud.

Coal to fuel—A method of producing liquid fuel from coal developed by Fischer and Tropsch for Germany during WWII. Gave rise to GTL (Gas to Liquid) and BTL (Biomass to Liquid) fuels.

Combustion chamber—The area inside each cylinder of an engine in which the mixture of fuel and air is compressed by the piston and ignited by either a spark or by the heat generated by the compression itself.

Compression ignition—An engine that operates by first compressing air and then injecting fuel. Also known as a "diesel" engine. Contains no spark plugs.

Continuous flow (biodiesel) plants—Facilities that produce biodiesel fuel continuously, as opposed to "batch process" plants.

Conventional oil—Oil that can be recovered or produced using conventional, current-day technology. Excludes oil that can be recovered from tar sands.

Cost per Kilowatt Hour—The cost of producing one kilowatt (kW) of electricity in one hour. Used as a means of determining how competitive different forms of electricity generation are.

Erucic acid—An inedible acid found in rapeseed oil that is not found in its hybridized cousin, canola.

Depleted uranium—The primary by-product of nuclear power plants, the main use of which is in the manufacture of weapons and the storage of which poses considerable security and health risks.

Diesel, Dr. Rudolf Christian Karl—(March 18, 1858–September 30, 1913)—Inventor of the diesel engine. Author of a book on the equitable distribution of wealth as well as numerous papers on combustion efficiency.

Diesel engine—See Compression ignition.

Diesel fuel—A fuel derived from the distillation of oil that is heavier than gasoline but lighter than engine oil and heavy oils. Diesel fuel is generally separated into two fuels: diesel number 1 (Diesel No. 1) and diesel number 2 (Diesel No. 2). Diesel No. 1 is similar to kerosene and is lighter than Diesel No. 2. While Diesel No. 2 is sold most of the time, Diesel No. 1 is sold during winter in very cold climates because it doesn't cloud or gel as easily as Diesel No. 2.

Direct injection (diesel)—Refers to a diesel engine in which fuel is injected directly into the combustion chamber under high pressure. Direct injection engines are more efficient than their predecessors. See Indirect injection engines.

Electrolysis—The process of separating bonded elements by passing a current through them. Electrolysis also refers to using electricity to split water into hydrogen and oxygen. There is always less energy present in the resulting hydrogen gas than was used in the electrolysis process to separate it from oxygen.

Energy balance ratio—The ratio of how much energy a given energy carrier takes to produce versus how much energy the carrier contains. An energy balance ratio of less than one indicates an energy carrier that takes more energy to produce than it contains (such as hydrogen). An energy balance ratio of greater than one indicates the carrier took less energy to produce than it contains (such as biodiesel).

Energy carrier—Any fuel, such as hydrogen, biodiesel, or oil and any energy storage device, such as batteries or ultra capacitors that is used to move energy from one place to another. Ultimately, most energy carriers originated with solar energy (i.e. algae that got their energy from the sun and were transformed, over the course of millions of years, into oil).

Energy sources—Include the sun and the atomic force.

Ethanol (C_2H_5OH)—Also known as ethyl alcohol and grain alcohol. A flammable, colorless chemical compound found in alcoholic beverages that can also be used as a fuel for gasoline engines. Ethanol is created by the fermentation of starches into sugars by yeast. Ethanol can be made from many natural sources of cellulose, including sugarcane, sugar beets, corn, barley, potatoes, stalks, sawdust, straw, and corncobs. Ethanol burns very cleanly, producing only water and carbon dioxide. Ethanol also has an octane rating of 113, considerably higher than premium gasoline's octane rating of 93. Brazil produces almost 50% of its fuel as ethanol from sugarcane. Ethanol is cheaper in Brazil than gasoline. The result is that car manufacturers such as Volkswagen now produce dual fuel vehicles for the Brazilian market that can run on gasoline or ethanol or a combination.

Euro IV Emissions Standards—EU-wide emissions standards adopted in 2005 as a progressive measure toward meeting Kyoto Protocol standards. Euro V Standards will be introduced in 2008.

Expeller press—A device used to crush oilseeds and separate vegetable oil from meal.

Externality or external cost—Costs associated with the production of energy that are borne by a third party. Such costs include pollution, sickness, and ecological destruction.

Fatty acid—A long chain organic acid, generally based on acetate (CH_3CO_2) and containing an even number of carbons.

Free fatty acid—A fatty acid not attached to a glycerin molecule but still present in some vegetable oils, especially hydrogenated vegetable oils. The higher its percentage of free fatty acids, the more difficult a vegetable oil is to process into biodiesel.

Feedstock—The basic input for the creation of a biofuel. Biodiesel feedstocks include soybeans and rapeseed. Ethanol feedstocks include corn, wheat, and switch grass.

Fischer Tropsch—See Gas to Liquid

Fission reaction—The splitting of atoms, which, in a nuclear power plant, gives off heat, which boils water, which creates steam, which drives a turbine, which makes electricity.

Flashpoint—The temperature at which a fuel ignites.

Fluroelastomer—A synthetic compound from which hoses compatible with biodiesel are made.

Fossil fuel—Oil, coal, and natural gas.

Fuel cell—An electrochemical device that converts hydrogen into electricity.

Fuel cell vehicle—An electric vehicle (EV) that is powered by electricity generated by a fuel cell.

Gas to Liquid (GTL)—A process similar to Coal to Liquid in which natural gas or gases comprised primarily of methane or carbon dioxide are converted into a liquid fuel.

Gasoline extender—An additive such as ethanol that decreases the amount of gasoline used thereby "extending" fuel supplies.

Gel point—The temperature at which the fuel is past its "cloud point" and beginning to gel, thereby making operation of fuel systems impossible.

General Agreement on Tariffs and Trades, (GATT)—Established in 1947 as an international forum to encourage free trade between member states by regulating and reducing tariffs on traded goods and by providing a means to resolve trade disputes.

Geothermal (energy)—Energy generated by the earth's crust. Geothermal energy can be converted into electricity in geothermal plants.

Ghawar Field—The largest oil field on Earth. Located in northeastern Saudi Arabia, about 60 miles from the city of Dharan and next to the Persian Gulf. Supplies approximately 6% of the world's daily oil supply. Controlled entirely by Saudi Aramco, which is in turn controlled by the Royal House of Saud.

Ghost loads—Electrical loads such as VCRs and microwaves, which when not in use still consume electricity.

Global Warming—The theory that a sustained and increased level of carbon dioxide in the earth's atmosphere is leading to a corresponding increase in average yearly global temperatures. Supported by scientists and countries involved in the Kyoto Protocol (not including the United States and Australia).

Glow plugs—Heating elements that, in a diesel engine, create the needed heat to start the engine. Unlike spark plugs, which are used continuously while a gasoline engine is operational, glow plugs only activate when a diesel engine is starting.

Glycerin—Also called glycerol. A heavy, sweet alcohol that is part of the vegetable oil triglyceride and must be "broken off" during transesterification. Glycerin is the by-product of the biodiesel process. Glycerin is hydroscopic (water soluble) and is used in over one thousand industrial, cosmetic, and food applications.

"Greenwashing" —A term given to using marketing and public relations to appear to be an environmentally responsible company while simultaneously engaging in environmentally destructive practices.

Half-life—The time it takes for half of a given quantity of a radioactive substance to decay. In the case of plutonium, which is one of the radioactive elements contained in spent nuclear reactor rods, its half-life is 24,400 years. To fully decay, a radioactive substance must undergo over 7 half-lives. Thus, radiation from man made plutonium will exist on Earth for over half a million years.

Hubbert's Peak—See also Peak Oil. In 1956 a prestigious geologist named M. King Hubbert shocked the petroleum industry by predicting that U.S. oil production would peak between 1970-1971. He graphed U.S. oil production in a bell-curve, rising to a peak and then falling. Hubbert's prediction was correct. Those subscribing to the "Peak Oil Theory" believe what Hubbert predicted for the United States will soon occur worldwide as total oil production peaks and then declines.

Hybrid vehicle—A vehicle that uses more than one form of motive power to achieve a higher efficiency. There are gasoline-electric hybrids (like the Toyota Prius) and diesel-electric hybrids (like every train in America). None of the current generation of hybrid vehicles must be plugged in to charge.

Hydrocarbon chains—Chains of carbon and hydrogen atoms that form the basis for fossils fuels like gasoline and biofuels like ethanol and biodiesel.

Hydrogen—Most plentiful and simplest element in the universe. Can be used as a gaseous fuel made by splitting water molecules or natural gas.

Hydrogen fuel cell - See fuel cell.

Indirect injection (diesel)—Refers to a diesel engine in which fuel is injected first into a pre chamber where it swirls and mixes with air before entering a combustion chamber. See also Direct injection.

Inorganic theory of oil—A theory promoted by the late Thomas Gold in which oil originates from a primordial source deep within the Earth. The theory is largely unsupported by the geological community and remains unproven.

Intercooler—An "air radiator" which cools air as it comes out of the turbocharger of a diesel engine. Intercoolers increase the efficiency of diesel engines by insuring the intake air is as dense as possible (containing as much oxygen as possible) before entering the combustion chamber.

Liquified Natural Gas, (LNG)—Natural gas (methane) which has been cooled to the point of liquefaction. Liquefying the gas makes it easier to transport over great distances. LNG storage and transport represents a high security risk due to the explosive potential of the fuel.

Liquefied Propane Gas, (LPG)—A gaseous fuel stored in low pressure tanks. Used to heat homes, in barbecues, and as a limited vehicle fuel.

LOHAS – An acronym for Lifestyles of Health and Sustainability, which describes a marketplace for goods and services that appeal to consumers who value health, the environment, social justice, personal development, and sustainable living. The estimated U.S. LOHAS market is approximately 68 million consumers, roughly 32% of adults, and is valued at $227 billon in annual sales.

Lubricity—The lubricating quality of a fuel. In a diesel engine high lubricity fuels are critical to maintaining proper engine functionality. Without any lubricity in its fuel, the diesel engine will fail.

Lubricity agent—Diesel fuel by itself has very low lubricity. Biodiesel has very high lubricity and can actually be added to diesel fuel in small quantities of between 1-5% as a "lubricity agent."

Maschinenfabrik Augsburg-Nürnberg AG, (MAN)—The German company which fostered the development of both the diesel and gasoline engines. Currently manufactures engines, trucks, buses, and parts for the aeronautics and aerospace industries. Now the third largest manufacturer in Europe.

Methane (CH_4)—The simplest hydrocarbon. A gas comprised of four atoms of hydrogen and one atom of carbon. The primary component of natural gas.

Methanol—A colorless, poisonous liquid fuel created by the conversion of natural gas (methane) into alcohol in a Gas to Liquid process. Methanol is also typically used in as the alcohol ingredient in the biodiesel reaction but the nontoxic alcohol, ethanol, can be used instead.

Multifeedstock (biodiesel plant)—A facility that can make biodiesel from various feedstocks. Most multifeedstock plants can make biodiesel from either virgin vegetable oil and used cooking oil.

N-parrafins—A group of hydrocarbon chains which are unique to algae and fossil oil, showing a direct chemical link between oil and ancient waterborne algae.

National Biodiesel Board (NBB)—The national clearinghouse for information and regulations regarding biodiesel.

The National Renewable Energy Laboratory (NREL)—the nation's primary laboratory for renewable energy and energy efficiency research and development. NREL is the principle research laboratory for the United States Department of Energy Office of Energy Efficiency and Renewable Energy.

Natural gas—A fossil fuel made primarily of methane (CH_4).

Nitrogen oxides (NO_x)—The emissions created from burning anything (including any liquid fuel) in Earth's atmosphere. Diesel engines have traditionally emitted higher levels of NO_x than their gasoline counterparts. However, newer diesel technology has resulted in engines that have greatly reduced NO_x emissions.

Non renewable energy—An energy that is based on ancient stored solar energy, is fixed in quantity, and if produced at a constant (or increasing) rate will "peak" and decline (i.e. oil).

Octane rating—The measure of a gasoline fuel's combustibility. The higher the octane rating, the more easily a fuel will burn in a gasoline engine.

Octane enhancer—An additive that increases the bonded oxygen available in a fuel, thereby making the fuel burn more cleanly and completely. Such enhancers include the controversial carcinogenic compound MTBE (methyl tertiary butyl ether), ethanol, and ETBE (ethyl tertiary butyl ether), a nontoxic additive made from ethanol.

Omnibus—Latin meaning "for all." Also refers to a (federal) bill that covers many separate, even conflicting, issues under one title. For example, many versions of the Omnibus Energy Bill have contained billions of dollars of support for coal, oil, natural gas, and nuclear, as well as limited support for biofuels and liability waivers for companies using MTBE.

Organic theory of oil—The generally accepted theory that oil comes from organic sources such as algae that lived millions of years ago. Supported by the preponderance of geological evidence as well as the n-paraffins link between algae and fossil oil.

Organization of Petroleum Exporting Countries, (OPEC)—Includes: Algeria, Lybia, Nigeria, Iran, Iraq, Kuwait, Qatar, Saudi Arabia, the United Arab Emirates, Venezuela, and Indonesia. Originally started by Alfonzo Perez, Venezuela's Prime Minister, to maintain price of oil.

Ozone forming— The specific combination of VOCs and NOx that results in low-level ozone formation, which is the precursor to smog.

Peak oil theory—See also Hubbert's Peak. Originally advanced by Dr. M. King Hubbert in 1956. States that there is a fixed quantity of conventional oil in Earth's crust. Once approximately half of the oil has been produced, production is said to have "peaked" and thereafter will decline. The U.S. reached peak oil production in 1971, as correctly predicted by Hubbert.

Photosynthesis—The process through which plants and algae transform sunlight, water and carbon dioxide into hydrocarbon-based plant tissue and oxygen.

Photovoltaic panels (PVs)—Silicon-based panels that transform sunlight into electricity.

Polymerize—Placing certain molecules under intense heat and pressure can transform them into a form of plastic, or polymerize them. This can occur inside a modern diesel engine into which a user pours straight vegetable oil.

Polymers—Chemical compounds used in anti-gel additives for diesel fuel. Such formulas are not applicable to biodiesel.

Prechamber—In older indirect injection diesel engines, a small chamber into which fuel and air swirl together before entering the combustion chamber.

Propane—See Liquefied Propane Gas.

Rapeseed—The primary feedstock used in Europe for the production of biodiesel. In the summer and winter, much of rural Germany and France is blanketed with the yellow rapeseed flowers.

Reforming—The energy intensive process of catalytically stripping hydrogen from fuels like methanol.

Regasifier—A device used to transform LNG back into uncompressed natural gas.

Renewable energy—An energy that is based on solar income and does not run out. For example, wind energy is renewable. See also "non renewable energy."

Reported oil reserves—the quantity of oil that a country 'reports' it has discovered. As in the case of Saudi Arabia, there is no independent verification of whether or not such reports are based on actual discoveries.

Reservoir rock—porous, permeable rock into which oil migrated and inside which oil is generally found. Generally, reservoir rock is either sandstone or limestone.

Royal House of Saud—Royal family of Saudi Arabia. Currently contains approximately 30,000 members and is expected to double within a decade.

Rule of 72—The Rule of 72 refers to a simplified equation to determine the time required for a given principal to double or halve. Assuming n = 1 conversion period for compound interest, the true equation is written $2P = P(1+r)t$ where "P" is principle, "r" is the rate, and "t" is time (in years). The equation can be summarized: $t = 0.72/r$.

Saudi Aramco (Saudi Arabian Oil Company)—Oil company controlling Saudi Arabia's oil reserves (the largest in the world), as well as the production of that oil. Refuses to disclose exact quantity of reserves held by Saudi Arabia.

Security margin —The "buffer" between the oil a given nation consumes and produces. The lower the security margin, the lower the energy security of a country.

Seven Sisters—The seven large oil conglomerates that emerged during the World Wars. They were: British Petroleum, Royal Dutch Shell, Exxon, Mobil, Texaco, Chevron, and Gulf Oil. Due to shrinking worldwide oil discoveries, these companies have consolidated into four sisters: BP, Shell, Exxon Mobil and Chevron/Texaco.

Smog—A brown haze common to large cities resulting from the reaction of volatile organic compound emissions primarily from gasoline vehicles, nitrogen oxide emissions primarily from diesel vehicles, and coal power plants, sunlight, particles, and dust. Smog has been cited as a contributor to respiratory illnesses including asthma and lung cancer.

Sodium hydroxide (NaOH)—Also known as "lye" and once sold as a common household drain cleaner. A caustic, metallic catalyst with an extremely basic pH, sodium hydroxide is used in very minute quantities in the biodiesel reaction. It should be noted that the nontoxic substitute potassium hydroxide (KOH) can also be used. Sodium hydroxide is highly caustic and can cause chemical burns, scarring, and blindness. When it reacts with water and certain fluids, it can become hot enough to cause fires.

Source rock—The porous rock in which fossil oil and gas are stored underground.

Spark ignition engine—An engine that operates by compressing a mixture of fuel and air and then igniting the mixture with a spark. (As opposed to a "compression ignition" engine, which uses only compression to ignite its fuel.) Also known as a gasoline engine.

Sulfur dioxide (SO_2)—Emissions resulting from burning fuel containing sulfur, such as coal or traditional diesel fuel (which contained sulfur as a lubricant). Sulfur dioxide is the primary component of acid rain. Biodiesel contains no sulfur and produces no sulfur dioxide when burned.

Super capacitor—A solid-state device made of metal plates encased in ceramic material (capacitor) with the ability to store a considerable electrical charge and act as a battery.

Swing producer—A company or country that has the ability to increase its crude oil production to meet changes in market demand. Traditionally, swing producers were countries with substantial excess oil production capacity. Saudi Arabia is the world's only remaining swing producer and questions have been raised about its ability to reliably increase its oil production.

Tallow—Fat produced from the slaughter of animals for the food industry that can be turned into biodiesel.

Tar sands—Near surface sands into which oil has seeped. Production of one barrel of oil from tar sands requires 2 tons of tar sands and uses more energy than it produces.

Turbo Direct Injection (TDI)—A relatively new diesel engine technology, in which fuel is injected into the compression chamber at extremely high pressure, resulting in a more complete fuel burn, lower emissions, and a higher overall efficiency.

Texas Railroad Commission—U.S. predecessor to OPEC. Set oil prices in Texas and later the entire United States.

Trade deficit—When the balance of the money earned by an economy minus the money spent by that economy is negative. Stated another way, when the value of products imported into a country exceeds the value of the products exported by that country. The United States has a growing trade deficit due mainly to the increasing quantity and value of its prinmary import, oil, and the decreasing value of its primary export, agricultural foodstuffs.

Transesterification—The process of transforming triglycerides into a combination of mono alkyl esters and long chain fatty acids, or in other words transforming vegetable oil into biodiesel. The actual chemical reaction for transesterification takes less than one hour and involves a mixture of approximately 80-90% vegetable oil, 10-20% alcohol, and less than 1% catalyst.

Triglyceride—A molecule consisting of three fatty acids attached at the base by a glycerin molecule. Triglycerides are the molecules that make up vegetable oil.

Turbocharger—A small turbine that is spun on one side by exhaust gases leaving an engine. The other side of the turbine forces more air into the combustion chamber, allowing for a more complete, more efficient fuel burn and more power output from the engine. Turbochargers are not affected by the use of biodiesel. See also intercooler.

Turbodiesel engine—A diesel engine in which a turbocharger is incorporated into the basic design and operation of the engine. These engines are unaffected by the use of biodiesel.

Ultra Low Sulfur Diesel (ULSD)—Until recently in the United States, diesel fuel was lubricated with sulfur. Sulfur in diesel fuel created two problems. First, it produced sulfur dioxide (SO_2) emissions, which contributed to acid rain. Second, due to the corrosive nature of the sulfur dioxide emissions, emissions technologies that were effectively reducing the other diesel emissions (such as NO_x) in Europe were not allowed into the United States, resulting in the ban of the sale of diesel passenger cars in California, Massachusetts, Vermont, and New York. In 2006, all U.S. diesel fuel will switch to ULSD, allowing a new breed of diesel vehicles and diesel emissions technologies to be sold in the United States. See also sulfur dioxide.

Ultimate Recoverable Reserves (URR)—The quantity of oil a country estimates that it can produce by using current and near-term technologies.

Uranium—A limited, toxic, metallic, and radioactive element mined for use as a fuel for nuclear power plants or for nuclear weapons.

Volatile organic compounds (VOCs)—Organic chemical compounds that easily vaporize, enter the atmosphere, and participate in photochemical reactions to produce smog. VOCs include methane and benzene, which has been linked to cancer. Recent studies indicate that it is the level of VOCs that must be first be limited (not NO_x emissions, as previously thought) in order to reduce smog.

Water cut—When oil production in a large oilfield begins to decline, water may be injected into the field to "push" the remaining oil out. The amount of water in the produced oil is the water cut.

Water injection—The practice of injecting water and/or steam into a large oilfield to push the oil out. Seawater is generally used in water injection, resulting in extreme corrosion of the oil processing equipment in a field as well as potential contamination of the oilfield with bacteria. Water injection also decreases the value of the oil produced, since the oil must be further processed to remove the intermixed water. In many parts of the world, such as Saudi Arabia, there are no environmental restrictions on the oil content of the discharged water and water containing crude oil and other contaminants is pumped back into seas and oceans.

Wildcatters—Early explorers who looked for oil by drilling on rumors and hunches.

Yellow grease—The oils and greases produced in the fast food industry and collected by the rendering industry.

Yom Kippur War—Also known as "The October War." Attack by Syria and Egypt on Israel that led to the 1973 oil crisis.

E N D N O T E S

Chapter 1 - America's Crude History

1. Coal, however, is formed from larger life forms such as plants and trees that grew primarily in swampy areas. In this case, the preserved organic matter is compressed and forms peat, which is eventually transformed into coal.

2. Paraffin is a common name for hydrocarbons with the general formula C_nH_{2n+2}. Paraffins can be arranged either in straight chains (normal paraffins or n-paraffins) or branched chains (isoparaffins). Most of the paraffin compounds in naturally occurring crude oils are normal paraffins, while isoparaffins are frequently produced in refinery processes. "So-called n-paraffins, with odd numbers of carbon atoms, are synthesized in living organisms, and such molecules found in oil are true biological markers inherited from the living organisms from which they were derived. C_{15}, C_{17}, and C_{19} characterize microscopic organisms including algae, whereas molecules of above C_{21} typify plants. These chemical links give the game away, showing that oils come primarily from algae." Colin J. Campbell, *The Coming Oil Crisis,* 19.

3. Thomas Gold, *"The Deep, Hot Biosphere,"* July 2002. http://people.cornell.edu/pages/tg21/DHB.html

4. Julie Creswell, "Oil Without End," *Fortune Magazine*, February 17, 2003, 46.

5. Ibid.

6. It should be noted that Edison did not, as is commonly believed, invent the light bulb. An English inventor named Joseph Swan unveiled a carbon filament light bulb 10 years before Edison's "discovery" and Swan's discovery was published in *Scientific American.* The American courts would eventually rule Edison's patents invalid and would force him to name Swan as a partner in the Edison and Swan United Electric Company.

7. Whale Watch. KaiKoura, New Zealand. 1997. http://www.whalewatch.co.nz/sperm.htm

8. Laura Saunders, "Blubber Capitalism," *Forbes Magazine*, October 11, 2004. http://www.forbes.com/forbes/2004/1011/096_print.html

9. Lance Davis, *In Pursuit of Leviathan: Technology, Institutions,*

Productivity, and Profits in American Whaling (Chicago: University of Chicago Press, 1997), 342.

10. Karl Brandt, *Whale Oil: An Economic Analysis* (Stanford: Food Research Institute Stanford University, 1940), 53-54.

11. S. Mintz, "The Politics of Oil," Digital History, May 10, 2005. http://www.digitalhistory.uh.edu/historyonline/oil.cfm

12. Ibid.

13. William Cran, *The Prize: The Epic Quest for Oil, Money and Power.* VHS, Cassette 2. (Chicago: Public Media Video, 1993).

14. *Interssen Gemeinschaft Farben* was assembled and funded in large part by American investors from Wall Street. Even Henry Ford merged his German assets with I.G. in 1928. I.G. also made the chlorine gas the Germans used in WWI and Zyklon B, the lethal gas used in Auschwitz and other concentration camps. I.G. Farben was awarded the Nobel Prize for Chemistry.

15. William Cran, *The Prize: The Epic Quest for Oil, Money and Power.* VHS, Cassette 2. (Chicago: Public Media Video, 1993).

16. Joseph S. Szylioxicz, *Energy Crisis and US Foreign Policy* (London: Praeger Publishers, 1975), 90.

17. The Texas Railroad Commission maintained the domestic price of U.S. oil. It went to great lengths to keep production down in the United States and pushed for high taxes on imported oil.

18. Daniel Yergin, *The Prize* (New York: Free Press, 1991).

19. Ultimate Recoverable Reserves refer to the actual number of barrels of oil that can be extracted from a given region. It is based on hard seismic data and is as close to the real number of barrels of oil as is possible.

20. Daniel Yergin, *The Prize* (New York: Free Press, 1991), 567.

21. Ibid.

22. Ted Thornton, *Sources of the Iranian Revolution* (History of the Middle East Database, October 2003). http://www.nmhschool.org/tthornton/mehistorydatabase/sources_of_the_iranian_revolutio.htm

23. William Cran, *The Prize: The Epic Quest for Oil, Money and Power.* VHS, Cassette 4. (Chicago: Public Media Video, 1993).

24. Jimmy Carter, "The Crisis of Confidence" (public address, July 15, 1979). http://usa.usembassy.de/etexts/speeches/rhetoric/jccrisis.htm

25. Jimmy Carter, "State of the Union Address 1981" (public address, Washington D.C., January 16, 1981). http://www.jimmycarterlibrary.org/documents/speeches/su81jec.phtml

26. Ibid.

Chapter 2 - The End of Cheap Oil

1. Matthew R. Simmons, *The World's Giant Oilfields* (Houston: Simmons & Company International, 2002).
2. Colin Campbell, "Peak Oil: A Turning Point for Mankind" (lecture, Technical University of Clausthal, Clausthal-Zellerfeld, Germany, December 2000). http://www.geologie.tu-clausthal.de/Campbell/lecture.html
3. Ibid.
4. Colin J. Campbell and Jean H. Laherrère, "The End of Cheap Oil," *Scientific American,* March 1998, 79.
5. Ibid, 81.
6. Matthew R. Simmons, *The World's Giant Oilfields* (Houston: Simmons & Company International, 2002).
7. Colin J. Campbell and Jean H. Laherrère, "The End of Cheap Oil," *Scientific American*, March 1998, 79-80.
8. Matthew R. Simmons, "Twilight in the Desert: The Fading of Saudi Arabia's Oil" (presentation, Hudson Institute, Washington, D.C., September 9, 2004), slide 13.
9. Jeff Gerth, "Forecast of Rising Oil Demand Challenges Tired Saudi Fields," *New York Times*, February 24, 2004, late edition.
10. The Rule of 72 refers to a simplified equation to determine the time required for a given principal to double or halve. Assuming n = 1 conversion period for compound interest, the true equation is written 2P = P(1+r)t where "P" is principle, "r" is the rate, and "t" is time (in years). The equation can be summarized: t = 0.72/r. http://mathworld.wolfram.com/
11. r = 8% or 0.08, t is unknown. Thus 0.72/0.08 = 9 years.
12. Vijay Vaitheeswaran, "Big Oil's Biggest Monster," *The Economist*, January 8, 2005, 51.
13. Jeff Gerth, "Forecast of Rising Oil Demand Challenges Tired Saudi Fields," *New York Times*, February 24, 2004, late edition.
14. Simmons International. http://www.simmonsco-intl.com/
15. Matthew R. Simmons, *The World's Giant Oilfields* (Houston: Simmons & Company International, 2002), 20.
16. Jeff Gerth, "Forecast of Rising Oil Demand Challenges Tired Saudi Fields," *New York Times*, February 24, 2004, late edition.
17. Peter Huber and Mark Mills, "Oil, Oil, Everywhere...," *Wall Street Journal*, January 27, 2005, Eastern edition.

18. Tim Appenzeller, "The End of Cheap Oil," *National Geographic,* June 2004.
19. Sonia Shah, "Crude: The Story of Oil" (lecture, Global Public Media, October 1, 2004). http://www.globalpublicmedia.com/transcripts/sonia _shah_on_crude_the_story_of_oil
20. Peter Huber and Mark Mills, "Oil, Oil, Everywhere...," *Wall Street Journal,* January 27, 2005, Eastern edition.
21. Peter Huber and Mark Mills, *The Bottomless Well* (New York: Basic Books, 2005), 44.
22. Ibid, 176.
23. Energy Information Administration, *Annual Energy Outlook 2004* (Washington D.C.: U.S. Department of Energy, January 2004).
24. Rate: Brian Handwerk, "China's Car Boom Tests Safety, Pollution Practices," *National Geographic News*, June 28, 2004. http://news.nationalgeographic.com/news/2004/06/0628_040628 _chinacars.html#main; Car production per month: Chetan Ahya and Andy Xie, "New Tigers of Asia," Morgan Stanley, July 26, 2004. http://www.ibef.org/attachdisplay.aspx?cat_id=135&art_id=3150
25. Matt Simmons, "Senate Budget Committee Testimony" (Senate testimony, Washington, D.C., January 30, 2001). http://www.senate .gov/~budget/republican/about/hearing2001/simmons.htm
26. David L. Greene and Nataliya I. Tishchishyna, *Cost of Oil Dependence: A 2000 Update* (Oak Ridge National Laboratory, Oak Ridge, Tennessee, May 2000). http://www-cta.ornl.gov/cta/Publications/ pdf/ORNL_TM_2000_152.pdf
27. Institute for the Analysis of Global Security, *How Much Are We Paying for a Gallon of Gas?* (Institute for the Analysis of Global Security, 2005). http://www.iags.org/costofoil.html
28. Institute for the Analysis of Global Security, *NDCF Report: The Hidden Cost of Imported Oil* (Institute for the Analysis of Global Security, October 30, 2003). http://www.iags.org/n1030034.htm
29. Colin Campbell, *The Coming Oil Crisis* (Multi-Science Publishing Company, 1998).
30. Ibid, 9.
31. Energy Information Administration, *Annual Energy Outlook 2004* (Washington D.C.: U.S. Department of Energy, January 2004), figure 5.20.
32. Mac Thornberry, "Oil Imports Threaten Our Security," *Roll Call,* http://www.anwr.org/features/thornber.htm (access May 10 2005).
33. U.S. Department of Commerce, "February 2005 U.S. Foreign Trade

Developments," *Monthly Trade Update*, April 12, 2005. http://www
.ita.doc.gov/TD/Industry/OTEA/usftu/current.pdf; Energy Information
Administration, *Annual Energy Review 2003* (Washington D.C.: U.S
Department of Energy, September 2003), 75 table 3.5.
http://www.eia.doe.gov/emeu/aer/pdf/pages/sec3_11.pdf
34. Colin Campbell, "Peak Oil: A Turning Point for Mankind" (lecture,
Technical University of Clausthal, Clausthal-Zellerfeld, Germany,
December 2000).
http://www.geologie.tu-clausthal.de/Campbell/lecture.html
35. "Green Light for BP-Arco Merger," *BBC News*, April 14, 2000.
http://news.bbc.co.uk/1/hi/business/712962.stm
36. Hermann Scheer, *The Solar Economy: Renewable Energy for a
Sustainable Global Future* (London: Earth Scan Publications, 2002), 145.
37. "Solar Energy Helps BP Meet 10% Savings Target," *BP News*,
August 1, 2001.http://www.bp.co.nz/bin/press/item.pl?id=996627341
&showarchive=yes
38. British Petroleum, *BP Sustainability Report 2003*. http://www.
bp.com/liveassets/bp_internet/globalbp/STAGING/global_assets/
downloads/B/BP_Sustainability_Report_2003.pdf
39. Hermann Scheer, *The Solar Economy: Renewable Energy for a
Sustainable Global Future* (London: Earth Scan Publications, 2002), 145.

Chapter 3 - Diesel: the Man and His Vision

1. Greg Wilson, "Feature: VW 1-Litre-Car," *Canadian Driver,* June 5,
2002. http://www.canadiandriver.com/articles/gw/vw1litre.htm
2. 80 mpg car: Audi Company Press Center, "A World First: The A2,"
Audi United Kingdom, October 24, 1999. http://www.audi.co.uk/
company/pressrelease.jsp?id=552&backPage=presscentre; 80-300 mpg
concept cars: Greg Wilson, "Feature: VW 1-Litre-Car," *Canadian Driver,*
June 5, 2002. http://www.canadiandriver.com/articles/gw/vw1litre.htm
3. Morton Grosser, *Diesel: The Man and the Machine* (Brattleboro,
Vermont: Book Press, 1978), 81.
4. Ibid, 90.
5. Rudolf Diesel, introduction to *Diesel Engines for Land and Marine
Work*, by A.P. Chalkley (London: Constable & Company, Limited, 1922), 4.
6. Morton Grosser, *Diesel: The Man and the Machine* (Brattleboro,
Vermont: Book Press, 1978), 23-24.

7. Ibid, 24.

8. Steve Tally, "Plant Oils Will Replace Petroleum in Coming Years," *Purdue News*, August 2000. http://www.purdue.edu/UNS/html4ever/0007.Tao.biofuels.html

9. David P. Morgan, *Diesels West!* (Milwaukee, Wisconsin: Kalmbach Publishing Co., 1963), 91.

10. Chris Carlson, "1978 Ninety-Eight," *Encyclopedia of Oldsmobiles,* 2005, http://encyclopedia.classicoldsmobile.com/ninetyeight/78.html (accessed May 11, 2005).

11. Diesel Technology Forum, "Diesel-Electric Hybrid Vehicles," Diesel Technology Forum, http://www.dieselforum.org/whitepaper/downloads/diesel-electric.pdf (accessed May 11, 2005).

12. Ibid.

13. "Jeep Liberty 2.8L CRD," Jeep Co., http://www.jeep.com/autoshow/news/2004_04_02_05_jeep_liberty_crd_68888 .html?context=home&type=promo3_img; Kellen Schefter, "Jeep Liberty CRD," *Green Car Journal Online*, 2005. http://www.greencar.com/index.cfm?content=topstory3

14. PerotSystems, "Volkswagen of America: A Success Story in Customer Satisfaction," 2002. http://www.perotsystems.com/library/SuccessStory_Volkswagen.pdf (accessed November 1, 2005).

15. Reuters, "Volkswagen, ADM team up to develop biodiesel fuel," January 6, 2004. (accessed November 1, 2005). http://www.planetark .com/dailynewsstory.cfm?newsid=23321&newsdate=06-Jan-2004

16. National Biodiesel Board, "Volkswagen Extends Warranty Coverage for B5 Biodiesel Fuel," March 17, 2005. www.biodiesel.org/resources/pressreleases/pas/20050318_vw_b5.pdf

17. Drive 55 Conservation Project, "VW Beetle wins fuel economy prize: 76 mpg" http://www.drive55.org/pn/modules.php?op=modload &name=News&file=article&sid=64 (accessed November 1, 2005).

18. European New Car Assessment Program, "Audi A2," European New Car Assessment Program, http://www.euroncap.com/content/safety_ratings/details.php?id1=1&id2=111(accessed May 11, 2005).

19. Amory Lovins, *Winning the Oil End Game* (Colorado: Rocky Mountain Institute, 2004), 58. http://www.oilendgame.org/pdfs/WtOEg_72dpi.pdf

20. (cD = 0.25); "Audi A2 1.2 TDI: The three-liter car from Audi," *Audi World*, November 28, 1999.

http://www.audiworld.com/news/99/a2_2/content.shtml
21. "EU IV Diesel Range: Less Taxing... More Rewarding," Audi Co., http://www.audi.co.uk/acs/ownershipbenefits/details.jsp?id=11615 (accessed May 11, 2005).
22. "Audi A2 1.2 TDI: The Three-Liter Car from Audi," *Audi World*, November 28, 1999.
http://www.audiworld.com/news/99/a2_2/content.shtml
23. "A World First: The Audi A2," Audi Co., October 24, 1999. http://www.audi.co.uk/company/pressrelease.jsp?id=552&backPage =presscentre; "Audi Picks Up 10 Awards at Challenge Bibendum," *Green Car Congress*, October 29, 2004.
http://www.greencarcongress.com/2004/10/audi_picks_up_1.html
24. Ricardo Incorporated, *Annual Diesel Report 2004*.
http://www.ricardo.com/pages/dieselreport.asp
25. Ricardo Incorporated, *Annual Diesel Report 2004*.
http://www.ricardo.com/pages/dieselreport.asp

Chapter 4 - Alternative Fuels 101

1. U.S. Census Bureau, *Statistical Abstract of the United States: 2004-2005*, 124th ed., (Washington: Government Printing Office, 2005), 7, table 2. http://www.census.gov/prod/2004pubs/04statab/pop.pdf
2. Charles Siegel, *The End of Economic Growth* (Berkeley: Preservation Institute Policy Study, 1998). http://www.preservenet.com/endgrowth/ EndGrowth.html
3. Energy Information Administration, *Annual Energy Review 2003* (Washington, D.C.: U.S. Department of Energy, 2003), xxv, figure 22. http://www.eia.doe.gov/aer/pdf/aer.pdf
4. Latent Semantic Analysis, University of Colorado at Boulder, http://lsa.colorado.edu/summarystreet/texts/solar.htm (accessed May 16, 2005).
5. Gas stations: Amory Lovins and others, *Winning the Oil End Game* (Colorado: Rocky Mountain Institute, 2004), 237.; Passenger cars: U.S. Census Bureau, *Statistical Abstract of the United States: 2004-2005*, 124th ed., (Washington: Government Printing Office, 2005), 674, table 1047. http://www.census.gov/prod/2004pubs/04statab/trans.pdf; Diesel vehicles: Diesel Technology Forum, "In Wake of High Gas Prices, News Reports Indicate Growing Market for Diesel Vehicles," Diesel Technology Forum, 2005. http://www.dieselforum.org/news/

mar_30_2005.html; Miles of pipeline: U.S. Census Bureau, *Statistical Abstract of the United States: 2004-2005*, 124th ed., (Washington: Government Printing Office, 2005),709, table 1110. http://www.census .gov/prod/2004pubs/04statab/trans.pdf; Diesel-electric locomotives: U.S. Census Bureau, *Statistical Abstract of the United States: 2004-2005*, 124th ed., (Washington: Government Printing Office, 2005), 707, table 1106. http://www.census.gov/prod/2004pubs/04statab/trans.pdf; Miles of railroad track: U.S. Census Bureau, *Statistical Abstract of the United States: 2004-2005*, 124th ed., (Washington: Government Printing Office, 2005), 707, table 1106. http://www.census.gov/prod/2004pubs/04statab/trans.pdf

6. Energy Information Administration, *Residential Energy Consumption Survey 2001: Consumption and Expenditure Data Tables* (Washington, D.C.: U.S. Department of Energy, 2001), table CE1-4c. http://www.eia .doe.gov/emeu/recs/recs2001/ce_pdf/enduse/ce1-4c_housingunits2001 .pdf; Energy Information Administration, *1999 Commercial Buildings Energy Consumption Survey: Consumption and Expenditures Tables* (Washington, D.C.: U.S. Department of Energy, 1999), 165, table C9. http://www.eia.doe.gov/emeu/cbecs/pdf/allce.pdf

7. "Quick Facts Regarding U.S. Energy Usage and the Benefits of Energy Efficiency," Alliance to Save Energy, 2003. http://www.ase.org/section/ _audience/consumers/powerful_avings_campaign/ps_did_you_know/

8. Office of Energy Efficiency and Renewable Energy, "Energy Efficiency," U.S. Department of Energy, 2005. http://www.eia.doe.gov/ kids/energyfacts/saving/efficiency/savingenergy.html

9. "Energy Savings: Tip of the Day," Seattle City Light, 2005. http://www.cityofseattle.net/light/conserve/tips/cv6tip_24.htm

10. Ibid.

11. Energy Star, "Change a Light, Change the World," U.S. Environmental Protection Agency, 2005. http://www.energystar.gov/index.cfm?c=lighting.pr_lighting

12. Office of Energy and Renewable Energy, "Save Energy with Home Improvements," U.S. Department of Energy, June 28, 2004. http://www.eere.energy.gov/consumerinfo/saveenergy/save_nocost.html; "Too 'Plugged In'," Alliance to Save Energy, http://www.ase.org/section/ quickfacts/ (accessed May 12, 2005).

13. Energy Information Administration, "Voluntary Reporting of Greenhouse Gases Program: Fuels and Energy Source Codes and Emissions Coefficients," U.S. Department of Energy, 2003.

http://www.eia.doe.gov/oiaf/1605/coefficients.html
14. "The Air Car: Lifestyle, Ecology, Economy," Moteur Developpment International, 2002. http://www.theaircar.com/models.html
15. Natural gas (CH4) + oxygen (2O2) ==> carbon dioxide (CO2), water (2H2O), and energy (891 kilojoules).
16. Gregory Piraino (principal, Applied Engineering), personal communication, March 17, 2005.
17. Julian Darley, *High Noon for Natural Gas* (White River Junction, Vermont: Chelsea Green, 2004), 8.
18. Donella H. Meadows, Dennis L. Meadows, and Jorgen Randers, *Beyond the Limits* (White River Junction, Vermont: Chelsea Green, 1992), 73.
19. Matt Simmons, interviewed by Julian Darley, *Global Public Media*, May 19, 2004. http://www.globalpublicmedia.com/transcripts/213
20. Julian Darley, *High Noon for Natural Gas* (White River Junction, Vermont: Chelsea Green, 2004), 59.
21. Office of Energy and Renewable Energy, "Propane Vehicles," U.S. Department of Energy, March 3, 2005.
http://www.eere.energy.gov/afdc/afv/prop_vehicles.html
22. Julian Darley, *High Noon for Natural Gas* (White River Junction, Vermont: Chelsea Green, 2004), 85.
23. Methanex Company. www.methanex.com
24. Office of Energy Efficiency and Renewable Energy, "Hydrogen Production & Delivery," U.S. Department of Energy, March 4, 2005.
http://www.eere.energy.gov/hydrogenandfuelcells/production/basics.html
25. The strength of the carbon hydrogen covalent bond in natural gas (methane) is among the strongest in all hydrocarbons. Breaking those bonds to manufacture hydrogen gas transforms the majority of energy contained in the natural gas into heat.
26. Joseph J. Romm, *The Hype About Hydrogen* (Washington: Island Press, 2004), 68.
27. Energy Information Administration, *Annual Energy Outlook 2004* (Washington D.C.: U.S. Department of Energy, January 2004), 76, figure 60.
28. "KU Researchers Develop Clean-Burning Synthetic Diesel Fuel," *Science Daily*, October 20, 1998 (adapted from a University of Kansas News Release).
http://www.sciencedaily.com/releases/1998/10/981020073822.htm
29. United States Environmental Protection Agency, "Clean Alternative Fuels: Fischer-Tropsch," United States Environmental Protection Agency Fact Sheet # EPA420-F-00-036, March, 2002.

http://www.epa.gov/otaq/consumer/fuels/altfuels/420f00036.pdf
30. "Landfill Gas," Prometheus Energy Company, 2004.
http://www.prometheus-energy.com/landfillgas.html
31. "A History of Biodiesel/Biofuels," Yokayo Biofuels, 2003.
http://www.ybiofuels.org/bio_fuels/history_biofuels.html
32. Robert A. Hoppe, ed., *Structural and Financial Characteristics of U.S. Farms: 2001 Family Farm Report,* (Washington, D.C.: U.S. Department of Agriculture, May 2001), 6, figure 2.
http://www.ers.usda.gov/publications/aib768/aib768.pdf
33. Ibid.
34. David Blume, *Alcohol Can Be a Gas!* (International Institute for Ecological Agriculture, 1983), http://www.permaculture.com/alcohol/book/intro.shtml (accessed May 16, 2005).
35. "U.S. Ethanol Production," Kansas Corn Commission, March 8, 2005. http://www.ksgrains.com/ethanol/useth.html
36. John M. Urbanchuk, *The Contribution of the Ethanol Industry to the American Economy in 2004* (Wayne, PA: LECG, March 12, 2004), 2.
http://www.ncga.com/ethanol/pdfs/EthanolEconomicContributionREV.pdf
37. A mixture of 10% ethanol with 90% gasoline is called "E10." Automakers have also produced millions of vehicles capable of 85% ethanol mixed with gasoline (called E85), but very few E85 fuel stations exist. According to David Blume, author of *Alcohol Can Be a Gas*, the Toyota Prius has a flexible fuel computer installed and can run ethanol at any percentage.
38. Hosein Shapouri, James A. Duffield, and Michael Wang, *The Energy Balance of Corn Ethanol: An Update* (Washington, D.C.: U.S. Department of Agriculture, July 2002). http://web.mit.edu/1.149/www/Corn.EtOH.pdf
39. Energy Information Administration, *Annual Energy Review 2003* (Washington D.C.: U.S. Department of Energy, 2003), 222, figure 8.2a.
http://www.eia.doe.gov/emeu/aer/contents.html
40. Energy Information Administration, "North America, The Energy Picture," North America Energy Working Group, Energy Information Administration, June 2002.
http://www.eia.doe.gov/emeu/northamerica/engsupp.htm
41. "Nuclear Waste Storage," Oracle Education Foundation, 1998.
http://library.thinkquest.org/17940/texts/nuclear_waste_storage/nuclear_waste_storage.html
42. Ibid.

43. In a speech to the National Association of Science Writers (New York City September 16, 1954) Lewis L. Strauss, chairman of the U.S. Atomic Energy Commission, coined the term. "Too Cheap to Meter?" Canadian Nuclear Society, April 2, 2005. http://www.cns-snc.ca/media/toocheap/toocheap.html

44. Eric S. Beckjord, executive director, *The Future of Nuclear Power* (Cambridge, MA: Massachusetts Institute of Technology, 2003). http://web.mit.edu/nuclearpower/

45. Matt Chambers, "Uranium Prices Are Set to Climb," *International Herald Tribune Online,* January 5, 2005. http://www.iht.com/bin/print_ipub.php?file=/articles/2005/01/04/bloomberg/sxnuke.html; Eric S. Beckjord, executive director, *The Future of Nuclear Power* (Cambridge, MA: Massachusetts Institute of Technology, 2003). http://web.mit.edu/nuclearpower/

46. Cass Peterson, "Continuing Cleanup: $1 Billion and Counting," *The Washington Post*, March 28, 1998, A08.

47. Joby Warrick, "Study Links Three Mile Island Radiation Releases to Higher Cancer Rates," *The Washington Post*, February 24, 1997, A06.

48. The original concept for The Solar Bank was created under the Carter Administration to lend money to solar-energy based enterprises. Jimmy Carter, "The Crisis of Confidence," July 15, 1979. http://usa.usembassy.de/etexts/speeches/rhetoric/jccrisis.htm

49. Energy Information Administration, *Country Analysis Briefs: United States of America* (U.S. Department of Energy, January 2005). http://www.eia.doe.gov/emeu/cabs/usa.html; Assumes 12% efficient photovoltaics and a national electricity consumption of 3,641 terawatt hours per year. Arthur Weaver (president, Renovus Energy, Ithaca, NY), personal communication, March 2005.

50. "What Kills Birds?" Curry & Kerlinger, LLC, http://www.currykerlinger.com/birds.htm (accessed May 17, 2005).

51. Ron L. Lehr and Will Guild, *Listening to Customers: How Deliberative Polling Helped Build 1,000 MW Of Renewable Energy Projects in Texas* (Golden, CO: National Renewable Energy Laboratory, June 2003), 10. http://www.gldgrp.com/PDF%20Files/NREL%20Report.pdf

Chapter 5 - Farming Fuel

1. Christopher Conte, *An Outline of the U.S. Economy* (Washington, D.C.: U.S. Department of State, February 2001). http://usinfo.state.gov/products/pubs/oecon/chap8.htm

2. Robert A. Hoppe, ed., *Structural and Financial Characteristics of U.S. Farms: 2001 Family Farm Report* (Washington D.C., U.S. Department of Agriculture, May 2001). http://www.ers.usda.gov/publications/aib768/

3. Robert E. Scott, *Exported to Death: The Failure of Agricultural Deregulation* (Economic Policy Institute, July 1999), 1. http://www.epinet.org/content.cfm/briefingpapers_exportdeath

4. Environmental Working Group, *What's the Plan: U.S. Farm Subsidies, 1995 through 2003* (Farm Subsidy Database, 2005). http://www.ewg.org/farm/findings.php

5. Ibid.

6. Ibid.

7. ASEED Europe Genetic Engineering Campaign, "Dupont: The Merger," Amsterdam, The Netherlands. http://www.groundup.org/dupont/merger.htm.

8. "Pioneer Merger Another Major Step in DuPont Life Sciences Strategy," DuPont Press Release, March 16, 1999. http://www.gene.ch/genet/1999/Mar/msg00055.html

9. Dale McDonald, "Industry Giants: Part II," *Farm Industry News*, March 1, 2001. http://farmindustrynews.com/mag/farming_industry_giants_part/

10. Ibid.

11. Economic Research Service, *Farm Income and Costs* (U.S. Department of Agriculture, October 28, 2003). http://www.ers.usda.gov/briefing/farmincome/Glossary/def_debt.htm

12. Robert E. Scott, *Exported to Death: The Failure of Agricultural Deregulation* (Economic Policy Institute, July 1999), 1. http://www.epinet.org/content.cfm/briefingpapers_exportdeath

13. Ibid.

14. Ibid, 4.

15. Ibid.

16. Ibid.

17. Scott Kilman, "Surging Imports of Food Threaten Wider Trade Gap: U.S. Agriculture Exports, Relied on to Ease Deficit, Feel Heat of Competition," *Wall Street Journal*, November 8, 2004, eastern edition.

18. *Farm Security and Rural Investment Act of 2002*, Public Law 107-171d, 107th Cong., 2nd sess. (May 13, 2002), 357, 359. http://www.usda.gov/farmbill/conference_report/title9.pdf

19. Scott Kilman, "Surging Imports of Food Threaten Wider Trade Gap: U.S. Agriculture Exports, Relied on to Ease Deficit, Feel Heat of Competition," *Wall Street Journal*, November 8, 2004, eastern edition.

20. Sustainable Agriculture Research and Extension Program, *The New American Farmer* (Washington D.C.: U.S. Department of Agriculture, 2001). http://www.sare.org/publications/naf/naf.pdf

21. Alan Weber, personal communication, March 3, 2005.

22. Food and Agricultural Policy Research Institute, *Impacts of Increased Ethanol and Biodiesel Demand*, (Food and Agricultural Policy Research Institute, October 2001). http://www.fapri.missouri.edu/outreach/publications/2001/FAPRI_UMC_Report_13_01.pdf

23. John M. Urbanchuk, *An Economic Analysis of Legislation for a Renewable Fuels Requirement for Highway Motor Fuels* (AUS Consultants, November 7, 2001).

24. Sevim Erhan, *New Uses of Vegetable Oils* (International Starch Technology Conference, 2003). http://www.ars.usda.gov/research/publications/publications.htm?SEQ_NO_115=145286

25. American Soybean Association, *Soy Stats: U.S. Biodiesel Consumption* (American Soybean Association, 2004). http://www.soystats.com/2004/Default-frames.htm; National Biodiesel Board, "Missouri and Iowa Biodiesel Plants Join Growing Number of Production Facilities," National Biodiesel Board, April 29, 2005. http://www.biodiesel.org/resources/pressreleases/far/20050429_midambiofuels.pdf

26. United Soybean Board, *Soybean Almanac* (United Soybean Board, 2002). http://www.unitedsoybean.org/soystats2002/ussoystats/soybeancrush.html

27. Canola Canada, Canola Council of Canada 2005. http://www.canola-council.org; Timothy N. Gorsky, "An Oily Urban Legend," *American Council on Science and Health*, April 1, 2001. http://www.acsh.org/healthissues/newsID.605/healthissue_detail.asp

28. K. Shaine Tyson, Jack Brown, and Matthew Morra, *Industrial Mustard Crops for Biodiesel and Biopesticides* (Golden, Colorado: National Renewable Energy Laboratory). http://www.bioproducts-bioenergy.gov/pdfs/bcota/abstracts/19/z347.pdf

29. James A. Duke, *Handbook of Energy Crops* (Purdue University

Center for New Crops & Plant Products, 2003), s.v. "mustard."
http://www.hort.purdue.edu/newcrop/med-aro/factsheets/
MUSTARD.html

30. James A. Duke, *Handbook of Energy Crops* (Purdue University
Center for New Crops & Plant Products, 2003), s.v. "peanut." http://
www.hort.purdue.edu/newcrop/Crops/Peanut.html; John W. Goodrum,
Review of Biodiesel Research at the University of Georgia (University
of Georgia, 1996). http://www.biodiesel.org/resources/reportsdatabase/
reports/gen/19960601_gen-073.pdf

31. Diane Relf, Virginia Cooperative Extension, "Sunflowers," *The
Virginia Gardener Newsletter*, Virginia Polytechnic Institute and State
University. http://www.ext.vt.edu/departments/envirohort/factsheets2/
annperbulb/aug94pr2.html; *Interactive European Network for Industrial
Crops and their Applications*, Crops Database, s.v. "sunflower." http://
www.ienica.net/cropsdatabase.htm

32. *Interactive European Network for Industrial Crops and their
Applications*, Crops Database, s.v. "maize." http://www.ienica.net/crops/
maize.pdf

33. National Corn Growers Association, *Corn Production Trends*
(National Corn Growers Association, July 17, 2003).
http://www.ncga.com/02profits/main/index.html

34. Eric Schlosser, *Fast Food Nation: The Dark Side of the All American
Meal* (New York: Houghton Mifflin Company, 2001), 3-10.

35. Gary G. Pearl, "Biodiesel Production in the U.S.," (presentation,
Australian Renderers Association, 6th International Symposium, July 25-
27, 2001).
http://www.rendermagazine.com/August2001/TechTopics.html

36. Judy Jarnefeld and John Urbanchuk, *Statewide Feasibility Study for
a Potential New York State Biodiesel Industry, Final Report* (Albany,
NY: New York State Energy Research and Development Authority, April
2004). http://www.nyserda.org/publications/biodieselreport.pdf

37. Animal By-Products Regulation EC 1774/2002 (ABPR); Food
Standards Agency, *Waste Cooking Oil from Catering Premises* (Food
Standards Agency, November 9, 2004). http://www.food.gov.uk/
foodindustry/guidancenotes/foodguid/wastecookingoil

38. Alisa Harrison and Tim McNeilly, *USDA Establishes a Pilot Project
for Renewable Energy Funding Small Businesses that Generate Energy
Production from Cattle Products* (U.S. Department of Agriculture, May
17, 2004).

39. John Sheehan, Terri Dunahay, John Benemann, and Paul Roessler, *A Look Back at the U.S. Department of Energy's Aquatic Species Program: Biodiesel from Algae* (Golden, Colorado: National Renewable Energy Laboratory, July 1998).

40. Ibid.

41. Energy Information Administration, *Fuel Oil and Kerosene Sales 2002* (Washington D.C.: U.S. Department of Energy, 2003), table 13. http://www.eia.doe.gov/pub/oil_gas/petroleum/data_publications/fuel_oil_and_kerosene_sales/current/pdf/table13.pdf

42. Michael Briggs, "Widescale Biodiesel Production from Algae," University of New Hampshire Biodiesel Group, August 2004. http://www.unh.edu/p2/biodiesel/article_alge.html

43. Charles L. Peterson and Dick L. Auld, "Technical Overview of Vegetable Oil as a Transportation Fuel," (Moscow, Idaho: University of Idaho, 1991). http://www.biodiesel.org/resources/reportsdatabase/reports/gen/19910101_gen-292.pdf

44. Michael Briggs, "Widescale Biodiesel Production from Algae," University of New Hampshire Biodiesel Group, August 2004. http://www.unh.edu/p2/biodiesel/article_alge.html

Chapter 6 - Got Biodiesel?

1. National Biodiesel Board, "Biodiesel Production Graph." http://www.biodiesel.org/pdf_files/fuelfactsheets/production%20graph%20slide(2004).pdf

2. Senter Novem, *The Development of Biodiesel* (Senter Novem, October 21, 2004). http://www.senternovem.nl/mmfiles/The%20Development%20of%20Biodiesel_tcm24-117024.pdf

3. Ibid.

4. John Campbell, personal communication, April 25, 2005.

5. National Biodiesel Board, "Standards and Warranties." http://www.biodiesel.org/resources/fuelfactsheets/standards_and_warranties.shtm (accessed May 5, 2005).

6. Ibid.

7. National Biodiesel Board, "National Biodiesel Day Marked by Unstable Petroleum Prices," March 17, 2005. http://www.biodiesel.org/resources/pressreleases/gen/20050317_nat_biod_day.pdf

8. Greg Phal, *Biodiesel: Growing a New Energy Economy* (White River

Junction, VT: Chelsea Green, 2005), 153.

9. National Biodiesel Board, "Current and Proposed Biodiesel Production Plants," April 2005. http://www.biodiesel.org/buyingbiodiesel/ producers_marketers/ProducersMap-existingandpotential.pdf

10. Shaine K. Tyson, *Biodiesel Handling and Use Guidelines* (U.S. Department of Energy: Office of Energy Efficiency and Renewable Energy, September 2004), 1. http://www.nrel.gov/vehiclesandfuels/npbf/ pdfs/tp36182.pdf

11. National Biodiesel Board, "Chicago School Buses Adopt Biodiesel," April 22, 2005. http://www.biodiesel.org/resources/pressreleases/sch/ 20050422_chicagoschoolbusesearthday.pdf

12. Shaine K. Tyson, *Biodiesel Handling and Use Guidelines* (U.S. Department of Energy: Office of Energy Efficiency and Renewable Energy, September 2004), 1. http://www.nrel.gov/vehiclesandfuels/npbf/ pdfs/tp36182.pdf

13. British Petroleum Company, "Frequently Asked Questions: Emissions Control Diesel," 2003. http://ecdiesel.com/faq/index.asp

14. National Biodiesel Board, "Safer, Cleaner Market for Government Fleets," http://biodiesel.org/markets/fle/default.asp (accessed May 8, 2005).

15. Alaska Oceans Program, "Fifty Key Facts about Seas and Oceans." http://www.alaskaoceans.org/facts/fiftyfacts.htm (accessed April 29, 2005).

16. Shaine K. Tyson, *Biodiesel Handling and Use Guidelines* (U.S. Department of Energy: Office of Energy Efficiency and Renewable Energy, September 2004).

17. National Biodiesel Board, "Lifecycle Summary," http://www. biodiesel.org/pdf_files/fuelfactsheets/LifeCycle_Summary.PDF (accessed May 24, 2005).

18. Hosein Shapouri, James A. Duffield, and Michael S. Graboski, *Estimating the Net Energy Balance of Corn Ethanol* (U. S. Department of Agriculture, July 1995). http://www.ers.usda.gov/publications/aer721/ aer721.pdf; J. Sheenan, V. Camobreco, J. Duffied, M. Graboski, and H. Shapouri, *Life Cycle Inventory of Biodiesel and Petroleum Diesel for Use in an Urban Bus* (U.S. Department of Commerce, Springfield, July 1998).

19. J. Sheenan, V. Camobreco, J. Duffied, M. Graboski, and H. Shapouri, *Life Cycle Inventory of Biodiesel and Petroleum Diesel for Use in an Urban Bus* (U.S. Department of Commerce, Springfield, July 1998).

20. Alternative Fuel Vehicle Program, *Report on Biodiesel* (Harvard University, August 13, 2001). http://www.biofuels.coop/archive/ harvard_biodiesel.pdf

21. C. Lindhjem and A. Pollack, *Impact of Biodiesel Fuels on Air Quality and Human Health: Task 1 Report* (National Renewable Energy Laboratory, May 2003). http://www.nrel.gov/docs/fy03osti/33794.pdf

22. National Biodiesel Board, *Summary Results from NBB/USEPA Tier I Health and Environmental Effects Testing for Biodiesel Under the Requirement for USEPA Registration of Fuels and Fuel Additives* (National Biodiesel Board, March 1998). http://www.biodiesel.org/resources/reportsdatabase/reports/gen/19980301_gen-063.pdf

23. Lovelace Respiratory Research Institute, *Tier 2 Testing of Biodiesel Exhaust Emissions* (Albuquerque, New Mexico, May 22, 2000). http://www.worldenergy.net/pdfs/TierIIReport.pdf

24. Werner Körbitz, *The Technical, Energy and Environmental Properties of BioDiesel* (Körbitz Consulting, Vienna, Austria, 1993).

25. Tom Krawzcyk, "Biodiesel Alternative Fuel Makes Inroads But Hurdles Remain," *INFORM* (International News on Fats, Oils, and Related Materials), Vol. 7, no.8, August 1996, 801-815.

26. Biodiesel Association of Australia, "Biodiesel Fact Sheet: Emissions." http://www.biodiesel.org.au/biodieselfacts.htm#EMISSIONS (accessed May 9, 2005).

27. "Green Diesel Technology" in Environmental, Health and Safety Report for Navistar International Corporation; "Emissions Standards: U.S.A. Cars and Light Duty Trucks." DieselNet, Diesel Emissions Online Web site, http://www.dieselnet.com (accessed April 30, 2005).

28. Ford Motor Company, *Corporate Citizenship Report 2003-2004.* http://www.ford.com/en/company/about/corporateCitizenship/report/principlesProductsPerformanceDiesel.htm

29. "Health Effects Associated with Diesel Emissions," Sierra Club, August 20, 2003. http://www.sierraclub.org/cleanair/factsheets/diesel.asp

30. "Pollution with Particulate Matter, Ozone and Nitrogen Dioxide," Report on a WHO Working Group, Bonn, Germany, January 13-15, 2003.

31. Steven F. Hayward and Joel Schwartz, "Emissions Down, Smog Up. Say What?" *American Enterprise Institute Online*, January 20, 2004. http://www.aei.org/publications/pubID.19746/pub_detail.asp

32. Ibid.

33. "Technical and Economic Assesment of Biodiesel for Vehicular Fuel Use," Booz-Allen & Hamilton, Inc., April 1994.

34. Nicolas B.C. Ahouissoussi and Michael E. Wetzstein, "A Comparative Cost Analysis of Biodiesel, Compressed Natural Gas, Methanol, and Diesel for Transit Bus Systems," Department of Applied

Agricultural Economics, University of Georgia.

35. Shaine K. Tyson, *Biodiesel Handling and Use Guidelines* (U.S. Department of Energy: Office of Energy Efficiency and Renewable Energy, September 2004), 24-25. http://www.nrel.gov/vehiclesandfuels/npbf/pdfs/tp36182.pdf

36. Paul Nazarro, personal communication, February 21, 2005.

37. "Greening the National Park Service: Yellowstone National Park's Biodiesel Truck," National Park Service, December 8, 1998. http://www.nps.gov/renew/yellbio.htm

38. National Biodiesel Board, "Frequently Asked Questions," http://www.biodiesel.org/resources/faqs/ (accessed May 5, 2005).

39. "Biodiesel Fuel in John Deere Diesel Engines," statement number KX50441, September 14, 2001.

40. Steve Howell, Technical Director, NBB. Working Position Paper by the National Biodiesel Board (NBB) On Non-Allowance of Un-modified Vegetable Oils or Animal Fats for Use in Diesel Engines. February, 2005.

41. Steve Howell, personal communication, February 26, 2005.

42. Ibid.

43. Nile Ramsbottom (Executive Vice President of Soy and Nutrition, West Central Cooperative), personal communication, April 28, 2005.

Chapter 7 - Biodiesel Goes to Washington

1. Carolyn L. Orr, *Rural Implications of the American Jobs Creation Act: HR 4520* (Council of State Governments, New York, 2004). http://www.csgeast.org/pdfs/agriculture/JOBSanalysis.pdf

2. *Energy Policy Act of 1992*, Public Law 102-486, 102nd Cong. 2d sess. (October 24, 1992). http://www.dnr.state.la.us/sec/execdiv/techasmt/resources/legislation/Energy_Policy_Act_1992.pdf

3. Office of Energy Efficiency and Renewable Energy, *Environmental Policy Act* (U.S. Department of Energy, March 16, 2005). http://www.eere.energy.gov/vehiclesandfuels/epact/

4. Ibid.

5. William J. Clinton, *Executive Order no. 13,149— Greening the Government through Federal Fleet and Transportation Efficiency* (Presidential Documents, April 21, 2000). http://ceq.eh.doe.gov/nepa/regs/eos/eo13149.html

6. National Biodiesel Board, "Safer, Cleaner Market for Government

Fleets," Jefferson City, Missouri, 2005. http://www.biodiesel.org/
markets/fle/default.asp
7. William J. Clinton, *Executive Order no. 13,149— Greening the
Government through Federal Fleet and Transportation Efficiency*
(Presidential Documents, April 21, 2000). http://ceq.eh.doe.gov/nepa/
regs/eos/eo13149.html
8. Ibid.
9. *Center for Biological Diversity, Bluewater Network, and Sierra Club
v. Spencer Abraham, et al.*, U.S. Dist. Ct. M.D. Cal., 218 F. Supp.2d 1143
(July 26, 2002).
10. "Agencies Ordered to Obey Alternative Vehicle Law," *Environmental
News Service*, August 8, 2002.
http://www.ens-newswire.com/ens/aug2002/2002-08-08-06.asp
11. Office of Energy Efficiency and Renewable Energy, *EPAct
Fleet Information and Regulations, 2003/2004 Annual Report* (U.S.
Department of Energy, September 2004). http://www.nrel.gov/docs/
fy04osti/36690.pdf
12. National Aeronautics and Space Administration, *Fleet Alternative
Fuel Vehicle Program Report for Fiscal Year 2004* (National Aeronautics
and Space Administration, December 29, 2004).
www.logistics.hq.nasa.gov/AFV/PDF/NASA_AFV_2004.pdf
13. National Renewable Energy Laboratory, *EPAct Fleet Information
and Regulations: EPAct Programs Celebrate Regulated Fleet Successes*
(U.S. Department of Energy, May 2003). http://www.nrel.gov/docs/
fy03osti/33827.pdf
14. "2005 Closing the Circle Awards - Minimizing Petroleum Usage in
Transportation United States Postal Service Biodiesel Utilization and
Fuel System Testing Program," http://ofee.tteam.com/usps_ofee/apply/
uploads/CTC_05_USPS_Biodiesel_MinPetUsage.doc
(accessed June 14, 2005).
15. Wayne Arny, "Department for the Navy Environmental Policy
Memorandum 05-01; Biodiesel Fuel use in Diesel Engines," (U.S.
Department of the Navy, January 18, 2005). http://www.biodiesel.org/
resources/3rd_party_misc/20050317_Navy_Biodiesel_Policy.pdf
16. Office of Energy Efficiency and Renewable Energy, *EPAct
Fleet Information and Regulations, 2003/2004 Annual Report* (U.S.
Department of Energy, September 2004). http://www.nrel.gov/docs/
fy04osti/36690.pdf
17. National Aeronautics and Space Administration, *Fleet Alternative*

Fuel Vehicle Program Report for Fiscal Year 2004 (National Aeronautics and Space Administration, December 29, 2004). www.logistics.hq.nasa.gov/AFV/PDF/NASA_AFV_2004.pdf
18. Office of Energy Efficiency and Renewable Energy, *Energy Policy Act (EPAct): Private and Local Government Fleet Rule* (U.S. Department of Energy, March 2005). http://www.eere.energy.gov/vehiclesandfuels/epact/private/
19. Office of Energy Efficiency and Renewable Energy, "Clean Cities Program," U.S. Department of Energy, December 15, 2004. http://www.eere.energy.gov/cleancities/index.html
20. U.S. Environmental Protection Agency, *Asthma and Indoor Environments*, April 5, 2005. http://www.epa.gov/asthma/about.html#How%20does%20Asthma%20Affect%20Children
21. U.S. Environmental Protection Agency, *About Asthma*, April 5, 2005. http://www.epa.gov/asthma/about.html#How%20does %20Asthma%20Affect%20Children; Environment and Human Health, Inc., *Children's Exposure to Diesel Exhaust on School Buses* (EHHI Reports& Publications), http://www.ehhi.org/reports/diesel/summary.htm (accessed May 2, 2005).
22. U.S. Environmental Protection Agency, *Clean School Bus USA,* April 15, 2005. http://www.epa.gov/cleanschoolbus
23. National Biodiesel Board, *EPA Clean School Bus Grants to Fund Biodiesel Programs in Five States* (National Biodiesel Board, July 14, 2004). http://www.biodiesel.org/resources/pressreleases/sch/20040715 _epa_clean_schoolbus_grants.pdf
24. U.S. Environmental Protection Agency, *Clean Diesel Trucks and Buses Rule*, March 25, 2005. http://www.epa.gov/otaq/diesel.htm#hd2007
25. U.S. Environmental Protection Agency, *EPA420-F-03-022: Diesel Exhaust in the United States*, June 2003. http://www.epa.gov/otaq/retrofit/documents/420f03022.pdf
26. *Energy Policy Act of 2003*, S. 2095, 108th Cong., 2nd sess. (February 12, 2004). http://energy.senate.gov/legislation/energybill2004/full_text.pdf
27. Taxpayers for Common Sense, "Oppose the $89 Billion Energy Bill," *TCS Energy Bill Watch.* http://www.taxpayer.net/energy/pdf/EBillOppApr19.pdf (accessed May 2, 2005).
28. Taxpayers for Common Sense, "Energy Campaign," http://www.taxpayer.net/energy/index.htm (accessed May 2, 2005).

29. *To ensure jobs for our future with secure, affordable, and reliable energy* H.R.6 http://thomas.loc.gov/cgi-bin/bdquery/z?d109:h.r.00006: (accessed October 10, 2005).

30. Marcy Kaptur, "Kaptur Calls for a Renewable Fuels Standard," March 17, 2005. http://www.kaptur.house.gov/PressRelease. aspx?NewsID=1358

31. "Senate Finance Committee Approves Excise Tax Exemption for Biodiesel," *The Soy Daily,* April 4, 2003. http://www.thesoydailyclub.com/BiodieselBiobased/nbb04042003.asp

32. *American Jobs Creation Act of 2004,* 108th Cong, October 21, 2004. GovTrack web site. http://www.govtrack.us/congress/bill.xpd?bill=h108-4520

33. American Soybean Association, *Soy Stats* (American Soybean Association 2003). http://www.soystats.com/2003/Default-frames.htm

34. National Biodiesel Board "Tax Incentive Fact Sheet," http://www.biodiesel.org/news/taxincentive/ (accessed April 20, 2005).

35. Personal communication with Mark Palmer. March 25, 2005.

36. National Biodiesel Board Press Release, "Senate Passes Last Year's Version of Energy Bill with Biodiesel Tax Provisions," August 1, 2003. http://www.iasoybeans.com/whatnew/nbb080103.html

37. United States Senate Biography: Blanche Lambert Lincoln United States Senator, Arkansas http://lincoln.senate.gov/html/biography.html (accessed April 20, 2005)

38. Tina Caparella, "Washington Gets Biodiesel Friendly," *Render Magazine*, June 2003. www.rendermagazine.com/June2003/BiodieselBulletin.html

39. Minnesota State Legislature, *The Minnesota Biodiesel Mandate* (Minnesota Session Laws, chapter 239 SF-1495, March 15, 2002). http://www.revisor.leg.state.mn.us/slaws/2002/c244.html

40. The New Rules Project *Biodiesel Mandate-Minnesota* (The New Rules Project: Agriculture Sector, March 15, 2002). http://www.newrules.org/agri/biodieselmn.html

41. American Soybean Association, *Soy Stats* (American Soybean Association 2004). http://www.soystats.com

42. Mark Steil, "Biodiesel Production Begins in Minnesota," *Minnesota Public Radio, January 7, 2005.* http://news.minnesota.publicradio.org/features/2004/01/07_steilm_biodiesel/

43. Douglas G. Tiffany, "Biodiesel: A Policy Choice for Minnesota," University of Minnesota Staff Paper Series, May 2001.

www.misa.umn.edu/programs/biodiesel.pdf
44. Illinois General Assembly, "Bill Status of HB0112: Short
Description: Biodiesel Fuel-Use & Taxes" Illinois General Assembly
Legislative Information System. http://www.ilga.gov/legislation/
BillStatus.asp?DocNum=0112&GAID=8&DocTypeID=HB&LegID=142
55&SessionID=50&GA=94 (accessed April 21, 2005)
45. Illinois Environmental Protection Agency, *Recent Illinois Clean
School Bus Activities* (Illinois Clean School Bus Program, 2004). http://
www.epa.state.il.us/air/cleanbus/activities.html
46. Judy Jarnefeld and John Urbanchuk, *Statewide Feasibility Study for
a Potential New York State Biodiesel Industry* (New York State Energy
Research and Development Authority (NYSERDA), April 2004).
http://www.nyserda.org/publications/biodieselreport.pdf
47. Oregon Environmental Council *2005 Legislative Agenda.* http://
www.orcouncil.org/Laws/2005%20agenda.htm (accessed April 21, 2005)

Chapter 8 - Biodiesel's Speedy Growth

1. Matt Curry, "Willie Nelson's New Gig: Biodiesel," *The Associated
Press*, January 14, 2005. http://msnbc.msn.com/id/6826994/
2. VoiceYourself. http://www.voiceyourself.com/11_sol/11_sol.php
3. Gordon Scott, "Green Queen, Eco-activist Daryl Hannah Wants to
Save the World," *High Times,* April 2005.
4. "Eco-Activist's Tale Headed to Big Screen," *Reuters News Service*,
October 6, 2004. http://www.planetark.com/dailynewsstory.cfm/
newsid/27532/story.htm
5. "Lollapalooza 2003 Powers Tour with Cleaner Burning
Biodiesel," *The Soy Daily,* 2003. http://www.thesoydailyclub.com/
BiodieselBiobased/lollapalooza07082003.asp
6. Bob Callanan, "President Bush: "I Believe in Biodiesel,'" National
Biodiesel Board , September 7, 2004. http://www.biodiesel.org/resources/
pressreleases/gen/20040907_Bush_believe.pdf
7. Elliott Minor, "Conference will focus on Georgia's potential for
biodiesel," *The Associated Press*, August 20, 2003. http://www
.ledger-enquirer.com/mld/ledgerenquirer/news/politics/6577308.htm
8. William J. Clinton, *Executive Order 13101—Greening the Government
Through Waste Prevention, Recycling, and Federal Acquisition*
(Presidential Documents, April 21, 2000). http://www.epa.gov/

EPA-WASTE/1998/September/Day-16/f25023.htm
9. Senator John Kerry, interviewed by Jon Stewart, *The Daily Show*, Comedy Central, August 24, 2004. http://www.comedycentral.com/ tv_shows/thedailyshowwithjonstewart/videos_celeb.jhtml
10. Cari Spivack "Worth the Drive" Google Blog, September 14, 2004. http://www.google.com/googleblog/2004/09/worth-drive_13.html
11. Nicholas Brown, "Quicksilver Yacht on Epic Voyage," *Portsmouth Herald*, July 24, 2004. http://thecrossing.quiksilver.com/about.aspx
12. "Welcome to L. L. Bean," *Edge: Ryder's Business eMagazine.* (accessed April 28, 2005) http://ryder.ed4.net/minisite4/mini/Articles/edge4_article4_llbean.htm
13. Office of the National Park Service *Greening the National Park Service: Biodiesel in the National Parks* (U.S. Department of the Interior, February 28, 2005). http://www.nps.gov/renew/NPSBiodiesel.xls
14. The Willie Nelson Biodiesel Company. http://www.wnbiodiesel.com/company.html (accessed April 28, 2005)
15. Office of Energy Efficiency and Renewable Energy *U.S. Military Uses Biodiesel* (U.S. Department on Energy, June 25, 2003). http://www.eere.energy.gov/afdc/progs/new_success_ddown.cgi?122
16. Wayne Arny, "Department for the Navy Environmental Policy Memorandum 05-01; Biodiesel Fuel use in Diesel Engines," (U.S. Department of the Navy, January 18, 2005). http://www.biodiesel.org/ resources/3rd_party_misc/20050317_Navy_Biodiesel_Policy.pdf
17. "U.S. Navy to Produce Its Own Biodiesel," National Biodiesel Board, October 30, 2003. www.biodiesel.org/resources/pressreleases/ gen/ 20031030_navy_to_produce_biodiesel.pdf
18. "School Buses," National Biodiesel Board, July 18, 2004. http://www.biodiesel.org/markets/sch/default.asp
19. Environment and Human Health, Inc., *Diesel Exhaust and Children: EHHI Releases Original Research Report, Children's Exposure to Diesel Exhaust on School Buses* (Environment and Human Health, Inc., February 7, 2002). http://www.ehhi.org/diesel/pr_dieselreport.htm
20. California Air Resources Board, "Characterizing the Range of Children's Pollutant Exposure During School Bus Commutes," October 10, 2003. http://cleanenergy.org/pdf/CARB%20Report.pdf
21. Environment and Human Health, Inc., *Diesel Exhaust and Children: EHHI Releases Original Research Report, Children's Exposure to Diesel Exhaust on School Buses* (Environment and Human Health, Inc.,

February 7, 2002). http://www.ehhi.org/diesel/pr_dieselreport.htm

22. American Lung Association, "Asthma and Children Fact Sheet," June 2004. http://www.lungusa.org/site/pp.asp?c=dvLUK9O0E&b=44352 (accessed June 16, 2005).

23. U.S. Environmental Protection Agency, *Clean Diesel Trucks and Buses Rule,* May 31, 2005. http://www.epa.gov/otaq/diesel.htm (accessed June 15, 2005).

24. U.S. Environmental Protection Agency, *Clean School Bus USA: Grants and Funding,* April 12, 2005. http://www.epa.gov/otaq/schoolbus/funding.htm

25. U.S. Environmental Protection Agency, *Clean School Bus USA: Demonstration Projects,* June 14, 2005. http://www.epa.gov/otaq/schoolbus/demo_projects.htm#2004

26. National Biodiesel Board, *EPA Clean School Bus Grants to Fund Biodiesel Program in Five States,* National Biodiesel Board, July 14, 2004. http://www.biodiesel.org/resources/pressreleases/sch/20040715 _epa_clean_schoolbus_grants.pdf

27. Claudia Graziano, "Clean My Ride," *Edutopia,* September, 2004. http://www.edutopia.org/magazine/ed1article.php?id=art _1157&issue=sept_04

28. Dave Williamson, personal communication, June 4, 2005.

29. National Biodiesel Board, "National Biodiesel Board, Daimler Chrysler Set Energy Security Example," National Biodiesel Board, November 17, 2004. http://www.biodiesel.org/resources/pressreleases/ pas/20041117_jeep_liberty_ride_drive.pdf

30. John Deere, "John Deere to Use B2 Biodiesel Fuel in U. S. Manufacturing Plants," 2005 News Releases and Information, February 1, 2005. http://www.deere.com/en_US/newsroom/2005/releases/ farmersandranchers/050201_biodiesel.html

31. John Gartner, "Automakers Give Biodiesel a Boost," *Wired News,* September 23, 2004. http://www.wired.com/news/print/0,1294,65054,00.html

32. "Diesel Share of New Passenger Cars in Western Europe at 51.9%," *DieselNet,* December 20, 2004. http://www.dieselnet.com/news/ 0412bosch.html

33. Jim Kerr, "Bio-diesel—a Renewable Energy Source," *Canadian Driver,* August 25, 2004. http://www.canadiandriver.com/articles/ jk/040825.htm

34. Marianne Lavelle, "Living Without Oil," *U.S. News,* February 17,

2003. http://www.usnewsclassroom.com/issue/030217/usnews/17oil.htm
35. Peter Bell, "Will the Oil Companies Resist Biodiesel?" *Distribution Drive*, 2002. http://www.distributiondrive.com/Article12.html
36. National Biodiesel Board, "Lubricity Benefits." http://www.biodiesel. org/pdf_files/fuelfactsheets/Lubricity.PDF (accessed June 14, 2005).
37. National Biodiesel Board, "Bioheat Frequently Asked Questions," http://www.biodiesel.org/markets/hom/faqs.shtm (accessed May 2, 2005).
38. Robert S. Cerio, "Warwick Public Schools Heating Oil Project," (presentation, Warwick, RI). http://www.biodiesel.org/multimedia/ powerpoint/WarwickPresenationCerio.ppt (accessed June 14, 2005).
39. National Oilheat Research Alliance (NORA), "About NORA." http://www.nora-oilheat.org/ (accessed May 2, 2005).
40. Don Comis, *ARS Center to Heat With Soy-Based Biodiesel This Winter* (United States Department of Agriculture, Agricultural Research Service, October 31, 2000). http://www.ars.usda.gov/is/pr/2000/001031.htm
41. Erik Baard, "Choo-Choo Trains on Energy Crunch," *Wired News*, July 3, 2002. http://www.wired.com/news/technology/0,1282,53591,00.html
42. Mario Osava, "Biodiesel Trains on the Right Track," *Inter Press Service News Agency*, December 26, 2003. http://ipsnews.net/interna.asp?idnews=21707
43. Alaska Oceans Program, "Fifty Key Facts about Seas and Oceans," 2005. http://www.alaskaoceans.net/facts/fiftyfacts.htm
44. Office of the National Park Service, *Channel Islands National Park Launches Marine Biodiesel Program* (U.S. Department of the Interior, August 8, 2000). http://www.nps.gov/chis/press8800.htm
45. U.S. Coast Guard Academy, "Cadets Launch Operation Soy Boat in an Effort to Turn the Coast Guard 'Green,'" *Academy News*. http://www.cga.edu/newsstoriesread3462.htm
46. Department of Aviation Sciences Baylor University, *Development of a Bio-Based Fuel for Turbine Engines* (Waco, Texas: Baylor University, October 1998). http://www.biodiesel.org/resources/reportsdatabase/ reports/gen/19981001_gen-106.pdf
47. The Japanese and Germans used diesel aircraft engines in the 1950s. Aviation diesels are currently being manufactured and/or prototyped by Zoche Diesel, Thielert (TAE), Delta Hawk, and others.
48. "California Requires Dispenser Labeling; Florida Embraces

Biodiesel" *RenderMagazine*, June 2004.
http://www.rendermagazine.com/June2004/BiodieselBulletin.html
49. Office of Energy Efficiency and Renewable Energy, *Fleet Successes: Salt Lake City International Airport*, (U.S. Department of Energy, July 7, 2003). http://www.eere.energy.gov/cleancities/vbg/fleets/progs/success_ddown.cgi?7
50. Dieter Bockey, *Biodiesel Flowerpower* (Union for the Promotion of Oil and Protein Bearing Plants (UFOP) second edition, January, 2004). http://www.biodiesel.org/resources/reportsdatabase/reports/gen/20040101_gen-331.pdf
51. Raffaelo Garofalo, "Biodiesel in Europe and World-Wide: Overview and Development Perspectives," (Presentation at Trieste, June October 12, 2004). http://www.biodiesel-canada.org/resources/publication_files/200406_European_Biodiesel_Board_Presentation.pdf

Chapter 9 - Turning Biodiesel Into Bucks

1. Jenna Higgins (director of communications, National Biodiesel Board), personal communication, March 10, 2005.
2. Joel Glatz (co-owner of Frontier Energy), personal communication.
3. Hart Moore (product manager of biodiesel division, Griffin Industries), personal communication, January 31, 2005.
4. Jenna Higgins (director of communications, National Biodiesel Board), personal communication, March 10, 2005.
5. Gene Gebolys (chief executive officer, World Energy), personal communication, January 31, 2005.
6. Russ Teall (chief executive officer, Biodiesel Industries), personal communication, January 31, 2005.
7. Kelly King (marketing director and secretary, Pacific Biodiesel), personal communication, January 31, 2005.
8. At the time of writing this standard is ASTM D6751.
9. Kelly King (marketing director and secretary, Pacific Biodiesel), personal communication, January 31, 2005.
10. Gene Gebolys (chief executive officer, World Energy), personal communication, January 31, 2005.
11. Jeff Irvin (president, Petroleum Marketers Association of America), personal communication, April 8, 2005.
12. It should be noted that the screw press process used by at the Ralston

plant is no longer the most common type of oil extraction. Today most vegetable oil producers use a closed-loop hexane extraction system that involves less mechanical force and produces vegetable oil at a lower cost.

13. Gene Gebolys (chief executive officer, World Energy), personal communication, January 31, 2005.

14. Kelly King (marketing director and secretary, Pacific Biodiesel), personal communication, January 31, 2005.

15. Rudi Wiedemann (chief executive officer, Biodiesel Soltions), personal communication, February 17, 2005.

16. Steve Howell (president, MARC IV Consulting), personal communication, May 17, 2005.

17. National Biodiesel Board, "Missouri and Iowa Biodiesel Plants Join Growing Number of Production Facilities," April 29, 2005. http://www
.biodiesel.org/resources/pressreleases/far/20050429_midambiofuels.pdf

18. John M. Urbanchuk, *An Economic Analysis of Legislation for a Renewable Fuels Requirement for Highway Motor Fuels* (AUS Consultants, November 7, 2001).
http://www.ncga.com/ethanol/pdfs/Urbanchuk_Final_Report.pdf

19. Renewable Fuels Association, "Bush Signs Important Pro-Ethanol Tax Measures Into Law," *Ethanol Report*, November 8, 2004.
http://www.ethanolrfa.org/ereports/er110804.html

Chapter 10

1. Dan Ackman, "Oil Hits $55 Alarm; Greenspan Hits Snooze," *Forbes Magazine*, October 18, 2004.
http://www.forbes.com/energy/2004/10/18/cx_da_1018topnews.html

2. Institute for the Analysis of Global Security, "Energy Security: Iraq Pipeline Watch," March 28, 2005.
http://www.iags.org/iraqpipelinewatch.htm

3. Robert Baer, "The Fall of the House of Saud," *Atlantic Monthly*, May 2003, 54, 58.

4. Anthony H. Cordesman, Nawaf Obaid, and Khalid Al-Rodhan, *Saudi Arabia's "Sustainable" Capacity and Global Energy Supply and Demand* (The Center for Strategic and International Studies, Washington D.C., May, 2005).
http://www.csis.org/burke/saudi21/050428_SaudiOilCapBrief.pdf

5. Robert Baer, "The Fall of the House of Saud," *Atlantic Monthly*, May

2003, 55-56, 59.

6. Ibid, 54.

7. Defense Policy Board is a group of prominent intellectuals and former senior officials that counsel the Pentagon.

8. Thomas E. Ricks, "Briefing Depicts Saudis as Enemies, Ultimatum Urged to Pentagon Board," *Washington Post*, August 6, 2002.

9. Robert Baer, "The Fall of the House of Saud," *Atlantic Monthly*, May 2003, 62.

10. Unemployment rate: Central Intelligence Agency, *The World Factbook* (Washington D.C.: Central Intelligence Agency, 2005), s.v. "Saudi Arabia." http://www.cia.gov/cia/publications/factbook/geos/sa.html; Daryl Champion, "The Kingdom of Saudi Arabia: Elements of Instability Within Stability," *Middle East Review of International Affairs*, December 1999. http://meria.idc.ac.il/journal/1999/issue4/jv3n4a4.html

11. Institute for the Analysis of Global Security, *Set America Free: A Blueprint for U.S. Energy Security* (Institute for the Analysis of Global Security, 2004). http://www.iags.org/safn.pdf

12. Hudson Institute, *Voters See Saudi Arabia as Greatest Source of Global Terror* (Hudson Institute, August 20, 2004). http://www.hudson.org/index.cfm?fuseaction=publication_details&id=3444&pubType=HI_NEW@HUDSON

13. Ibid.

14. Amory B. Lovins and others, *Winning the Oil End Game* (Colorado: Rocky Mountain Institute, 2004), 14.

15. Ibid.

16. Ibid, 3.

17. Ibid, 33.

18. According to David Blume, author of *Alcohol Can Be a Gas*, the Toyota Prius has a "smart fuel" chip that makes the car a multifuel vehicle capable of running on ethanol or gasoline.

19. Amory B. Lovins and others, *Winning the Oil End Game* (Colorado: Rocky Mountain Institute, 2004), 175.

20. Brian Dumaine, "The New Color of Oil," *Fortune Small Business*, February 2005.

21. Amory B. Lovins and others, *Winning the Oil End Game* (Colorado: Rocky Mountain Institute, 2004), 127.

22. Ibid, 128.

INDEX

A

A2 (see Audi)
Abbot & Mills 216
Advanced Fuel Solutions 175
Afghanistan 6
Africa 1, 28, 67, 91, 98, 220
AFV (see alternative fuel vehicles)
Ag. Processing Inc. (AGP) 160, 161
agrarian communities 66
Agriculture Committee 199, 200
Air Car 91
Air Force Space Command 208
Air Quality Management District
    (AQMD) 207
al-Jazeera 242
al-Qaeda 242, 243
Alaska 34, 50, 72, 165, 217
Alaska Oceans Program 165, 217
Alberta 45, 46
Alfonzo, Juan Pablo Pérez 30, 45
algae 17, 19, 146, 147, 148, 151, 152,
    153
Algeria 48
Alliance to Save Energy 87
Allied forces 29
Alsup, William. Federal District Court
    Judge 186, 188
alternative fuel 91, 92, 95, 104, 156,
    160, 168, 181, 185, 186, 187,
    188, 189, 190, 196, 197, 200,
    206, 238, 254
alternative fuel vehicles (AFVs) 185,
    186, 187, 188
American Civil War 25
American Gothic 117
American Jobs Creation Act 145, 174,
    183, 193, 194

American Society for Testing and Ma-
    terials (ASTM) 161, 177, 179,
    180, 215, 230, 236
Archer Daniels Midland (ADM) 126
ASTM (see American Society for
    Testing and Materials)
ASTM (D 6751) 161, 180, 215
Arab Oil Embargo 7, 33
Atlantic Oil 25
Atlantic Richfield Co. 53
atomization 68
Audi 73, 78, 79
    Audi A2 73, 78, 79
Augsburg 59, 62
AUS Consultants 135, 238
Axis Powers 27
Ayatollah Khomeini 35

B

B10 197, 216, 218
B20 164, 168, 174, 175, 176, 181,
    185, 186, 188, 194, 197, 203,
    204, 206, 208, 213, 214, 216,
    217, 218, 223, 226, 231
B100 161, 165, 168, 175, 181, 185,
    186, 188, 198, 204, 207, 213,
    219, 223
baby boom 242
Bakhtiari, Ali Mortexa Sasam 44
basement rock 19
batch process plants 232
Baylor University International Center
    for Aviation and the Environ-
    ment's Clean Airports Program
    218

Baylor University Renewable Avia-
tion Fuels Development Center
(RAFDC) 218
Beetle (see VW Beetle)
Bell, Alexander Graham 62
Berkeley Ecology Center 213
Beyond Petroleum (BP) 25, 30, 52,
    53, 54, 155, 165, 214, 230, 248
Bintulu, Malaysia 98
Biodegradability 165
Biodiesel 155, 156, 157, 159, 160,
    161, 162, 164, 165, 166, 168,
    169, 170, 174, 175, 176, 178,
    180, 181, 183, 184, 185, 186,
    189, 192, 193, 194, 195, 196,
    197, 198, 200, 203, 204, 209,
    210, 215, 217, 218, 219, 220,
    221, 223, 224, 225, 226, 227,
    229, 230, 231, 232, 233, 234,
    235, 236, 237, 239, 251, 254,
    257
Biodiesel America 6
Biodiesel Industries 229
Biodiesel Rule 185, 186
Biodiesel Solutions 236
biofuel(s) 122, 123, 145, 160, 192,
    198, 200, 253
Biofuels Energy Independence Act of
    2005 192
biomass 98, 99, 100, 154, 192, 196,
    206, 249
biorefinery 99, 233
Biotane 230
BioWillie 204
Bio G-3000 230
Bissell, George 22
bitumen 45
black grease 144
Black Mistress 60, 61
blended 102, 103, 164, 175, 192, 194,
    199, 215, 223, 226, 238
blubber 20

Blue Sun Biodiesel 141
Boeing 206
Bottomless Well, The 45
Bond, Kit Senator 200
Booz-Allen 174
Bosch, Robert 214
BP (see Beyond Petroleum)
BP Solar 53
BQ-9000 180, 181, 230, 232
Brandt, Karl 21
Briggs, Michael 152, 153
British 28, 34, 53, 64, 65, 166, 203
British Diesel Company 64
British Petroleum 53
British Thermal Units (BTU's) 95,
    166
Brown, former Defense Secretary
    Harold 243
Browne, Lord John 53, 54
Brown grease 144
BTU's (see British Thermal Units)
Bud Boat 218
bulk plants 223
Busch, Adolphus 62, 218
Bush, President George W. 183, 191,
    192, 193, 205, 246

C

CAFE (see Corporate Average Fuel
    Economy)
California Air Resources Board
    (CARB) 168, 173, 210, 211
Campbell, Colin 38, 49
Campbell, John 159
Camp Lejeune Marine Corps Base 208
Canada 44, 45, 49, 96, 129, 130, 180
cancer 86, 96, 108, 168, 189, 210,
    211, 229
canola 139, 140, 142, 147
Capitol Hill 50, 159, 246
CARB (see California Air Resources
    Board)

carbon dioxide (CO$_2$) 18, 75, 86, 88, 92, 100, 104, 108, 146, 147, 168, 169, 170
carcinogenic 104, 168, 170
carcinogens 89
Career Intelligence Medal 243
Carels, George 65
Cargill 125, 126
Carnot, Sadi 67, 68
Carter, President James E. 6, 7, 35, 36, 205
CCC (see Commodity Credit Corporation)
cellulostic ethanol production 104
Census of Agriculture 123
Center for Middle East Policy 245
Channel Islands National Park Service 218
Chase Manhattan Bank 44
Cheney, Vice President Richard 44
Chevron 25, 30, 46, 52, 53, 231
Chevrolet 79
Chrysler 75, 155
CIA 243
Citroen 214
Clean Air Act 168
Clean Air Non-Road Diesel Rule 190
Clean Cities 188, 189, 219, 225
Clean Diesel Trucks and Buses program 190
Clean School Bus USA program 188, 189, 212, 213
Clif Bar 206, 207
Clinton, President William J. 186, 205, 206
closed carbon cycle 5, 170
cloud point 175
CNG (see compressed natural gas)
coal-to-fuel 29
coal oil 23
Coertsen (Belgian steamer) 65
cold weather 104, 174, 175, 181, 225, 230

Coleman, Senator Norm 200
Colorado School of Mines 162
combustion chamber 68, 69, 178
Coming Oil Crisis, The 49
Commodity Credit Corporation (CCC) 133
common rail 75
Common Rail Diesel (CRD) 74, 75
compressed natural gas (CNG) 73, 92, 213
compression ignition 60, 68
Congress 34, 132, 133, 184, 185, 190, 193, 194, 195, 248, 250
Conoco 25
Continental Oil 25, 125, 126
continuous flow plants 232
conventional oil 39, 45, 46, 47, 91, 140
corn 99, 101, 103, 104, 125, 126, 128, 129, 130, 134, 142, 143, 167, 183, 198, 254
Corporate Average Fuel Economy (CAFE) 250
Corpus Christi 222
counter-cyclical payments 132
Crazy Horse 203
CRD (see Common Rail Diesel)
Crisis in Confidence Speech 35
crops 5, 104, 118, 119, 120, 124, 133, 135, 136, 137, 139, 141, 142, 143, 151, 152, 159, 162, 200, 207
crushing facility 233, 236
Cummins 72, 238

D

Daily Show, The 206
Daimler, Gottlieb 60
DaimlerChrysler 73, 75, 200, 214, 238
Darley, Julian 96
Daschle, Senator Tom 159

Declaration of Independence 257
Deep Hot Biosphere, The 19
Defense Energy Support Center
    (DESC) 208
Defense Policy Board 243
Department of Energy (see U.S. De-
    partment of Energy)
Department of Energy's National
    Renewable Energy Laboratory
    (NREL) (see National Renew-
    able Energy Lab)
Department of Transportation (see
    U.S. Department of Transporta-
    tion)
DESC (see Defense Energy Support
    Center)
Detroit 249, 256
Diesel, Rudolf Christian Karl 58, 59
diesel-electric hybrids 73, 74, 90
diesel-powered 26, 70, 71, 72, 168,
    188, 208, 214
diesel engine 57, 58, 60, 61, 62, 65,
    66, 68, 69, 70, 71, 72, 75, 78,
    88, 89, 90, 104, 142, 158, 160,
    162, 170, 172, 181, 204, 214
diesel pickup truck 204
direct injection 70
Dodge 72, 73, 79
Dodge "ESX4" 73
DOE (see U.S. Department of En-
    ergy)
DOT ((see U.S. Department of Trans-
    portation)
Dow 44, 125
Dow Chemical Company 44
Drake, Edwin L. 22, 59
Dresden 29, 65
Drive to Survive 205
Dupont 125
Dustbowl 255

E

E320 CDI sedan (Mercedes) 214
Earthrise Farms 146
Earth Day 226, 227
Eastern Europe 23
East Texas 23
Eaton Corporation 73
EC (see European Commission)
Economic Policy Institute 130
ECRA (see Energy Conservation
    Reauthorization Act)
electrolysis 97, 112
electromagnetic fields 86
Elephants 39, 40, 41
emissions 68, 73, 74, 75, 80, 86, 87,
    88, 100, 104, 105, 109, 110,
    146, 164, 165, 168, 169, 170,
    171, 172, 173, 174, 179, 181,
    184, 189, 190, 199, 207, 212,
    213, 215, 217, 220, 228, 232,
    250
energetic hydrocarbon chains 104
energy balance 5, 85, 86, 97, 103,
    104, 105, 166, 167
energy carriers 85, 251, 257, 258
Energy Conservation Reauthorization
    Act (ECRA) 185, 186
energy crisis 2, 45, 258
Energy Information Administration
    47, 50, 98
Energy Policy Act (EPAct) 164, 184,
    185, 186, 187, 188, 189, 190,
    200, 206, 228
ENERGY STAR 87, 88
Enterprise 52
Environmental Protection Agency
    (EPA) 71, 164, 165, 168, 173,
    179, 184, 186, 189, 190, 211,
    212, 215
Environmental Working Group
    (EWG) 124

Environment and Human Health, Inc. 210

Environment and Public Works Committee 199

EPA (see Environmental Protection Agency)

EPAct (see Energy Policy Act)

ethanol 36, 88, 99, 101, 102, 103, 104, 122, 143, 150, 154, 167, 183, 185, 191, 192, 193, 195, 198, 200, 225, 251, 258

ethyl vinyl acetate 175

EU (see European Union)

Europe 1, 20, 23, 26, 60, 62, 63, 73, 79, 80, 81, 129, 139, 140, 144, 157, 172, 176, 214, 219, 220, 238

European Commission (EC) 144, 145

European New Car Assessment Program (EURONCAP) 78

European Union (EU) 129, 138, 144, 145, 219

Euro IV 80

Everett Naval Station 208

EWG (see Environmental Working Group)

Executive Order 13, 149, 164, 186

expeller presses 233

externalities 86, 248

Exxon 25, 29, 53

ExxonMobil 25, 39, 46, 53, 230

F

FAA (see Federal Aviation Administration)

Farmers Union Marketing and Processing Association (FUMPA) 198

Farm Bill 127, 128, 130, 131, 132, 200

Farm Progress Show 205

Farm Security and Rural Investment Act 132

farm subsidies 118, 123, 124

Farrell, Perry 205

Far East 27

Federal Aviation Administration (FAA) 218

Federal Energy Regulatory Commission 94

Federal Express 73

Federal Institute for Agricultural Engineering (BLT) 156

feedstock 98, 140, 141, 142, 143, 145, 146, 152, 166, 175, 234, 236

Fetzer Vineyards 207

Finance Committee 195, 199

Fischer Tropsch 98

Fisher, Franz 98

Fisk Corporation 44

fission reaction 106

flashpoint 166

Florida Energy Office 219

fluroelastomer 176

Foley, former House speaker Thomas 243

Food and Agricultural Policy Research Institute (FAPRI) 135

Ford 25, 72, 73, 78, 79, 83, 90, 101, 102, 103, 158, 159, 172, 214, 225, 248, 252

Ford, Henry 25, 78, 83, 101, 102, 103, 252

Ford Escape SUV 90

Ford Motor Company 25, 83, 172

Ford "Prodigy" diesel-electric hybrid 73

Fortune Small Business (FSB) 252

fossil fuel 17, 18, 19, 27, 66, 88, 99, 105, 107, 184, 193, 222

Fred M. Schildwachter & Sons 216

Frist, Senate Majority Leader Bill 191

Frontier Energy 225

FSB (see Fortune Small Business)

Ft. Leonard Wood 208, 209

fuel cell 89, 96, 98, 105, 112, 114

fuel jobber 223
fuel rack 223

G

gasoline-electric hybrid vehicle
    (GHEV) 90
gasoline extender 102
Gas to Liquid Fuel (GTL) 98, 99
GATT (see General Agreement on
    Tariffs and Trade)
Gavett, Earle 157
gel 104, 175
General Accounting Office 193
General Agreement on Tariffs and
    Trade (GATT) 128, 129
General Motors (GM) 70, 71, 72, 73,
    204, 214
Georgia 35, 120, 142, 174, 205, 209
geothermal 105, 108, 109
Germany 26, 27, 28, 29, 57, 60, 64,
    81, 98, 101, 139, 140, 145, 219,
    220
Gesner, Abraham 23
Ghawar 37, 40, 41, 42, 43, 44, 244
GHEV (see gasoline-electric hybrid
    vehicle)
ghost loads 88
Gingrich, former House Speaker Newt
    243
Glatz, Joel 225, 226
global warming 18, 100, 207
glow plugs 68
glycerin 163, 164, 178, 234
GM (see General Motors)
GM 350 72
Gold Coast Clean Cities Coalition
    219
Golf (see VW Golf)
Gonzalez, Elian 227
Google 206
Go Further 204
Grassley, Senator Chuck 195, 196,
    238

Great Depression 255
Greening the Government Executive
    Order 186, 206
greenwashing 53
Green Energy Parks Program 207
Griffin Industries 226
Grosser, Morton 62, 71
GTL (see Gas to Liquid Fuel)
Gulf Oil 214
Gulf War 41, 159, 185

H

half-life 106
Halliburton 44
Hamburg 29, 57
Hamilton, Inc. 174
Hannah, Daryl 204
Haradh field 43
Harkin, Senator Tom 200
Harkins, Edward 213
Harrelson, Woody 204
Harrelson's Simple Organic Living
    (SOL) Tour 204
Harvard University 168, 210
Harvard University's Alternative Fuel
    Vehicle Program 168
Higgins, Jenna 159, 224, 225, 227
Hiroshima 29
Hitler, Adolph 27, 28
Holliday, Charles O. 125
Honda 90, 248
Honda Insight 90
Hoover Dam 109
House Appropriations Committee
    199, 200
House of Saud 242, 243
Howell, Steve 179, 180, 236, 237
Hubbert, M. King 32, 33
Hubbert's Peak 32
Huber, Peter 45, 46
Hudson Institute 244, 245
Hulshof, Representative Kenny 200

hybrid 57, 70, 72, 73, 81, 87, 90, 91, 140, 189, 248, 249
hybrid electric vehicle (HEV) 90
hydro (see hydropower)
hydrocarbons 20, 68, 85, 98, 104, 168, 170, 172
hydroelectricity generation (see hydropower)
hydrogen 4, 20, 54, 57, 85, 88, 89, 96, 97, 98, 105, 110, 112, 113, 114, 154, 185, 249, 251, 252, 258
hydrogen fuel cell 4, 105
hydropower 84, 105, 109, 110
Hype About Hydrogen, The 97

I

I.G. Farben 28
IBM 148
Illinois 184, 196, 198, 199
Illinois Soybean Association 199
Indiana 25, 184, 196
indirect injection 70
Indonesia 27, 48
industrial age 25, 27, 37
Industrial Revolution 20, 62, 251, 257
injunctive relief 187
inorganic theory 19
Interchem, Inc. 158
intercoolers 69
International Harvester 127
Iowa Department of Transportation 208
Iowa State University 135
Iran 6, 31, 34, 35, 48
Iraq 27, 31, 45, 49, 86, 241, 242, 244
Irvin, Jeff 231, 232
ISO9000 180
ITL 231, 232

J

Janus Capital 44
jatropha 66

Jeep Cherokee 74
Jeep Liberty CRD 74, 75
Jeep Willys 74
Jefferson, Thomas 257
Jetta (see VW Jetta)
Jobs, Steve 252
JOBs creation act, 2004 145, 174, 183, 193, 194, 195, 238
Johannes, Kenlon 158, 160
Johnson, Senator Tim 200
John Deere 127, 157, 177, 178, 214, 238

K

Kamikaze 28
Kansas 158, 197, 210
Kaptur, Senator Macy 192, 200
kerosene 23, 175
Kerosene Works company 23
Kerry, Senator John 193, 206
Kilman, Scott 133
King, Bob 229, 235, 236
King, Kelly 229, 231, 235
Kissinger, former Secretary of State Henry 243
Kuwait 31, 49

L

L. L. Bean 207, 226
Langen, Eugen 60, 64
LECG 199
Lee, Robert 75
Lexus 75
Libya 49
Lifestyles of Health and Sustainability (LOHAS) 257
Lincoln, Abraham 257
Lincoln, Senator Blanche 195, 196, 200
Liquefied Natural Gas (LNG) 94
Liquefied Petroleum Gas (LPG) 95

liquid fuel 66, 86, 91, 93, 98, 100, 105, 134, 151, 152
liquid radiation 86
liquid solar fuel 104
Lollapalooza 205
Long Beach, California 222
Lovins, Amory 248, 249, 252, 253
lubricity 164, 165, 184, 215, 238
Luntz Research Company 244
Lupo (see VW Lupo)

M

mad cow disease 144
Maine's Technology Institute 226
Maize 142
Malayan fire piston 60
Marc IV Consulting 179, 236
Marina at the Lake of the Ozarks Lodge of the Four Seasons 218
Maschinenfabrik Augsburg-Nürnberg (MAN) 62
Mason-Dixon Line 194
Massachusetts Institute of Technology (MIT) 107
Materials Safety and Data Sheet (MSDS) 166
Maui Scuba Tours 218
Maybach, Wilhelm 60
McCarthy, Representative Karen 184
McFarlane, Robert C. 244
Mercedes Benz 71, 73
Mercedes R-Class 73
Mercedes Sprinter Van 79
Merrill Lynch Asset Management 44
methane 91, 92, 94, 97, 99, 100
Methanex 96
methanol 89, 91, 95, 96, 97, 103, 163, 164
methyl tertiary butyl ether (MTBE) 96, 190
Mexico 36, 49, 129, 130, 138, 146
Miami Dade Aviation Department 219

Miami International Airport 219
Middle East 1, 30, 31, 34, 35, 48, 49, 119, 123, 183, 229, 238, 244, 245, 246, 254, 256
Midwest 101, 102, 118, 119, 160, 228
Mid East (see Middle East)
Mills, Mark 45, 46
Minnesota Biodiesel Mandate 197
Missouri 1, 135, 157, 158, 159, 160, 184, 196, 197, 200, 208, 209, 225
Missouri Soybean Merchandising Council (MSMC) 158, 159, 160, 225
MIT (see Massachusetts Institute of Technology)
Mobil 25, 30, 53
mobile warfare 28
Model T 25, 101, 103
mono alkyl esters 157
Monsanto 125
Montana 123, 140, 184, 196, 212
Moore, Hart 226, 227
Mothership, The 204
MTBE (see methyl tertiary butyl ether)
multifeedstock 226, 233
multifeedstock plants 233

N

n-paraffins 17
NAFTA (see North American Free Trade Act)
Nagasaki 29
National Aeronautics and Space Administration (NASA) 96, 110, 164, 187, 207, 209
National Biodiesel Accreditation Commission (NBAC) 161
National Biodiesel Board (NBB) 1, 5, 139, 159, 160, 168, 174, 178, 180, 189, 224, 225, 226, 232, 237

National Defense Council Foundation (NDCF) 48, 51
National Energy Leadership Award 196
National Fire Protection Association 94
National Iranian Oil Company 44
National Oceanographic and Atmospheric Administration (NOAA) 208
National Parks and Recreation Service 227
National Renewable Energy Lab (NREL) 109, 113, 115, 141, 146, 147, 148, 152, 168, 216, 232
National SoyDiesel Development Board 160
Native Americans 22
natural gas 36, 45, 73, 85, 88, 91, 92, 93, 94, 95, 96, 97, 98, 100, 105, 107, 112, 156, 185, 189, 213, 216, 249
Navy 188, 208
Nazarro, Paul 175
Nazi 28, 29
NBAC (see National Biodiesel Accreditation Commission)
NDCF (see National Defense Council Foundation)
Negre, Guy 91
Nelson, Willie 203, 204, 225
New American Farmer, The 134
New Belgium Brewery 207
New Orleans 222
New York 22, 23, 25, 42, 73, 174, 213, 216, 217
New York Times, The 42
Nigeria 49
Nissan 73
nitrogen oxide (NOx) 73, 80, 105, 108, 165, 171, 172, 173

Nixon, President Richard M. 1, 6, 35, 36
nomenclature 139
NOPEC 161
Northern Oil Company 241
North Africa 28
North American Free Trade Act (NAFTA) 128, 129, 131
North Dakota 120, 140, 196
North Sea oil 50, 53
Novartis 125
NOx (see nitrogen oxide)
NREL (see National Renewable Energy Lab)
nuclear 84, 105, 106, 107, 112, 115, 190, 191
nutrition 18, 181, 207

O

Oak Ridge National Laboratories 52
octane enhancer 102
OEMs (see Original Equipment Manufacturers)
Office of Fuels Development (OFD) 146
Ohio 25, 192, 200, 209
Oil and Gas Journal, The 38
oil consumption 25, 26, 31, 36, 38, 46, 47, 247
Oil Creek 21
oil field 23, 39, 43, 44
oil imports 33, 36, 48, 49, 50, 51, 100, 247, 250
Oldsmobile "Ninety-Eight" 71
Oldsmobile Cutlass Supreme 71
Oldsmobile Delta 88 Royal 71
Oldsmobile Toronado 71
Old Brownie 158, 159, 225
oleaginous 136, 139, 146
Omnibus Energy Bill 127, 131, 190, 191, 192, 193, 194, 195, 196

OPEC (see Organization of the Petroleum Exporting Countries)
Operation Iraqi Freedom 241
organic theory 18
Organization of the Petroleum Exporting Countries (OPEC) 30, 31, 33, 34, 38, 41, 48, 49, 245
Original Equipment Manufacturers 161
Orinoco basin 46
Osama bin Laden 243
Otto, Nicolaus August 60, 61, 62, 64, 66
Otto & Cie 64
ozone 104, 105

P

Pacific Biodiesel 161, 229, 231
Pacific Whale Foundation 218
Palmer, Mark 194
Paris 59, 60, 66, 142
Parsons, Sir Charles 64, 65
Parsons Turbine 64
particulate emissions 73, 168, 169, 172, 173, 232
Partnership for a New Generation of Vehicles (PNGV) 72, 73
Passat (see VW Passat)
Patton, General George S. 29
peak oil 3, 32
Pearl Harbor, Hawaii 27
Pennsylvania 21, 22, 23, 24, 59, 107, 188, 196, 197, 217
Pennsylvania Turnpike Commission 188
Permanent Select Committee on Intelligence 50
Persian Gulf 1, 6, 34, 41, 99
Peterson, Bryan 158
Petro-Canada 44

petroleum 3, 4, 5, 6, 18, 20, 21, 23, 26, 29, 31, 32, 38, 46, 48, 49, 52, 53, 54, 55, 67, 85, 91, 95, 99, 123, 134, 151, 155, 156, 157, 161, 162, 164, 165, 166, 167, 169, 170, 173, 175, 180, 185, 186, 187, 189, 193, 194, 198, 199, 205, 206, 208, 213, 214, 217, 219, 222, 223, 224, 229, 231, 232, 248, 249
Petroleum Marketers Association of America (PMAA) 231
Peugeot 214
Pew Center for Global Climate Change 53
photosynthesis 17
photovoltaic (PV) 110, 112
physeter macrocephalus 20
Piech, Ferdinand 57
Pioneer Hi-Bred 125
PMAA (see Petroleum Marketers Association of America)
PNGV (see Partnership for a New Generation of Vehicles)
polymers 175
port authorities 94
Port Richmond 222
power generation 105, 110, 115
Power Too Cheap To Meter 107
Precept (Ford) 73
prechamber 70
Prize, The 24
Prohibition 102
Propane 85, 91, 95
protozoa 19
PV (see photovoltaic)
Pyle, George B. 117

Q

Qatar 49
Quayle, former Vice President Dan 243

Queen Elizabeth battleship 64
Quiksilver 206, 207

R

Raitt, Bonnie 205
Ramsbottom, Nile 181
rapeseed 139, 140, 142, 157
Reed, Dr. Thomas 162
reforming 97
regasifiers 94
Renault 74, 75, 214
renewable 5, 46, 53, 55, 84, 98, 99,
    101, 104, 105, 109, 113, 115,
    133, 146, 151, 153, 154, 156,
    166, 168, 185, 191, 192, 194,
    195, 196, 198, 200, 204, 205,
    206, 215, 216, 218, 232, 238,
    239, 247, 250, 251, 258
Renewable Fuels Standard (RFS) 196
reported oil reserves 38
respiratory illness 86, 211
Rhode Island 196, 212, 216
Rockefeller 24
Rocky Mountain Institute 46
rock oil 22, 25
Roll Call 50
Romm, Joseph J. 97
Roosevelt, President Theodore R. 101
Rough Rider 101
Royal Dutch Shell 46
Royal Technical High School 59
Rube-Goldberg 100
Rule of 72 42
runoff 86

S

Salt Lake City International Airport
    219
satellite terminals 223
Saudi Arabia 31, 37, 38, 40, 41, 42,
    43, 44, 49, 86, 151, 242, 243,
    244, 245

Saudi Aramco 42, 43
Scheer, Herman 55
Schlesinger, former Defense Secretary
    James 243
Schneeberger, Dr. Ken 157
school bus 189, 212
Schwarz, Joel 173
Scientific American 38
Scott, Robert E. 130
security margin 33, 34, 40
Senate Biofuels Caucus 200
Senate Centrist Coalition 196
Senate New Democrat Coalition, The
    196
Seneca Oil Company 22
September 11th 42, 242, 244, 256
Seven Sisters 29, 30, 52
Shah, Sonia 45
Shah of Iran 34
Shapouri, Dr. Hosein 103
Shell Oil 30, 32, 46, 52, 53, 98, 215,
    230
Shimkus, Representative John 184,
    200
Siljan 19
Silliman Jr., Benjamin 22
Simmons, Mathew 44
Simmons and Company International
    44
smog 105, 168, 171, 172, 173, 174
Société pour l'Instruction Élémentaire
    59
sodium hydroxide (NaOH) 163
Sohn, Sung Won 133
solar 36, 53, 54, 55, 85, 97, 98, 104,
    105, 110, 111, 112, 154, 167,
    191, 204, 251, 252, 254, 257,
    258
Solar Economy: Renewable Energy
    for a Sustainable Global Future,
    The 55
solar energy 36, 85, 104, 167, 252

Solar Energy and Energy Conservation Bank 36
solid waste 86
source rock 18
Southwest Research Institute 215
Soviet 6
SoyGold 230
SoyPower 230
spark ignition 68
Splash Tours 218
Sports Utility Vehicle (SUV) 75, 90
Stage IV smog requirements 172
Standard Oil 24, 25, 26, 29, 30, 101, 102
Standard Oil of California 25
Standard Oil of New Jersey 25, 26, 30
Standard Oil of New York 25
Standyne Automotive and Engineering Testing Services 215
State Building and Department of Motor Vehicles 216
state utility commissions 94
steam engine 61, 62, 64, 70
Straits of Hormuz 6
sub-terminal 223
Subcommittee on Agricultural Appropriations 200
submarines 26, 28, 64, 70
subsidy 119, 122, 123, 124, 129, 253
Sulaiman, Sana Toma 241
sulfur dioxide (SO$_2$) 86, 89, 104, 165, 168, 169, 172
sunflower 54, 142
Sunrider 158
super capacitor 90
Sweden 19, 220
swing producers 40

T

tailpipe emissions 105, 168
Talent, Senator Jim 200
Tariki, Sheikh Abdullah 31

tar sands 45, 46
Taylor, Brad 225
Teagle, Walter 'Boss' 26
Teall, Russ 229
Tesla, Nicola 62
Texaco 30, 46, 52, 53
Texas 23, 26, 30, 31, 50, 72, 115, 156, 184, 196, 210, 221, 222
Texas Gulf 221
Texas oilfields 26
Texas Railroad Commission 23, 30, 31
Thanksgiving Coffee 207
Third Reich 27
Thornberry, Mac 50, 51
Three Mile Island 107, 108
Tickell, Josh 5
Tier I and Tier II Health Effects Tests 168, 169
Titusville 21
toxicity 95, 136, 165
Toxic Air Contaminant 168
toxic waste 86
Toyota 73, 90, 248
Toyota Prius 90
trade deficit 5, 7, 48, 51, 131, 132, 133
transesterification 157, 163
triglyceride 157
Tropsch, Hans 98
Tuareg (see VW Tureg)
turbochargers 69
turbo diesel engines 67

U

U.S. Coast Guard 94, 218
U.S. Congress 184, 248
U.S. Department of Agriculture (USDA) 103, 121, 128, 134, 144, 145, 157, 159, 166, 183, 194, 216, 232

U.S. Department of Energy (DOE) 46,
    48, 50, 51, 52, 97, 98, 104, 106,
    109, 114, 134, 139, 140, 146,
    148, 156, 164, 175, 185, 187,
    188, 193, 219, 232
U.S. Department of Energy's Energy
    Information Administration
    (EIA) 47, 50, 98
U.S. Department of Transportation
    (DOT) 94, 208, 209, 227
U.S. Geological Survey (USGS) 19
U.S. Government 44
U.S. Navy 208
U.S. Postal Service (USPS) 164, 188,
    207, 209, 228
UCLA 172, 210
UCLA School of Medicine 172
UC Riverside 210
Ulmishek, Gregory 19
ULSD (see Ultra Low Sulfur Diesel)
Ultimate Recoverable Reserves (URR)
    41
Ultra Low Sulfur Diesel (ULSD) 172,
    184, 190, 215
Uncle Billy 22
Underwood, Gerry 157
United Arab Emirates 49
United Nations 54
United Nations International Gov-
    ernmental Panel on Climate
    Change 54
United Parcel Service (UPS) 166
United States 7, 20, 25, 27, 28, 29, 31,
    32, 33, 34, 35, 36, 41, 42, 47,
    48, 49, 51, 52, 54, 55, 62, 63,
    73, 75, 79, 81, 84, 85, 86, 88,
    89, 90, 92, 94, 95, 96, 98, 101,
    102, 103, 104, 105, 108, 112,
    113, 120, 127, 128, 132, 133,
    134, 138, 139, 140, 142, 143,
    144, 145, 146, 147, 149, 150,
    151, 152, 159, 161, 162, 177,
    179, 185, 194, 207, 211, 213,
    215, 226, 227, 229, 232, 237,
    238, 244, 246, 250, 251, 256
University of Georgia 142, 174
University of Graz 157
University of Missouri 135, 157, 158
University of Montana 123
University of New Hampshire 152
University of Southern California 210
Unterseebooten 64
UN Secretary Council 243
uranium 84, 106, 107
URR 32, 41
USDA (see U.S. Department of Agri-
    culture)
USDA Agricultural Research Center
    (ARS) 216

V

Van Dyne, Dr. Don 157
vegetable oil 20, 62, 66, 89, 104, 135,
    137, 143, 147, 150, 151, 156,
    157, 163, 167, 174, 177, 178,
    179, 233, 234, 236
Venezuela 45, 46, 49, 151
Ventura Harbor 218
Verry, Tom 159, 225
Vietnam War 256
VOC (see volatile organic com-
    pounds)
Vogel, Lucien 59, 61
volatile 92, 126, 172
volatile organic compound (VOC)
    172, 173
Volkswagen (VW) 57, 58, 71, 73, 78,
    79, 214
VW Beetle 79
VW Golf 79
VW Jetta 79
VW Lupo 73, 78
VW Passat 79
VW Tuareg 79

W

Wall Street Journal 45, 133
waste generation 86
water cut 43
Watson, Thomas 148
Weaver, Dennis 205
Weber, Alan 134, 135, 236, 237
Wiedemann, Rudi 236
Wellons, Fred 145
Wells Fargo & Co. 133
West Central Soy 161, 181, 203, 231,
        233, 234
whale oil 20, 21
Whale Oil, An Economic Analysis 21
wildcatters 37
Williamson, Dave 213
wind 84, 97, 98, 105, 112, 113, 114,
        115, 154, 191, 251, 252, 253,
        257, 258
wind farms 113, 114
Wolfsburg 57
Wood, Grant 117
Woolsey, R. James 244
World Bank, The 44, 220
World Energy 214, 228, 231
World Exhibition Paris 142
World Health Organization (WHO)
        172
World Nuclear Association 107
World Trade Organization (WTO)
        128
World War I (WW1) 26, 64, 74
World War II (WWII) 27
World's Giant Oilfields, The 44
Worley & Obetz of Manheim 217
Wright brothers 26, 62, 252
WTO (see World Trade Organization)
Wurmser, Dr. Mey 245
WWI (see World War I)
WWII (see World War II)

Y

Yale University 22, 210, 211
Yellowstone National Park 176, 207
Yellow Freight 166
yellow grease 143, 144, 184
Yergin, Daniel 24
Yom Kippur 33, 34
Young, Neil 203, 204, 225
Yucca Mountain Deep Geological
        Repository 106

Z

Zen Noh 126
Zetsche, Dieter 155
Zodiac Hurricane 158

The National Biodiesel Board (NBB) is the central coordinating body for biodiesel development in the United States. NBB was founded by American soybean farmers as a non-profit development group in the early 90s to work toward establishment of a domestic biodiesel industry. As development efforts succeeded, NBB evolved into the trade association that leads the biodiesel industry on regulatory, technical and educational initiatives. In partnership with other industry and agricultural organizations, NBB has driven significant accomplishments, including

- **Full compliance with the Clean Air Act and registration of biodiesel as a legal fuel and additive with the Environmental Protection Agency.**
- **Designation of biodiesel as an alternative fuel with the Department of Energy.**
- **Establishing of a fuel standard within the American Society for Testing and Materials (ASTM.)**
- **Recognition as one of the best-tested alternative fuels.**
- **Initiating BQ 9000, a fuel quality control program.**
- **Passage of a federal tax incentive for biodiesel, and other major federal initiatives.**
- **Favorable biodiesel legislation in more than 30 states.**
- **Improved acceptance by Original Equipment Manufacturers.**
- **A nationwide education program including the annual National Biodiesel Conference & Expo.**

NBB coordinates with a broad range of cooperators including industry, government and academia. Virtually all biodiesel producers are members of NBB. Membership is also made up of state, national, and international feedstock and feedstock processor organizations, fuel marketers and distributors, and technology providers.

You, too, can get involved with the biodiesel movement. Visit www.biodiesel.org to sign up to become a Biodiesel Alliance or Biodiesel Backer member. You will receive updates on biodiesel supply and activities in your area as well as other relevant topics to biodiesel supporters.

www.biodiesel.org

www.BiodieselAmerica.org

at BiodieselAmerica.org you can use our
interactive map to find...

Biodiesel Retail Pumps
Biodiesel Cooperative Groups
Biodiesel Distributors
& Diesel Cars for Sale

...near you.

Join our **on-line** forum to discuss the
different issues raised in this book.

Check out author **Josh Tickell's blog
and podcasts**.

Get **up-to-the-minute news alerts** about
biodiesel and related issues.

See reviews of all the **available diesel cars**
in the USA and internationally.

View **members profiles** and pictures and see
what they have to say about using biodiesel.

Get access to the most comprehensive range
of **biodiesel books and videos** anywhere.